2002 Krause-Minkus

Stamps & Prices

A Concise Catalog of United States Stamps

Edited by Maurice D. Wozniak

Published by

krause publications

700 E. State Street • Iola, WI 54990-0001
Telephone: 715/445-2214

Please call or write for our free catalog of publications.
Our toll-free number to place an order or obtain a free catalog is 800-258-0929
or please use our regular business telephone, 715-445-2214.

Library of Congress Catalog Number: 00-102618
ISBN: 0-87349-250-1

Printed in the United States of America

Contents

A brief introduction to United States stamps

By Maurice D. Wozniak, Editor

Most collectors trace the history of stamp collecting to 1840, when Great Britain revolutionized postal service by introducing adhesive stamps that signified the sender had paid the fee for delivery. That first stamp featured a portrait of the reigning British monarch, Queen Victoria, and the hobby of stamp collecting commenced almost simultaneously.

The United States followed with its first two postage stamps on July 1, 1847. Issued during the presidency of James K. Polk, the stamps featured two popular figures from the American Revolution – Benjamin Franklin, who had been named the first postmaster general in an age when delivery largely was entrusted to personal couriers or the good will of strangers; and George Washington, the general who became the first president of the republic.

Franklin's picture appeared on the 5¢ stamp, sufficient to carry an ordinary letter up to 300 miles, and Washington's picture was on the 10¢ stamp, used for letters requiring higher postage.

They were the world's first stamps to feature prominent persons of the past, and they set the tone for U.S. stamp-issuing policy. In the first 100 years, especially, portraits of America's heroes were prominent on stamps, which represented the country on mail sent to every country on the globe.

So-called commemorative stamps, issued typically in remembrance of a historical event or to highlight a current event, such as a large stamp exhibition, appeared first in 1893. Those first commemoratives were issued in support of the World's Columbian Exposition in Chicago, Ill., an event designed around the 400th anniversary of the voyage of Christopher Columbus, on which he is credited with the discovery of America.

The 16 stamps in that first commemorative set feature exquisite engravings of paintings of Columbus' voyage. The stamps were enormously popular with the public. In fact, more than 1 billion copies of the dull purple 2¢ stamp, the standard postal value at the time, were printed. That output dwarfs the production of almost all modern U.S. commemorative stamps.

People then could buy a 2¢ stamp as a souvenir of the anniversary and put it away for safekeeping. Many did. Today, you can buy that 2¢ stamp or its companion 1¢ value for less than $20 each. Postally used stamps might cost about 25¢. But the black $5 stamp in the set, which would have placed a strain on the budgets of most Americans at the end of the last century, is now valued at more than $2,500.

While commemoratives helped to sing the praises of America, the workhorse definitives could become dull to most mailers. In fact, for a period of more than 20 years in the early part of the 20th century, familiar portraits of either Washington or Franklin appeared on almost all U.S. stamps. Some collectors today specialize in finding the differences among that array of stamps.

The Presidential Series of definitive stamps, named because it featured profile busts of every deceased president in order of his term in office, extended over 16 years. The Liberty Series, the Prominent Americans Series, Americana Series, and the Great Americans Series, all of which continued to feature famous people and icons of history, followed it.

Then came the Transportation Series, which added an occasional touch of whimsy to the staid postage stamp. (A Tow Truck in a Transportation Series? An Elevator car?)

Today's regular issues are distinguished by variety – flags in various settings, birds and animals, symbols of culture, even berries.

Meanwhile, commemoratives went through a similar evolution in these changing times. Besides recalling famous people and events of history, U.S. stamps became blatantly political and considerably more expansive.

In the 1930s, they extolled the virtue of the Olympics Games, a Roosevelt administration program that was determined to be unconstitutional two years later, Mothers and Baseball.

Today, they have an obvious "topical" bent – art works, trains, professions, extinct animals, living animals, flowers and movie stars. More and more, they are designed to appeal to stamp collectors and entice more people to become stamp collectors. Some of the most difficult stamps to find today are those in the hands (and mounted on the walls) of non-traditional collectors – those for sports stars and Certified Public Accountants.

It may be a reflection of our democratic national character that the most famous U.S. stamp is an airmail error, the "Inverted Jenny" of

1918, on which the center vignette of an airplane was printed upside-down.

Since 1847, the United States has issued approximately 5,000 different postage stamps, not including stamped envelopes and postal cards. In addition, there have been thousands more stamps to raise revenues and signify other business transactions. All of these attract ardent collectors, and the hobby, while changing, remains popular and arguably more interesting than ever. We hope this mini catalog, a more portable version of the *Krause-Minkus Standard Catalog of® U.S. Stamps,* will enhance your enjoyment.

How to use this catalog

Stamps issued by the United States government are listed in chronological order according to Minkus catalog number. To the right of the number is a space for you to write in numbers assigned by other catalog makers for that stamp, if you wish. A cross-reference guide to the Scott catalog is available free from Krause Publications, Iola WI 54990-0001.

The date of issue, subject of the stamp image, denomination and color of the stamp are given to help in identification. The prices given for used and unused stamps are based on actual selling prices by dealers or at auction.

Five boxes are provided at the right of each listing for you to customize an inventory of your collection. For example, you might designate the boxes to indicate if you have, in order, a used copy, an unused copy, a mint (never-hinged) copy, a multiple (such as a plate block), and a copy on cover. If you mark the boxes to indicate you have a particular item, you will have a simple, illustrated inventory of your collection that you can carry with you to stamp bourses or stamp club meetings.

		UnFVF	UseFVF

REGULAR POSTAL ISSUES

1 _____ **1847. Benjamin Franklin Issue**

   5¢ **red brown**   4,500.00   500.00 ☐☐☐☐☐

SP1 _____ **1875. Benjamin Franklin Special Printing Issue**

   5¢ **red brown** (4,779 copies sold)   800.00   ☐☐☐☐☐

2 _____ **1847. George Washington Issue**

   10¢ **black**   17,500.00   1,250.00 ☐☐☐☐☐

NOTE: Government imitations of the 5¢ (in blue) and 10¢ (in Venetian red) were printed in 1947 and are listed as CM290 in the commemorative stamp section.

NOTE: The earliest known use of any U.S. stamp is a pen-canceled pair of No. 2 with a New York City postmark of "July 2," 1847, sent to Indianapolis, Ind.

SP2 _____ **1875. George Washington Special Printing Issue**

   10¢ **black** (3,883 copies sold)   950.00   ☐☐☐☐☐

3 _____ **1851. Benjamin Franklin Issue**

   1¢ **blue** Type I   175,000.00 35,000.00 ☐☐☐☐☐

4 _____ **1857. Benjamin Franklin Type Ia Regular Issue**

   1¢ **blue** Type Ia   25,000.00   6,500.00 ☐☐☐☐☐

5 _____ **1851. Benjamin Franklin Type Ib Issue**

   1¢ **blue** Type Ib   9,000.00   3,500.00 ☐☐☐☐☐

NOTE: Catalog prices for the above stamp are for nice examples of the type. Stamps with a slightly less complete design at the bottom are worth about one-fourth of the above prices.

6 _____ **1857. Benjamin Franklin Type II Issue**

   1¢ **blue** (Plate 1) Type II   500.00   95.00 ☐☐☐☐☐

7 _____ **1851. George Washington Issue**

   5¢ **blue** Type III   7,500.00   1,600.00 ☐☐☐☐☐

8 _____ **1851. Benjamin Franklin Type IIIa Issue**

   1¢ **blue** (Plate 1E) Type IIIa   2,400.00   550.00 ☐☐☐☐☐

9 _____ **1852. Benjamin Franklin Type IV Issue**

   1¢ **blue** Type IV (recut Type IV) (recut once at top & once at bottom)   600.00   100.00 ☐☐☐☐☐

10 _____ **1851. George Washington Issue**

   3¢ **orange brown** Type I   2,700.00   100.00 ☐☐☐☐☐

11 _____

   3¢ **Venetian red** Type I   220.00   10.00 ☐☐☐☐☐

12 _____ **1856. Thomas Jefferson Issue**

   5¢ **red brown** Type I   15,500.00   1,000.00 ☐☐☐☐☐

13 _____ **1855. George Washington Type I Issue**

   10¢ **green** Type I   13,000.00   700.00 ☐☐☐☐☐

14 _____ **1855. George Washington Type II Issue**

   10¢ **green** Type II   1,900.00   200.00 ☐☐☐☐☐

15 _____ **1855. George Washington Type III Issue**

   10¢ **green** Type III   1,900.00   200.00 ☐☐☐☐☐

16 _____ **1856. George Washington Type IV Issue**

   10¢ **green** Type IV (outer line recut at top only)   12,500.00   1,200.00 ☐☐☐☐☐

NOTE: All four types of the 10¢ stamp occur on the same sheet, so that pairs and blocks showing combinations of these types exist.

17 _____ **1851. George Washington Type I Issue**

   12¢ **black** Type I   2,600.00   225.00 ☐☐☐☐☐

18 _____ **1861. Benjamin Franklin Type I Issue**

   1¢ **blue** Type I   725.00   325.00 ☐☐☐☐☐

NOTE: The normal setting of the perforating machine was such that perforations cut the design on almost every stamp. Prices quoted are for such copies. Where the perforations do not cut the design, No. 18 stamps command very high premiums.

19 _____ **1857. Benjamin Franklin Type Ia Issue**

   1¢ **blue** Type Ia   12,000.00   3,250.00 ☐☐☐☐☐

1

1

SP1

2

2

SP2

3, 18

3

4, 19

5

6, 20

7

9

10, 11

10

12

13

13

14

15

16

17

	UnFVF	UseFVF	

20 _____ 1857. Benjamin Franklin Type II Issue
1¢ **blue** (Plate 2) Type II — 475.00 — 135.00 ☐☐☐☐☐

21 _____ 1857. Benjamin Franklin Type III Issue
1¢ **blue** Type III — 5,000.00 — 1,150.00 ☐☐☐☐☐

22 _____ 1857. Benjamin Franklin Type IIIa Issue
1¢ **blue** (Plate 4) Type IIIa — 800.00 — 260.00 ☐☐☐☐☐

23 _____ 1857. Benjamin Franklin Type IV Issue
1¢ **blue** Type IV recut top and once at bottom — 3,000.00 — 325.00 ☐☐☐☐☐

24 _____ 1857. Benjamin Franklin Type V Issue
1¢ **blue** Type V — 170.00 — 40.00 ☐☐☐☐☐

25 _____ 1857. George Washington Type I Issue
3¢ **rose** Type I — 1,900.00 — 70.00 ☐☐☐☐☐

NOTE: Fakes are known of the horizontal pair, imperforate vertically.

26 _____ 1857. George Washington Type II Issue
3¢ **Venetian red** Type II — 75.00 — 4.50 ☐☐☐☐☐

27 _____ 1857. George Washington Type III Issue
3¢ **Venetian red** Type III — 200.00 — 45.00 ☐☐☐☐☐

28 _____ 1857. Thomas Jefferson Type I Issue
5¢ **red brown** Type I — 3,000.00 — 260.00 ☐☐☐☐☐

28A _____ 1857. Thomas Jefferson Type I Issue
5¢ **henna brown (Indian red)** — 25,000.00 — 2,500.00 ☐☐☐☐☐

29 _____ 1858. Thomas Jefferson Type I Issue
5¢ **brick red** Type I — 10,000.00 — 900.00 ☐☐☐☐☐

30 _____ 1859. Thomas Jefferson Type I Issue
5¢ **brown** Type I — 1,500.00 — 250.00 ☐☐☐☐☐

31 _____ 1860. Thomas Jefferson Type II Issue
5¢ **brown** Type II — 1,500.00 — 200.00 ☐☐☐☐☐

32 _____ 1861. Thomas Jefferson Type II Issue
5¢ **orange brown** Type II — 1,100.00 — 800.00 ☐☐☐☐☐

33 _____ 1857. George Washington Type I Issue
10¢ **green** Type I — 8,250.00 — 500.00 ☐☐☐☐☐

34 _____ 1857. George Washington Type I Issue
10¢ **green** Type II — 2,500.00 — 200.00 ☐☐☐☐☐

35 _____ 1857. George Washington Type III Issue
10¢ **green** Type III — 2,600.00 — 200.00 ☐☐☐☐☐

36 _____ 1857. George Washington Type IV Issue
10¢ **green** Type IV, recut at top — 17,500.00 — 1,500.00 ☐☐☐☐☐

37 _____ 1859. George Washington Type V Issue
10¢ **green** Type V — 200.00 — 60.00 ☐☐☐☐☐

38 _____ 1857. George Washington Type I Issue
12¢ **black** Type I — 380.00 — 100.00 ☐☐☐☐☐

39 _____ 1859. George Washington Type II Issue
12¢ **black** Type II — 360.00 — 115.00 ☐☐☐☐☐

40 _____ 1860. George Washington Issue
24¢ **gray lilac** — 725.00 — 210.00 ☐☐☐☐☐

41 _____ 1860. Benjamin Franklin Issue
30¢ **orange** — 850.00 — 300.00 ☐☐☐☐☐

42 _____ 1860. George Washington Issue
90¢ **deep blue** — 1,300.00 — 5,500.00 ☐☐☐☐☐

NOTE: Many fake cancellations exist on this stamp.

SP3 _____ 1875. Benjamin Franklin Special Printing Issue
1¢ **brilliant blue** (3,846 copies sold) — 500.00 — ☐☐☐☐☐

SP4 _____ 1875. George Washington Special Printing Issue
3¢ **bright vermilion** (479 copies sold) — 2,000.00 — ☐☐☐☐☐

21

23

24

25

26

27

28-30

31, 32

33

33

34

35

36

37

38

39

40

41

42

		UnFVF	UseFVF

SP5 _____ **1875. Thomas Jefferson Special Printing Issue**

5¢ **bright orange brown** (878 copies) — 950.00

SP6 _____ **1875. George Washington Special Printing Issue**

10¢ **bluish green** (516 copies) — 1,750.00

SP7 _____ **1875. George Washington Special Printing Issue**

12¢ **greenish black** (489 copies) — 2,000.00

SP8 _____ **1875. George Washington Special Printing Issue**

24¢ **dark violet black** (479 copies) — 2,000.00

SP9 _____ **1875. Benjamin Franklin Special Printing Issue**

30¢ **yellow orange** (480 copies) — 2,000.00

SP10 _____ **1875. George Washington Special Printing Issue**

90¢ **indigo** (454 copies) — 3,300.00

NOTE: This set is known imperforated.

43 _____ **1861. Benjamin Franklin Issue**

1¢ **blue** — 150.00 — 16.00

44 _____ **1863. Andrew Jackson Issue**

2¢ **black** — 175.00 — 24.00

45 _____ **1861. George Washington Issue**

3¢ **pink** — 4,500.00 — 450.00

NOTE: It is almost impossible to describe a "pink" in words, but it should be kept in mind that the inking on a "pink" is rather heavy, and the lines of the design do not stand out as sharply as on the other shades. The color, while not as outstanding as a dull pink ribbon, is nevertheless on that order. It is not any of the shades of brown, dull red, rose red, or brown red so often mistaken for the real pink.

46 _____ **1861. George Washington Issue**

3¢ **brown carmine** — 125.00 — 2.50

47 _____ **1861. Thomas Jefferson Issue**

5¢ **buff** — 9,000.00 — 425.00

48 _____ **1862. Thomas Jefferson Issue**

5¢ **red brown** — 2,000.00 — 225.00

49 _____ **1863. Thomas Jefferson Issue**

5¢ **brown** — 1,000.00 — 100.00

50 _____ **1861. George Washington Type I Issue**

10¢ **green** Type I — 4,500.00 — 550.00

51 _____ **1861. George Washington Type II Issue**

10¢ **green** Type II — 325.00 — 30.00

52 _____ **1861. George Washington Issue**

12¢ **black** — 625.00 — 55.00

53 _____ **1866. Abraham Lincoln Issue**

15¢ **black** — 1,000.00 — 100.00

54 _____ **1861. George Washington Issue**

24¢ **violet** — 6,500.00 — 575.00

NOTE: No. 54 is found only on thin, semi-transparent paper, while Nos. 55 and 56 are on a thicker and more opaque paper.

55 _____ **1861. George Washington Issue**

24¢ **red lilac** — 800.00 — 80.00

56 _____ **1862. George Washington Issue**

24¢ **lilac** — 400.00 — 55.00

57 _____ **1861. Benjamin Franklin Issue**

30¢ **orange** — 650.00 — 75.00

58 _____ **1861. George Washington Issue**

90¢ **blue** — 1,500.00 — 250.00

SP11 _____ **1875. Benjamin Franklin Special Printing Issue**

1¢ **dark ultramarine** (3,195 copies) — 500.00 — 800.00

SP12 _____ **1875. Andrew Jackson Special Printing Issue**

2¢ **jet black** (979 copies) — 2,300.00 — 4,000.00

43

43

43

44

45

45

45

47

47

47

50

50

51

51

52

52

52

53

54-56

57

58

58
unissued design

58
issued design

		UnFVF	UseFVF

SP13 _____ **1875. George Washington Special Printing Issue**

3¢ **brown red** (465 copies) — 2,500.00 — 4,300.00 ☐☐☐☐☐

SP14 _____ **1875. Thomas Jefferson Special Printing Issue**

5¢ **light yellow brown** (672 copies) — 1,850.00 — 2,300.00 ☐☐☐☐☐

SP15 _____ **1875. George Washington Special Printing Issue**

10¢ **bluish green** (451 copies) — 2,000.00 — 3,750.00 ☐☐☐☐☐

SP16 _____

12¢ **deep black** (389 copies) — 2,800.00 — 4,500.00 ☐☐☐☐☐

SP17 _____ **1875. Abraham Lincoln Special Printing Issue**

15¢ **deep black** (397 copies) — 3,250.00 — 5,500.00 ☐☐☐☐☐

SP18 _____ **1875. George Washington Special Printing Issue**

24¢ **deep brown violet** (346 copies) — 3,250.00 — 6,000.00 ☐☐☐☐☐

SP19 _____ **1875. Benjamin Franklin Special Printing Issue**

30¢ **brown orange** (346 copies) — 3,500.00 — 6,000.00 ☐☐☐☐☐

SP20 _____ **1875. George Washington Special Printing Issue**

90¢ **dark blue** (317 copies) — 4,800.00 — 20,000.00 ☐☐☐☐☐

59 _____ **1867. George Washington w/Grill Issue**

3¢ **rose** grill A — 2,200.00 — 2,000.00 ☐☐☐☐☐

60 _____ **1867. Thomas Jefferson Grill A Issue**

5¢ **brown** grill A — 42,000.00 — — ☐☐☐☐☐

61 _____ **1867. Benjamin Franklin Grill A Issue**

30¢ **orange** grill A — — — 32,500.00 ☐☐☐☐☐

61A _____ **1868. George Washington Grill B Issue**

3¢ **rose** grill B — — — 150,000.00 ☐☐☐☐☐

62 _____ **1867. George Washington Grill C Issue**

3¢ **rose** grill C — 3,000.00 — 650.00 ☐☐☐☐☐

NOTE: No. 62 shows rows of grill points, not as heavily impressed as the normal grill, forming a grill whose total area is about 18 x 15mm. Caused by a failure to cut deep enough into the grill roller when it was being machined, which left a few areas on the roller only "partially erased."

63 _____ **1868. Andrew Jackson w/Grill D Issue**

2¢ **black** grill D — 9,500.00 — 1,500.00 ☐☐☐☐☐

64 _____ **1868. George Washington Grill D Issue**

3¢ **rose** grill D — 3,000.00 — 2,500.00 ☐☐☐☐☐

65 _____ **1868. Benjamin Franklin Grill Z Issue**

1¢ **blue** grill Z — — — 935,000.00 ☐☐☐☐☐

66 _____ **1868. Andrew Jackson Grill Z Issue**

2¢ **black** grill Z — 3,000.00 — 400.00 ☐☐☐☐☐

67 _____ **1868. George Washington Grill Z Issue**

3¢ **rose** grill Z — 5,000.00 — 1,200.00 ☐☐☐☐☐

68 _____ **1868. George Washington Grill Z Issue**

10¢ **green** grill Z — 47,500.00 — — ☐☐☐☐☐

69 _____ **1868. George Washington Grill Z Issue**

12¢ **black** grill Z — 4,000.00 — 600.00 ☐☐☐☐☐

69A _____ **1868. Abraham Lincoln Grill Z Issue**

15¢ **black** grill Z — 200,000.00 — — ☐☐☐☐☐

70 _____ **1868. Benjamin Franklin Grill E Issue**

1¢ **blue** grill E — 1,100.00 — 275.00 ☐☐☐☐☐

71 _____ **1868. Andrew Jackson Grill E Issue**

2¢ **black** grill E — 525.00 — 75.00 ☐☐☐☐☐

72 _____ **1868. George Washington Grill E Issue**

3¢ **rose** grill E — 375.00 — 10.00 ☐☐☐☐☐

73 _____ **1868. George Washington Grill E Issue**

10¢ **green** grill E — 2,000.00 — 175.00 ☐☐☐☐☐

	UnFVF	UseFVF	

74 _____ **1868. George Washington Grill E Issue**
   12¢ **black** grill E   2,250.00   210.00 ☐☐☐☐☐
75 _____ **1868. Abraham Lincoln Grill E Issue**
   15¢ **black** grill E   6,750.00   560.00 ☐☐☐☐☐
76 _____ **1868. Benjamin Franklin Grill F Issue**
   1¢   **blue** grill F   500.00   100.00 ☐☐☐☐☐
77 _____ **1868. Andrew Jackson Grill F Issue**
   2¢   **black** grill F   200.00   35.00 ☐☐☐☐☐
78 _____ **1868. George Washington Grill F Issue**
   3¢   **rose** grill F   175.00   3.50 ☐☐☐☐☐
79 _____ **1868. Thomas Jefferson Grill F Issue**
   5¢   **brown** grill F   1,500.00   225.00 ☐☐☐☐☐
80 _____ **1868. George Washington Grill F Issue**
   10¢ **yellow green** grill F   1,200.00   120.00 ☐☐☐☐☐
81 _____
   12¢ **black** grill F   1,500.00   125.00 ☐☐☐☐☐
82 _____ **1868. Abraham Lincoln Grill F Issue**
   15¢ **black** grill F   2,500.00   200.00 ☐☐☐☐☐
83 _____ **1869. George Washington Grill F Issue**
   24¢ **gray lilac** grill F   2,100.00   450.00 ☐☐☐☐☐
84 _____ **1868. Benjamin Franklin Grill F Issue**
   30¢ **orange** grill F   2,750.00   400.00 ☐☐☐☐☐
85 _____ **1869. George Washington Grill F Issue**
   90¢ **blue** grill F   5,000.00   850.00 ☐☐☐☐☐

NOTE: Most of the stamps that bear grills can be found with double grills, triple grills, split grills and quadruple split grills. Double grills are two impressions of the grill on the same stamp, triple grills are three impressions of the grill on the same stamp, split grills are those with about half of a normal grill on each end or on each side of the stamp and quadruple split grills are those that show just a small portion of the grill on each corner of the stamp. The split grill varieties were caused by misplacing the stamps under the grill roller so that the grills were not properly placed on the stamps. Fake grills exist.

86 _____ **1869. Benjamin Franklin Issue**
   1¢   **buff**   275.00   65.00 ☐☐☐☐☐
87 _____ **1869. Pony Express Issue**
   2¢   **brown**   225.00   28.00 ☐☐☐☐☐
88 _____ **1869. Early Locomotive Issue**
   3¢   **ultramarine**   175.00   12.00 ☐☐☐☐☐

59

62

65

86

87

88

		UnFVF	UseFVF

89 _____ **1869. George Washington Issue**
6¢ **ultramarine** — 950.00 — 100.00 ☐☐☐☐☐

90 _____ **1869. Shield and Eagle Issue**
10¢ **yellow** — 1,000.00 — 90.00 ☐☐☐☐☐

91 _____ **1869. Steamship Adriatic Issue**
12¢ **green** — 975.00 — 100.00 ☐☐☐☐☐

92 _____ **1869. Landing of Columbus Type I Issue**
15¢ **brown & blue** Type I — 2,500.00 — 350.00 ☐☐☐☐☐

93 _____ **1869. Landing of Columbus Type II Issue**
15¢ **brown & blue** Type II — 1,200.00 — 160.00 ☐☐☐☐☐

94 _____ **1869. Signing of the Declaration of Independence Issue**
24¢ **green & violet** — 3,100.00 — 550.00 ☐☐☐☐☐

95 _____ **1869. Shield, Eagle and Flags Issue**
30¢ **blue & carmine** — 3,100.00 — 350.00 ☐☐☐☐☐

96 _____ **1869. Abraham Lincoln Issue**
90¢ **carmine & black** — 6,000.00 — 1,800.00 ☐☐☐☐☐

SP21 _____ **1875. Benjamin Franklin Special Printing Pictorial Issue**
1¢ **buff** (approx. 2,750 copies sold) — 335.00 — 230.00 ☐☐☐☐☐

SP22 _____ **1875. Pony Express Special Printing Pictorial Issue**
2¢ **brown** (4,755 copies) — 385.00 — 330.00 ☐☐☐☐☐

SP23 _____ **1875. Early Locomotive Special Printing Pictorial Issue**
3¢ **ultramarine** (1,406 copies) — 3,000.00 — 10,000.00 ☐☐☐☐☐

SP24 _____ **1875. George Washington Special Pictorial Issue**
6¢ **ultramarine** (2,226 copies) — 900.00 — 600.00 ☐☐☐☐☐

SP25 _____ **1875. Shield and Eagle Special Printing Pictorial Issue**
10¢ **yellow** (1,947 copies) — 1,400.00 — 1,200.00 ☐☐☐☐☐

SP26 _____ **1875. Steamship Adriatic Special Printing Pictorial Issue**
12¢ **bright green** (1,584 copies) — 1,500.00 — 1,250.00 ☐☐☐☐☐

SP27 _____ **1875. Landing of Columbus Special Printing Pictorial Issue**
15¢ **brown & blue** Type III (1,981 copies) — 1,400.00 — 600.00 ☐☐☐☐☐

SP28 _____ **1875. Declaration of Independence Special Printing Pictorial Issue**
24¢ **deep green & violet** (2,091 copies) — 1,300.00 — 600.00 ☐☐☐☐☐

SP29 _____ **1875. Shield, Eagle and Flags Special Printing Pictorial Issue**
30¢ **bright blue & carmine** (1,356 copies) — 1,750.00 — 1,000.00 ☐☐☐☐☐

SP30 _____ **1875. Abraham Lincoln Special Printing Pictorial Issue**
90¢ **carmine & black** (1,356 copies) — 3,800.00 — 4,300.00 ☐☐☐☐☐

SP31 _____ **1880. George Washington Special Printing Pictorial Issue**
1¢ **buff** without gum (approx. 2,500 copies) — 210.00 — 190.00 ☐☐☐☐☐

97 _____ **1870. Benjamin Franklin Issue**
1¢ **ultramarine** grill H — 850.00 — 65.00 ☐☐☐☐☐

98 _____ **1870. Andrew Jackson Issue**
2¢ **red brown** grill H — 480.00 — 38.00 ☐☐☐☐☐

99 _____ **1870. George Washington Issue**
3¢ **green** grill H — 370.00 — 10.00 ☐☐☐☐☐

100 _____ **1870. Abraham Lincoln Issue**
6¢ **carmine** grill H — 2,000.00 — 300.00 ☐☐☐☐☐

101 _____ **1871. Edwin Stanton Issue**
7¢ **vermilion** grill H — 1,325.00 — 275.00 ☐☐☐☐☐

102 _____ **1871. Thomas Jefferson Issue**
10¢ **brown** — 1,800.00 — 450.00 ☐☐☐☐☐

103 _____ **1872. Henry Clay Issue**
12¢ **pale violet** — 14,000.00 — 1,750.00 ☐☐☐☐☐

104 _____ **1870. Daniel Webster Portrait Issue**
15¢ **orange** — 2,600.00 — 750.00 ☐☐☐☐☐

89

90

91

92

92

93 inverted center

93

94

95

96

97, 108

97, 108

98, 109

98, 109

99, 110

99, 110

100, 111

100, 111

101, 112

101, 112

102, 113

102, 113

103, 114

103, 114

104, 115

104, 115

		UnFVF	UseFVF	
105 _____	1870. Gen. Winfield Scott Issue			
24¢ purple		—	10,000.00	☐☐☐☐☐
106 _____	1870. Alexander Hamilton Issue			
30¢ black		3,750.00	550.00	☐☐☐☐☐
107 _____	1870. Oliver Perry Issue			
90¢ carmine		4,250.00	550.00	☐☐☐☐☐
108 _____	1870. Benjamin Franklin Issue			
1¢ ultramarine		120.00	5.00	☐☐☐☐☐
109 _____	1870. Andrew Jackson Issue			
2¢ red brown		90.00	3.50	☐☐☐☐☐
110 _____	1870. George Washington Issue			
3¢ green		90.00	.50	☐☐☐☐☐
111 _____	1870. Abraham Lincoln Issue			
6¢ carmine		175.00	7.50	☐☐☐☐☐
112 _____	1871. Edwin Stanton Issue			
7¢ vermilion		200.00	30.00	☐☐☐☐☐
113 _____	1870. Thomas Jefferson Issue			
10¢ brown		185.00	9.00	☐☐☐☐☐
114 _____	1870. Henry Clay Issue			
12¢ pale violet		400.00	40.00	☐☐☐☐☐
115 _____	1870. Daniel Webster Issue			
15¢ orange		400.00	50.00	☐☐☐☐☐
116 _____	1870. Gen. Winfield Scott Issue			
24¢ purple		400.00	50.00	☐☐☐☐☐
117 _____	1871. Alexander Hamilton Issue			
30¢ black		950.00	75.00	☐☐☐☐☐
118 _____	1872. Oliver Perry Issue			
90¢ carmine		950.00	100.00	☐☐☐☐☐
119 _____	1873. Benjamin Franklin Issue			
1¢ ultramarine		70.00	1.25	☐☐☐☐☐
120 _____	1873. Andrew Jackson Issue			
2¢ brown		115.00	7.00	☐☐☐☐☐
121 _____	1875. Andrew Jackson Issue			
2¢ vermilion		115.00	3.50	☐☐☐☐☐
122 _____	1873. George Washington Issue			
3¢ green		40.00	.20	☐☐☐☐☐
123 _____	1875. Zachary Taylor Issue			
5¢ Prussian blue		145.00	5.50	☐☐☐☐☐
124 _____	1873. Abraham Lincoln Issue			
6¢ dull Venetian red		140.00	7.00	☐☐☐☐☐
125 _____	1873. Edwin Stanton Issue			
7¢ vermilion		300.00	30.00	☐☐☐☐☐
126 _____	1873. Thomas Jefferson Issue			
10¢ brown		200.00	8.00	☐☐☐☐☐
127 _____	1874. Henry Clay Issue			
12¢ blackish violet		500.00	40.00	☐☐☐☐☐
128 _____	1873. Daniel Webster Issue			
15¢ yellow orange		475.00	37.50	☐☐☐☐☐
129 _____	1874. Gen. Winfield Scott Issue			
24¢ light purple		—	400,000.00	☐☐☐☐☐
130 _____	1874. Alexander Hamilton Issue			
30¢ gray black		600.00	37.50	☐☐☐☐☐

NOTE: The 30¢ Continental and 30¢ National are identical except in shade.

		UnFVF	UseFVF

131 _____ **1874. Oliver Perry Issue**

90¢ **rose carmine** — 1,100.00 — 105.00 ☐☐☐☐☐

NOTE: The 90¢ Continental and the 90¢ National are identical except in shade.

SP32 _____ **1875. Benjamin Franklin Special Printing of the 1873 Pictorial Issue**

1¢ **bright ultramarine** — 7,250.00 — ☐☐☐☐☐

SP33 _____ **1875. Andrew Jackson Special Printing Pictorial Issue**

2¢ **blackish brown** — 3,000.00 — ☐☐☐☐☐

SP34 _____ **1875. Andrew Jackson Special Printing Pictorial Issue**

2¢ **carmine vermilion** — 20,000.00 — ☐☐☐☐☐

SP35 _____ **1875. George Washington Special Pictorial Issue**

3¢ **bluish green** — 9,250.00 — ☐☐☐☐☐

SP36 _____ **1875. Zachary Taylor Special Printing Pictorial Issue**

5¢ **bright blue** — 27,500.00 — ☐☐☐☐☐

SP37 _____ **1875. Abraham Lincoln Special Printing Pictorial Issue**

6¢ **pale rose** — 8,000.00 — ☐☐☐☐☐

SP38 _____ **1875. Edwin Stanton Special Printing Pictorial Issue**

7¢ **scarlet vermilion** — 1,500.00 — ☐☐☐☐☐

SP39 _____ **1875. Thomas Jefferson Special Printing Pictorial Issue**

10¢ **yellow brown** — 8,000.00 — ☐☐☐☐☐

SP40 _____ **1875. Henry Clay Special Printing Pictorial Issue**

12¢ **black violet** — 2,750.00 — ☐☐☐☐☐

SP41 _____ **1875. Daniel Webster Special Printing Pictorial Issue**

15¢ **bright orange** — 8,000.00 — ☐☐☐☐☐

SP42 _____ **1875. Winfield Scott Special Printing Pictorial Issue**

24¢ **dull purple** — 1,750.00 — ☐☐☐☐☐

SP43 _____ **1875. Alexander Hamilton Special Printing Pictorial Issue**

30¢ **greenish black** — 5,750.00 — ☐☐☐☐☐

SP44 _____ **1875. Oliver Perry Special Printing Pictorial Issue**

90¢ **violet carmine** — 7,500.00 — ☐☐☐☐☐

132 _____ **1879. Benjamin Franklin Issue**

1¢ **dark ultramarine** — 75.00 — 1.00 ☐☐☐☐☐

133 _____ **1879. Andrew Jackson Issue**

2¢ **vermilion** — 45.00 — 1.00 ☐☐☐☐☐

134 _____ **1879. George Washington Issue**

3¢ **green** — 35.00 — .25 ☐☐☐☐☐

135 _____ **1887. George Washington Issue**

3¢ **vermilion** — 45.00 — 20.00 ☐☐☐☐☐

136 _____ **1879. Zachary Taylor Issue**

5¢ **blue** — 145.00 — 6.00 ☐☐☐☐☐

137 _____ **1879. Abraham Lincoln Issue**

6¢ **dull pink** — 257.00 — 8.50 ☐☐☐☐☐

138 _____ **1879. Thomas Jefferson Issue**

10¢ **brown** like No. 102, but no secret mark — 550.00 — 12.50 ☐☐☐☐☐

139 _____ **1879. Thomas Jefferson Issue**

10¢ **brown** like No. 126, with secret mark — 425.00 — 12.50 ☐☐☐☐☐

140 _____ **1879. Daniel Webster Issue**

15¢ **orange** — 300.00 — 21.00 ☐☐☐☐☐

141 _____ **1882. Alexander Hamilton Issue**

30¢ **black** — 300.00 — 22.50 ☐☐☐☐☐

142 _____ **1888. Alexander Hamilton Issue**

30¢ **orange brown** — 325.00 — 40.00 ☐☐☐☐☐

143 _____ **1880. Oliver Perry Issue**

90¢ **carmine** — 725.00 — 95.00 ☐☐☐☐☐

		UnFVF	UseFVF	

144 _____ **1880. Oliver Perry Issue**

90¢ **dark red violet** 750.00 85.00 ☐☐☐☐☐

SP45 _____ **1880. Special Printing of the 1879-88 Issue of 1879.**

1¢ **deep ultramarine** 4,000.00 ☐☐☐☐☐

145 _____ **1881-82. Re-Engraved Designs of 1873 Issue**

1¢ **ultramarine** 22.50 .35 ☐☐☐☐☐

146 _____ **1881. George Washington Issue**

3¢ **blue green** 27.50 .20 ☐☐☐☐☐

147 _____ **1882. Abraham Lincoln Issue**

6¢ **rose** 150.00 27.50 ☐☐☐☐☐

148 _____ **1882. Thomas Jefferson Issue**

10¢ **brown** 50.00 1.50 ☐☐☐☐☐

149 _____ **1887. Benjamin Franklin Issue**

1¢ **ultramarine** 32.50 .65 ☐☐☐☐☐

150 _____ **1883. George Washington Issue**

2¢ **red brown** 20.00 .20 ☐☐☐☐☐

151 _____ **1887. George Washington Issue**

2¢ **green** 15.00 .20 ☐☐☐☐☐

152 _____ **1883. Andrew Jackson Issue**

4¢ **deep bluish green** 80.00 4.00 ☐☐☐☐☐

SP59 _____ **1883. Special Printing Issue**

2¢ **red brown** 600.00 ☐☐☐☐☐

SP60 _____

4¢ **blue green** 14,500.00 ☐☐☐☐☐

153 _____ **1889. Andrew Jackson Issue**

4¢ **carmine** 75.00 7.50 ☐☐☐☐☐

154 _____ **1882. James Garfield Issue**

5¢ **olive brown** 80.00 3.00 ☐☐☐☐☐

SP58 _____ **1882. James Garfield Special Printing Issue**

5¢ **light brownish gray** (2,463 sold) 30,000.00 ☐☐☐☐☐

155 _____ **1888. James Garfield Issue**

5¢ **indigo** 75.00 4.00 ☐☐☐☐☐

156 _____ **1890. Benjamin Franklin Issue**

1¢ **dull blue** 17.50 .20 ☐☐☐☐☐

145

146

147

148

149

150

152

154

156

			UnFVF	UseFVF

157 _____ **1890. George Washington Issue**

   2¢ **lake**   125.00   .60 ☐☐☐☐☐

158 _____

   2¢ **carmine**   14.00   .20 ☐☐☐☐☐

159 _____ **1890. Andrew Jackson Issue**

   3¢ **dark lilac**   47.50   5.00 ☐☐☐☐☐

160 _____ **1890. Abraham Lincoln Issue**

   4¢ **dark brown**   47.50   2.00 ☐☐☐☐☐

161 _____ **1890. Ulysses S. Grant Issue**

   5¢ **chocolate**   47.50   2.00 ☐☐☐☐☐

162 _____ **1890. James Garfield Issue**

   6¢ **brown red**   50.00   15.00 ☐☐☐☐☐

163 _____ **1890. W. T. Sherman Issue**

   8¢ **purple brown**   50.00   11.00 ☐☐☐☐☐

164 _____ **1890. Daniel Webster Issue**

   10¢ **deep bluish green**   95.00   2.25 ☐☐☐☐☐

165 _____ **1890. Henry Clay Issue**

   15¢ **indigo**   145.00   16.00 ☐☐☐☐☐

166 _____ **1890. Thomas Jefferson Issue**

   30¢ **black**   225.00   19.00 ☐☐☐☐☐

167 _____ **1890. Oliver Hazard Perry Issue**

   90¢ **orange**   325.00   90.00 ☐☐☐☐☐

NOTE: Stamps of all values of the 1890 issue exist imperforate. They are considered finished proofs.

168 _____ **1894. Benjamin Franklin Issue**

   1¢ **ultramarine**   20.00   3.50 ☐☐☐☐☐

169 _____

   1¢ **blue**   47.50   2.00 ☐☐☐☐☐

170 _____ **1894. George Washington Issue**

   2¢ **pink** triangle I   15.00   3.00 ☐☐☐☐☐

171 _____

   2¢ **carmine lake** triangle I   95.00   2.00 ☐☐☐☐☐

172 _____

   2¢ **carmine** triangle I   17.50   .35 ☐☐☐☐☐

173 _____

   2¢ **carmine** triangle II   150.00   3.25 ☐☐☐☐☐

174 _____

   2¢ **carmine** triangle III   85.00   3.50 ☐☐☐☐☐

175 _____ **1894. Andrew Jackson Issue**

   3¢ **dark lilac**   60.00   6.50 ☐☐☐☐☐

176 _____ **1894. Abraham Lincoln Issue**

   4¢ **dark brown**   75.00   3.50 ☐☐☐☐☐

177 _____ **1894. Ulysses S. Grant Issue**

   5¢ **chocolate**   65.00   4.00 ☐☐☐☐☐

178 _____ **1894. James Garfield Issue**

   6¢ **red brown**   115.00   17.50 ☐☐☐☐☐

179 _____ **1894. William T. Sherman Issue**

   8¢ **purple brown**   120.00   12.50 ☐☐☐☐☐

180 _____ **1894. Daniel Webster Issue**

   10¢ **blue green**   150.00   8.50 ☐☐☐☐☐

181 _____ **1894. Henry Clay Issue**

   15¢ **indigo**   185.00   40.00 ☐☐☐☐☐

182 _____ **1894. Thomas Jefferson Issue**

   50¢ **orange**   275.00   75.00 ☐☐☐☐☐

183 _____ **1894. Oliver Hazard Perry Issue**

   $1 **black** Type I   575.00   225.00 ☐☐☐☐☐

			UnFVF	UseFVF	

184 _____

   $1   **black** Type II   1,500.00   450.00 ❏❏❏❏❏

185 _____   **1894. James Madison Issue**

   $2   **dark blue**   1,900.00   650.00 ❏❏❏❏❏

186 _____   **1894. John Marshall Issue**

   $5   **dark green**   2,900.00   1,250.00 ❏❏❏❏❏

187 _____   **1895-1898. Bureau of Engraving and Printing Portrait Designs on Watermarked Paper Issue**

   1¢   **deep blue**   5.00   .20 ❏❏❏❏❏

188 _____

   1¢   **deep green**   7.50   .20 ❏❏❏❏❏

189 _____

   2¢   **carmine** Type I   22.50   .90 ❏❏❏❏❏

190 _____

   2¢   **carmine** Type II   20.00   3.00 ❏❏❏❏❏

191 _____

   2¢   **carmine** Type III   4.00   .20 ❏❏❏❏❏

192 _____

   2¢   **red** Type III   7.50   .20 ❏❏❏❏❏

157, 158   159   160   161   162

163   164   165   166   167

168, 169, 187, 188   170-174, 189-192   170-72, 189 (I)   173, 190 (II)   174, 191-192 (III)

175, 193   176, 194, 195   177, 196, 197   178, 198, 199   179, 200

		UnFVF	UseFVF	
193				
3¢	**dark red violet**	27.50	1.00	❑❑❑❑❑
194				
4¢	**dark brown**	27.50	1.50	❑❑❑❑❑
195				
4¢	**chocolate**	22.50	.90	❑❑❑❑❑
196				
5¢	**dark orange brown**	27.50	1.65	❑❑❑❑❑
197				
5¢	**dark blue**	25.00	.75	❑❑❑❑❑
198				
6¢	**red brown**	55.00	4.00	❑❑❑❑❑
199				
6¢	**lake**	35.00	2.25	❑❑❑❑❑
200				
8¢	**purple brown**	50.00	1.25	❑❑❑❑❑
201				
10¢	**dark green** Type I	50.00	1.25	❑❑❑❑❑
202				
10¢	**brown** Type I	135.00	2.50	❑❑❑❑❑
203				
10¢	**orange brown** Type II	75.00	2.00	❑❑❑❑❑
204				
15¢	**indigo**	150.00	9.00	❑❑❑❑❑
205				
15¢	**olive green**	115.00	7.50	❑❑❑❑❑
206				
50¢	**orange**	200.00	20.00	❑❑❑❑❑
207				
$1	**black** Type I	450.00	55.00	❑❑❑❑❑
208				
$1	**black** Type II	900.00	125.00	❑❑❑❑❑
209				
$2	**dark blue**	775.00	250.00	❑❑❑❑❑
210				
$5	**dark green**	1,600.00	375.00	❑❑❑❑❑
211	**1902-03. Regular Issue**			
1¢	**deep bluish green**	9.00	.20	❑❑❑❑❑
212				
2¢	**carmine**	12.00	.20	❑❑❑❑❑
213				
3¢	**dark red violet**	52.50	2.25	❑❑❑❑❑
214				
4¢	**brown**	57.50	1.00	❑❑❑❑❑
215				
5¢	**deep blue**	57.50	1.15	❑❑❑❑❑
216				
6¢	**brown red**	70.00	2.00	❑❑❑❑❑
217				
8¢	**violet black**	42.50	1.60	❑❑❑❑❑
218				
10¢	**pale red brown**	60.00	1.15	❑❑❑❑❑
219				
13¢	**black brown**	42.50	6.50	❑❑❑❑❑

180, 201-203

181, 204, 205

182, 206

183, 194, 207, 208

183, 184, 207

184, 208

185, 209

186, 210

Double-line watermark 187

201, 202

203

211, 225, 228, 230

212

213

214, 226

215, 227, 229

216

217

218

219

		UnFVF	UseFVF	

		UnFVF	UseFVF	
220 _____				
15¢	olive green	150.00	4.50	⬜⬜⬜⬜⬜
221 _____				
50¢	orange	425.00	20.00	⬜⬜⬜⬜⬜
222 _____				
$1	black	750.00	45.00	⬜⬜⬜⬜⬜
223 _____				
$2	dark blue	1,075.00	140.00	⬜⬜⬜⬜⬜
224 _____				
$5	dark green	2,800.00	525.00	⬜⬜⬜⬜⬜

225 _____ 1906-08. Regular Issues of 1902-03

		UnFVF	UseFVF	
1¢	deep bluish green	20.00	17.50	⬜⬜⬜⬜⬜
226 _____				
4¢	brown	22,500.00	15,000.00	⬜⬜⬜⬜⬜
227 _____				
5¢	blue	375.00	475.00	⬜⬜⬜⬜⬜

NOTE: Please exercise caution in buying singles of this stamp, particularly used copies. Certification by respected authorities recommended.

228 _____ 1908. Coil Stamp 1902-03 Series Issue

		UnFVF	UseFVF	
1¢	blue green pair	68,500.00	—	⬜⬜⬜⬜⬜
229 _____				
5¢	blue pair	9,000.00	—	⬜⬜⬜⬜⬜

NOTE: Perforated 12 vertically.

		UnFVF	UseFVF	
230 _____				
1¢	blue green pair	6,000.00	—	⬜⬜⬜⬜⬜

231 _____ 1903. Two-Cent Shield Stamp Issue

		UnFVF	UseFVF	
2¢	carmine Type I	4.00	.20	⬜⬜⬜⬜⬜
232 _____				
2¢	lake Type II	7.50	.50	⬜⬜⬜⬜⬜

233 _____ 1903. Two-Cent Shield Coil Issue

		UnFVF	UseFVF	
2¢	carmine Type II	20.00	15.00	⬜⬜⬜⬜⬜
234 _____				
2¢	lake Type II	50.00	40.00	⬜⬜⬜⬜⬜

235 _____ 1903. Two-Cent Shield Coil Issue

		UnFVF	UseFVF	
2¢	carmine Type I pair	95,000.00	100,000.00	⬜⬜⬜⬜⬜

NOTE: Perforated 12 vertically.

		UnFVF	UseFVF	
236 _____				
2¢	scarlet Type II pair	7,000.00	4,250.00	⬜⬜⬜⬜⬜

237 _____ 1908-09 Washington & Franklin Issue

		UnFVF	UseFVF	
1¢	green	6.00	.20	⬜⬜⬜⬜⬜
238 _____				
2¢	carmine	6.00	.20	⬜⬜⬜⬜⬜

239 _____ 1908. George Washington Type I Issue

		UnFVF	UseFVF	
3¢	violet Type I	27.50	2.50	⬜⬜⬜⬜⬜
240 _____				
4¢	orange brown	30.00	1.00	⬜⬜⬜⬜⬜
241 _____				
5¢	blue	40.00	2.00	⬜⬜⬜⬜⬜
242 _____				
6¢	red orange	47.50	5.00	⬜⬜⬜⬜⬜
243 _____				
8¢	olive green	37.50	2.50	⬜⬜⬜⬜⬜
244 _____				
10¢	yellow	55.00	1.50	⬜⬜⬜⬜⬜

	UnFVF	UseFVF	
245 _____			
13¢ **blue green**	37.50	20.00	☐☐☐☐☐
246 _____			
15¢ **gray blue**	50.00	6.00	☐☐☐☐☐
247 _____			
50¢ **gray lilac**	250.00	17.50	☐☐☐☐☐
248 _____			
$1 **violet brown**	375.00	75.00	☐☐☐☐☐
249 _____ **1908. Washington & Franklin Type I Issue**			
1¢ **green**	6.00	4.00	☐☐☐☐☐
250 _____			
2¢ **carmine**	7.50	3.00	☐☐☐☐☐
251 _____			
3¢ **violet** Type I	17.50	20.00	☐☐☐☐☐
252 _____			
4¢ **brown**	27.50	22.50	☐☐☐☐☐
253 _____			
5¢ **blue**	42.50	30.00	☐☐☐☐☐
254 _____ **1908-10. Washington & Franklin Coil Issue**			
1¢ **green**	22.50	12.50	☐☐☐☐☐
255 _____			
2¢ **carmine**	37.50	8.00	☐☐☐☐☐
256 _____			
4¢ **brown**	85.00	70.00	☐☐☐☐☐
257 _____			
5¢ **blue**	100.00	85.00	☐☐☐☐☐
258 _____			
1¢ **green**	50.00	30.00	☐☐☐☐☐
259 _____			
2¢ **carmine**	47.50	7.50	☐☐☐☐☐
260 _____			
4¢ **brown**	115.00	55.00	☐☐☐☐☐

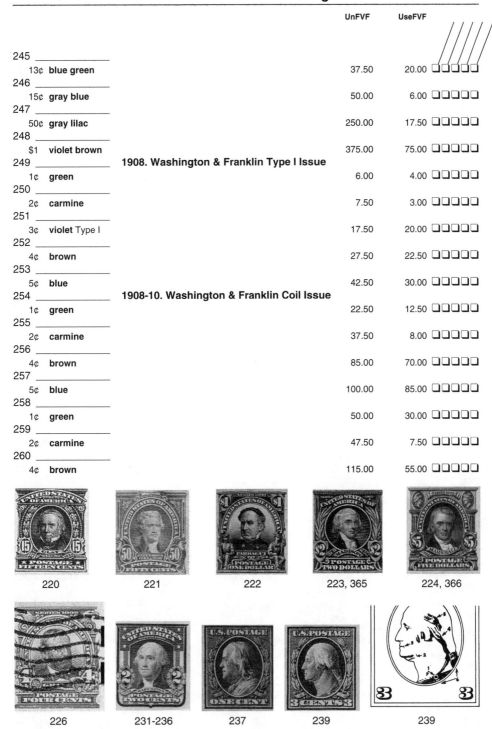

220   221   222   223, 365   224, 366

226   231-236   237   239   239

239 *George Washington. Type I: All stamps of this design and perforated 12 are Type I. Top line of toga from front of neck to top of button is very weak, as are upper parts of five lines of shading that join top line; line between the lips is thin.*

			UnFVF	UseFVF	
261 _____					
	5¢	blue	125.00	75.00	☐☐☐☐☐
262 _____					
	10¢	yellow	1,750.00	850.00	☐☐☐☐☐
263 _____		**1909. Washington & Franklin Issue**			
	1¢	green	85.00	85.00	☐☐☐☐☐
264 _____					
	2¢	carmine	75.00	70.00	☐☐☐☐☐
265 _____					
	3¢	deep violet Type I	1,600.00	1,600.00	☐☐☐☐☐
266 _____					
	4¢	orange brown	15,000.00	—	☐☐☐☐☐
267 _____					
	5¢	blue	3,500.00	3,750.00	☐☐☐☐☐
268 _____					
	6¢	red orange	1,150.00	1,000.00	☐☐☐☐☐
269 _____					
	8¢	olive green	16,000.00	—	☐☐☐☐☐
270 _____					
	10¢	yellow	1,400.00	1,150.00	☐☐☐☐☐
271 _____					
	13¢	blue green	2,350.00	1,450.00	☐☐☐☐☐
272 _____					
	15¢	pale ultramarine	1,150.00	1,000.00	☐☐☐☐☐
273 _____		**1910-14. Washington & Franklin Issue**			
	1¢	green	6.00	.20	☐☐☐☐☐
274 _____					
	2¢	carmine	5.75	.20	☐☐☐☐☐
275 _____					
	3¢	violet Type I	15.00	1.50	☐☐☐☐☐
276 _____		**1911. George Washington Issue**			
	4¢	brown	22.50	.75	☐☐☐☐☐
277 _____					
	5¢	blue	22.50	.75	☐☐☐☐☐
278 _____					
	6¢	red orange	30.00	.85	☐☐☐☐☐
279 _____					
	7¢	black	70.00	8.50	☐☐☐☐☐
280 _____					
	8¢	light olive green	95.00	12.50	☐☐☐☐☐
281 _____					
	10¢	yellow	85.00	4.00	☐☐☐☐☐
282 _____					
	15¢	pale ultramarine	225.00	15.00	☐☐☐☐☐
283 _____		**1910. George Washington Issue**			
	1¢	green	3.00	2.75	☐☐☐☐☐
284 _____					
	2¢	carmine	5.50	3.00	☐☐☐☐☐
285 _____		**1910. Washington & Franklin Coil Issue**			
	1¢	green	22.50	12.50	☐☐☐☐☐
286 _____					
	2¢	carmine	37.50	17.50	☐☐☐☐☐
287 _____					
	1¢	green	85.00	37.50	☐☐☐☐☐

		UnFVF	UseFVF	

288		575.00	250.00	☐☐☐☐☐
2¢	carmine			

1910. George Washington Orangeburg Coil Issue

289		28,500.00	7,000.00	☐☐☐☐☐
3¢	deep violet Type I			

1910. Washington & Franklin Coil Issue

290		4.50	5.00	☐☐☐☐☐
1¢	green			
291		30.00	12.50	☐☐☐☐☐
2¢	carmine			
292		20.00	20.00	☐☐☐☐☐
1¢	green			
293		40.00	10.00	☐☐☐☐☐
2¢	carmine			
294		50.00	50.00	☐☐☐☐☐
3¢	violet Type I			
295		50.00	50.00	☐☐☐☐☐
4¢	brown			
296		50.00	50.00	☐☐☐☐☐
5¢	blue			

1912. Modified George Washington Issue

297		5.00	.20	☐☐☐☐☐
1¢	green			
298		4.50	.20	☐☐☐☐☐
2¢	carmine Type I			
299		1.25	.60	☐☐☐☐☐
1¢	green			
300		1.30	.60	☐☐☐☐☐
2¢	carmine Type I			

1912. George Washington Modified Design Coil Issue

301		5.50	4.50	☐☐☐☐☐
1¢	green			
302		7.50	4.50	☐☐☐☐☐
2¢	carmine Type I			
303		22.50	6.25	☐☐☐☐☐
1¢	green			

273 275-262 276 297

298

298 *George Washington, Type I. The following detailed description is provided, although any 2¢ that fits Point 1 is a Type I.* 1. The line from the front of the neck to and over the top of the button is very weak. The shading lines that run into this line (top of toga) are thin in the area above the cross hatching lines. 2. One shading line in the first (upper) curve of the ribbon above the left numeral and one line in the second (middle) curve above the right numeral. 3. There is a white dash below the ear. 4. The shading lines of the face terminate in front of the ear and are not joined with each other. 5. The lock of hair behind the ear is formed at the bottom by two lines of shading, the lower one being considerably shorter than the other. 6. The hair lines above the ear and slightly to the right form an arrowhead. 7. The shading lines just to the left of the ear form a fairly solid color.

		UnFVF	UseFVF

304 _____
2¢   **carmine** Type I   35.00   1.25 ☐☐☐☐☐

305 _____   **1912-14. Benjamin Franklin Redesigned Issue**
8¢   **pale olive green**   30.00   1.25 ☐☐☐☐☐

306 _____
9¢   **salmon pink**   45.00   12.50 ☐☐☐☐☐

307 _____
10¢ **orange yellow**   32.50   .50 ☐☐☐☐☐

308 _____
12¢ **chocolate**   40.00   4.25 ☐☐☐☐☐

309 _____
15¢ **gray black**   65.00   4.00 ☐☐☐☐☐

310 _____
20¢ **gray blue**   150.00   17.50 ☐☐☐☐☐

311 _____
30¢ **orange red**   115.00   17.50 ☐☐☐☐☐

312 _____
50¢ **violet**   350.00   20.00 ☐☐☐☐☐

313 _____
50¢ **violet**   225.00   20.00 ☐☐☐☐☐

314 _____
$1   **violet brown**   425.00   65.00 ☐☐☐☐☐

315 _____   **1914-15. Washington & Franklin Issue**
1¢   **green**   2.75   .20 ☐☐☐☐☐

316 _____
2¢   **rose red** Type I   2.25   .20 ☐☐☐☐☐

317 _____
3¢   **violet** Type I   12.50   2.00 ☐☐☐☐☐

318 _____
4¢   **brown**   30.00   .75 ☐☐☐☐☐

319 _____
5¢   **blue**   27.50   .70 ☐☐☐☐☐

320 _____
6¢   **red orange**   45.00   2.00 ☐☐☐☐☐

321 _____
7¢   **black**   75.00   5.00 ☐☐☐☐☐

322 _____
8¢   **yellow olive**   30.00   1.25 ☐☐☐☐☐

323 _____
9¢   **salmon**   35.00   2.00 ☐☐☐☐☐

324 _____
10¢ **orange yellow**   40.00   .40 ☐☐☐☐☐

325 _____
11¢ **deep bluish green**   20.00   9.00 ☐☐☐☐☐

326 _____
12¢ **maroon**   23.00   4.25 ☐☐☐☐☐

NOTE: So-called vertical pair, imperforate between, really have at least one perforation hole between the stamps.

327 _____
15¢ **gray black**   110.00   8.50 ☐☐☐☐☐

328 _____
20¢ **pale ultramarine**   175.00   4.50 ☐☐☐☐☐

329 _____
30¢ **orange red**   225.00   20.00 ☐☐☐☐☐

330 _____
50¢ **violet**   525.00   22.50 ☐☐☐☐☐

		UnFVF	UseFVF	

331 _____ **1914-15. Benjamin Franklin Issue**

$1 **violet black** — 725.00 85.00 ☐☐☐☐☐

332 _____ **1915. George Washington Issue**

2¢ **rose red** Type I — 100.00 225.00 ☐☐☐☐☐

333 _____ **1914. George Washington Coil Issue**

1¢ **green** — 1.25 1.25 ☐☐☐☐☐

334 _____

2¢ **carmine** Type I — 8.50 8.00 ☐☐☐☐☐

335 _____

1¢ **green** — 22.50 7.50 ☐☐☐☐☐

336 _____

2¢ **carmine** Type I — 32.50 1.75 ☐☐☐☐☐

337 _____

3¢ **violet** Type I — 225.00 125.00 ☐☐☐☐☐

338 _____

4¢ **brown** — 120.00 47.50 ☐☐☐☐☐

339 _____

5¢ **blue** — 47.50 32.50 ☐☐☐☐☐

340 _____ **1914-16. Washington & Franklin Rotary Press Coil Issue**

1¢ **green** — 6.50 4.25 ☐☐☐☐☐

341 _____

2¢ **carmine** Type III — 10.00 4.25 ☐☐☐☐☐

342 _____ **1914. Washington Rotary Press Sidewise Coil Issue**

2¢ **carmine** Type I — 375.00 750.00 ☐☐☐☐☐

343 _____ **1914-16. Washington Issue**

1¢ **green** — 10.00 2.50 ☐☐☐☐☐

344 _____

2¢ **carmine** Type III — 10.00 1.15 ☐☐☐☐☐

345 _____

3¢ **violet** Type I — 225.00 115.00 ☐☐☐☐☐

346 _____

4¢ **yellow brown** — 27.50 20.00 ☐☐☐☐☐

305-314

315-321

322-331

333 and 340

341 *Type III. Same as Type II except two lines of shading in the curves of the ribbons.*

344

344 *Type II. Shading lines in ribbons same as Type I. The top line of toga rope is heavy and the rope is heavily shaded. The shading lines on the face, in front of the ear, are joined by a heavy vertical curved line.*

		UnFVF	UseFVF	

347 _____

   5¢ **blue** — 32.50 — 17.50 ⬜⬜⬜⬜⬜

348 _____   **1916-17. Washington & Franklin Issue**

   1¢ **green** — 6.00 — .50 ⬜⬜⬜⬜⬜

349 _____

   2¢ **carmine** Type I — 4.00 — .35 ⬜⬜⬜⬜⬜

350 _____

   3¢ **violet** Type I — 65.00 — 15.00 ⬜⬜⬜⬜⬜

351 _____

   4¢ **yellow brown** — 42.50 — 2.25 ⬜⬜⬜⬜⬜

352 _____

   5¢ **blue** — 65.00 — 2.25 ⬜⬜⬜⬜⬜

353 _____

   5¢ **carmine** — 550.00 — 700.00 ⬜⬜⬜⬜⬜

NOTE: 353 The "Five Cent Red Error" was caused by mistakenly using a 5¢ transfer roll in reentering three positions on plate 7942, a plate of the 2¢ stamps. Of the 400 positions on the plate, 397 copies were 2¢ and three copies were 5¢. The error was not discovered until a considerable number of sheets were in the post offices, and many of them were picked up by collectors. The errors exist perforated 10 (No. 353), perforated 11 (No. 385), and imperforate (No. 370). The shade actually is carmine, but the stamp commonly is called the "Red Error."

354 _____

   6¢ **red orange** — 80.00 — 7.50 ⬜⬜⬜⬜⬜

355 _____

   7¢ **black** — 100.00 — 12.50 ⬜⬜⬜⬜⬜

356 _____

   8¢ **yellow olive** — 55.00 — 6.50 ⬜⬜⬜⬜⬜

357 _____

   9¢ **salmon** — 50.00 — 15.00 ⬜⬜⬜⬜⬜

358 _____

  10¢ **orange yellow** — 95.00 — 1.25 ⬜⬜⬜⬜⬜

359 _____

  11¢ **deep bluish green** — 35.00 — 22.50 ⬜⬜⬜⬜⬜

360 _____

  12¢ **chocolate** — 45.00 — 5.50 ⬜⬜⬜⬜⬜

361 _____

  15¢ **gray black** — 165.00 — 12.50 ⬜⬜⬜⬜⬜

362 _____

  20¢ **pale blue** — 225.00 — 12.50 ⬜⬜⬜⬜⬜

362A _____

  30¢ **orange red** — 4,500.00 — — ⬜⬜⬜⬜⬜

NOTE: 362A Two sheets of 100 stamps of the 30¢ denomination were discovered without any trace of watermark, as authenticated by The Philatelic Foundation's expert committee.

363 _____

  50¢ **light violet** — 950.00 — 65.00 ⬜⬜⬜⬜⬜

364 _____

  $1 **violet black** — 625.00 — 20.00 ⬜⬜⬜⬜⬜

365 _____   **1917. James Madison Issue**

  $2 **dark blue** — 325.00 — 45.00 ⬜⬜⬜⬜⬜

366 _____   **1917. John Marshall Issue**

  $5 **light green** — 250.00 — 50.00 ⬜⬜⬜⬜⬜

367 _____   **1916-1917. George Washington Issue**

   1¢ **green** — 1.15 — 1.00 ⬜⬜⬜⬜⬜

368 _____

   2¢ **carmine** Type I — 1.40 — 1.30 ⬜⬜⬜⬜⬜

369 _____

   3¢ **violet** Type I — 15.00 — 8.50 ⬜⬜⬜⬜⬜

	UnFVF	UseFVF

370 _____

5¢ carmine   12,500.00   □□□□□

NOTE: This stamp commonly is called the "Red Error," but really is carmine. See note with No. 353.

371 _____   **1916-22. Washington Rotary Press Coil Issue**

1¢ green   .75   .20 □□□□□

372 _____

2¢ **carmine** Type III   3.00   1.75 □□□□□

373 _____

3¢ **violet** Type I   4.50   1.50 □□□□□

374 _____   **1916-22. Washington Issue**

1¢ green   .60   .20 □□□□□

375 _____

2¢ **carmine** Type III   8.50   .20 □□□□□

376 _____

3¢ **violet** Type II   11.50   1.25 □□□□□

377 _____

4¢ **yellow brown**   10.50   4.00 □□□□□

378 _____

5¢ **blue**   3.50   1.25 □□□□□

379 _____

10¢ **orange yellow**   19.00   12.50 □□□□□

380 _____   **1917-19 Washington & Franklin Issue**

1¢ green   .55   .20 □□□□□

381 _____

2¢ **rose red** Type I   .50   .20 □□□□□

NOTE: Type Ia is similar to Type I, but lines of the design are stronger. This is particularly noticeable on the toga button, toga rope and rope shading lines, which are heavy. Lines in the ribbons are similar to Type I.

382 _____

3¢ **violet** Type I   12.50   .20 □□□□□

382A _____

3¢ **violet** Type II   15.00   .40 □□□□□

383 _____

4¢ **yellow brown**   11.50   .30 □□□□□

384 _____

5¢ **blue**   8.50   .25 □□□□□

385 _____

5¢ **carmine**   400.00   500.00 □□□□□

NOTE: This stamp commonly is called the "Red Error" but really is carmine. See note with No. 353.

386 _____

6¢ **red orange**   12.50   .40 □□□□□

387 _____

7¢ **black**   25.00   1.25 □□□□□

388 _____

8¢ **yellow olive**   12.50   1.00 □□□□□

365

366

369

369 *3¢. On Type II the top line of the toga rope is heavy, and the rope shading lines are also heavy and complete. The line between the lips is heavy.*

			UnFVF	UseFVF	
389					
	9¢	**salmon**	14.00	2.50	☐☐☐☐☐
390					
	10¢	**orange yellow**	17.50	.25	☐☐☐☐☐
391					
	11¢	**deep bluish green**	9.00	3.00	☐☐☐☐☐
392					
	12¢	**brown purple**	9.00	.65	☐☐☐☐☐
393					
	13¢	**apple green**	10.50	6.50	☐☐☐☐☐
394					
	15¢	**gray black**	37.50	1.25	☐☐☐☐☐
395					
	20¢	**pale blue**	47.50	.50	☐☐☐☐☐
396					
	30¢	**orange red**	37.50	1.25	☐☐☐☐☐
397					
	50¢	**reddish violet**	65.00	.90	☐☐☐☐☐
398					
	$1	**black purple**	55.00	1.75	☐☐☐☐☐
399		**1917. George Washington Issue**			
	2¢	**carmine**	275.00	450.00	☐☐☐☐☐
400		**1918-20. Benjamin Franklin Issue**			
	$2	**orange & black**	650.00	225.00	☐☐☐☐☐
401					
	$2	**carmine & black**	190.00	40.00	☐☐☐☐☐
402					
	$5	**deep green & black**	225.00	35.00	☐☐☐☐☐
403		**1918-20. George Washington Issue**			
	1¢	**dull green**	2.00	.75	☐☐☐☐☐
404					
	2¢	**rose red** Type VII	17.50	.35	☐☐☐☐☐
404A					
	2¢	**rose red** Type V	15.00	1.00	☐☐☐☐☐
404B					
	2¢	**rose red** Type Va	8.00	.35	☐☐☐☐☐
404C					
	2¢	**rose red** Type VI	45.00	1.50	☐☐☐☐☐
404D					
	2¢	**rose red** Type IV	25.00	4.25	☐☐☐☐☐
405		**1918. George Washington Issue**			
	3¢	**purple** Type III	3.00	.40	☐☐☐☐☐
405A					
	3¢	**purple** Type IV	1.25	.20	☐☐☐☐☐
406		**1919-20. George Washington Issue**			
	1¢	**dull green**	10.00	8.50	☐☐☐☐☐
407					
	2¢	**rose red** Type IV	35.00	30.00	☐☐☐☐☐
407A					
	2¢	**rose red** Type V	190.00	85.00	☐☐☐☐☐
407B					
	2¢	**rose red** Type Va	12.50	8.50	☐☐☐☐☐
407C					
	2¢	**rose red** Type VI	35.00	22.50	☐☐☐☐☐

400, 401

402

403

Type IV: Top line of toga rope is broken. Lines inside toga button read "D (reversed) ID." The line of color in the left "2" is very thin and is usually broken.

Type V: Top line of the toga is complete. Five vertical shading lines in toga button. Line of color in left "2" is very thin and usually broken. Shading dots on nose form a triangle with six dots in third row from bottom.

Type Va: Same as Type V except on the shading dots on the nose, in which the third row from the bottom has only four dots instead of six.

Type VI: Same as Type V but there is a heavy line of color in the left "2."

Type VII: The line of color in the left "2" is clear and unbroken, heavier than on Type V or Va but not as heavy as on Type VI. An extra vertical row of dots has been added on the lip, making four rows of three dots instead of two dots. Additional dots have been added to the hair on top of the head.

404-404D

405

Type III: Top line of toga is strong but the fifth shading line is missing. The center shading line of the toga button consists of two vertical dashes with a dot between them. The "P" and "O" of "POSTAGE" have a line of color between them.

Type IV: The "P" and "O" of "POSTAGE" are joined with no line of color between them. The center shading line runs right through the dot in the toga button.

		UnFVF	UseFVF

407D _____
2¢   **rose red** Type VII — 1,500.00   575.00 ☐☐☐☐☐

408 _____
3¢   **violet** Type IV — 8.75   6.00 ☐☐☐☐☐

409 _____   **1919. George Washington Issue**
1¢   **dull green** — 14.00   16.50 ☐☐☐☐☐

410 _____   **1919. George Washington Issue**
1¢   **green** — 8.00   8.00 ☐☐☐☐☐

411 _____
2¢   **carmine red** Type II — 2,500.00   3,200.00 ☐☐☐☐☐

411A _____
2¢   **carmine red** Type III — 10.00   9.00 ☐☐☐☐☐

412 _____
3¢   **gray lilac** Type II — 32.50   35.00 ☐☐☐☐☐

413 _____   **1920. George Washington Issue**
1¢   **green** — 10.00   1.00 ☐☐☐☐☐

414 _____   **1921. George Washington Issue**
1¢   **green** — .55   .20 ☐☐☐☐☐

415 _____   **1922. George Washington Issue**
1¢   **green** — 12,000.00   2,400.00 ☐☐☐☐☐

416 _____   **1921. George Washington Issue**
1¢   **green** — 120.00   130.00 ☐☐☐☐☐

417 _____
2¢   **carmine** Type III — 85.00   115.00 ☐☐☐☐☐

418 _____   **1925. Nathan Hale Issue**
1/2¢ **olive brown** — .30   .20 ☐☐☐☐☐

419 _____   **1923. Benjamin Franklin Issue**
1¢   **green** — 1.50   .20 ☐☐☐☐☐

420 _____   **1925. Warren Harding Issue**
1-1/2¢ **yellow brown** — 2.50   .25 ☐☐☐☐☐

NOTE: See also CM60-63, a 2¢ black Harding of the same design as 420. Some include it with the 1922-34 Regular Issue Series.

421 _____   **1923. George Washington Type I Issue**
2¢   **carmine** Type I — 1.25   .20 ☐☐☐☐☐

422 _____   **1923. Abraham Lincoln Issue**
3¢   **reddish violet** — 18.00   .65 ☐☐☐☐☐

423 _____   **1923. Martha Washington Issue**
4¢   **yellow brown** — 20.00   .20 ☐☐☐☐☐

424 _____   **1922. Theodore Roosevelt Issue**
5¢   **Prussian blue** — 20.00   .20 ☐☐☐☐☐

425 _____   **1922. James Garfield Issue**
6¢   **red orange** — 35.00   .55 ☐☐☐☐☐

426 _____   **1923. William McKinley Issue**
7¢   **black** — 9.00   .35 ☐☐☐☐☐

427 _____   **1923. Ulysses S. Grant Issue**
8¢   **yellow olive** — 50.00   .85 ☐☐☐☐☐

428 _____   **1923. Thomas Jefferson Issue**
9¢   **carmine rose** — 15.00   .75 ☐☐☐☐☐

429 _____   **1923. James Monroe Issue**
10¢   **orange yellow** — 19.00   .25 ☐☐☐☐☐

430 _____   **1922. Rutherford B. Hayes Issue**
11¢   **turquoise blue** — 2.50   .30 ☐☐☐☐☐

NOTE: No. 430 is known in a wide range of color shades between yellow green and light blue.

431 _____   **1923. Grover Cleveland Issue**
12¢   **maroon** — 6.25   .20 ☐☐☐☐☐

410

411

412

416

417

418, 473

419, 443, 446, 448,
449A 450, 461,
469, 474, 495, 506

420, 444, 451,
462, 470, 472,
475, 496, 507

421, 445, 447, 449,
452, 463, 471,
476, 476A, 497, 508

422, 453, 464,
477, 498, 509

423, 454, 465,
478, 499, 510

424, 455, 466,
479, 500, 511

425, 456, 467,
480, 501, 512

426, 457,
481, 502, 513

427, 458,
482, 503, 514

428, 459,
483, 504, 515

429, 460, 468,
484, 505, 516

430, 485

431, 486

432, 487

433, 488

434, 489

435, 490

436, 491

437, 492

438, 493

439, 494

440

			UnFVF	UseFVF	
432 _____		**1926. Benjamin Harrison Issue**			
	13¢ **green**		10.00	.30 ☐☐☐☐☐
433 _____		**1923. American Indian Issue**			
	14¢ **blue**		4.75	.50 ☐☐☐☐☐
434 _____		**1922. Statue of Liberty Issue**			
	15¢ **gray black**		25.00	.20 ☐☐☐☐☐
435 _____		**1925. Woodrow Wilson Issue**			
	17¢ **black**		12.00	.20 ☐☐☐☐☐
436 _____		**1923. Golden Gate Issue**			
	20¢ **carmine red**		22.50	.20 ☐☐☐☐☐
437 _____		**1922. Niagara Falls Issue**			
	25¢ **green**		19.00	.50 ☐☐☐☐☐
438 _____		**1923. Bison Issue**			
	30¢ **olive brown**		35.00	.50 ☐☐☐☐☐
439 _____		**1922. Arlington Issue**			
	50¢ **gray lilac**		57.00	.20 ☐☐☐☐☐
440 _____		**1923. Lincoln Memorial Issue**			
	$1 **purple brown**		47.00	.50 ☐☐☐☐☐
441 _____		**1923. U. S. Capitol Issue**			
	$2 **blue**		100.00	6.00 ☐☐☐☐☐
442 _____		**1923. Head of Freedom Issue**			
	$5 **carmine & blue**		200.00	13.50 ☐☐☐☐☐
443 _____		**1923. Issue**			
	1¢ **green**		7.50	3.00 ☐☐☐☐☐
444 _____					
	1-1/2¢ **yellow brown**		1.50	1.00 ☐☐☐☐☐

NOTE: No. 444 exists in a rotary press printing, No. 472.

			UnFVF	UseFVF	
445 _____					
	2¢ **carmine**		1.50	1.00 ☐☐☐☐☐
446 _____		**1923-24. Rotary Press Printings**			
	1¢ **green**		90.00	90.00 ☐☐☐☐☐
447 _____					
	2¢ **carmine**		75.00	85.00 ☐☐☐☐☐
448 _____		**1923-24. Rotary Press Printing Issue**			
	1¢ **green**		15,000.00	4,000.00 ☐☐☐☐☐
449 _____					
	2¢ **carmine**		285.00	300.00 ☐☐☐☐☐

NOTE: Nos. 448 and 449 were made from coil waste. Design 18 1/2 to 19mm wide by 22 1/2mm high.

			UnFVF	UseFVF	
449A _____					
	1¢ **green**		—	42,500.00 ☐☐☐☐☐
450 _____		**1923-26. Rotary Press Printing Issue**			
	1¢ **green**		7.50	1.00 ☐☐☐☐☐
451 _____					
	1-1/2¢ **yellow brown**		3.75	1.00 ☐☐☐☐☐
452 _____					
	2¢ **carmine**		2.00	.35 ☐☐☐☐☐
453 _____					
	3¢ **reddish violet**		20.00	2.50 ☐☐☐☐☐
454 _____					
	4¢ **yellow brown**		14.00	.80 ☐☐☐☐☐
455 _____					
	5¢ **blue**		14.00	.80 ☐☐☐☐☐
456 _____					
	6¢ **orange**		6.25	.75 ☐☐☐☐☐

		UnFVF	UseFVF	
457 _____				
	7¢ **black**	9.00	6.50	❑❑❑❑❑
458 _____				
	8¢ **yellow olive**	20.00	4.00	❑❑❑❑❑
459 _____				
	9¢ **red**	4.25	2.50	❑❑❑❑❑
460 _____				
	10¢ **orange yellow**	50.00	.45	❑❑❑❑❑
461 _____	**1923-26. Rotary Press Coil Issue**			
	1¢ **yellow green**	.35	.20	❑❑❑❑❑
462 _____				
	1-1/2¢ **yellow brown**	.75	.20	❑❑❑❑❑
463 _____				
	2¢ **carmine** Type I	.45	.20	❑❑❑❑❑
464 _____				
	3¢ **reddish violet**	5.50	.30	❑❑❑❑❑
465 _____				
	4¢ **yellow brown**	3.75	.50	❑❑❑❑❑
466 _____				
	5¢ **blue**	1.75	.20	❑❑❑❑❑
467 _____				
	6¢ **orange**	9.50	.35	❑❑❑❑❑
468 _____				
	10¢ **orange yellow**	3.50	.20	❑❑❑❑❑
469 _____	**1924. Rotary Press Coil Issue**			
	1¢ **yellow green**	.35	.20	❑❑❑❑❑
470 _____				
	1-1/2¢ **yellow brown**	.35	.20	❑❑❑❑❑
471 _____				
	2¢ **carmine**	.35	.20	❑❑❑❑❑
472 _____	**1926. Rotary Press Issue**			
	1-1/2¢ **yellow brown**	2.25	2.00	❑❑❑❑❑
473 _____	**1926-34. Rotary Press Issue**			
	1/2¢ **olive brown**	.25	.20	❑❑❑❑❑
474 _____				
	1¢ **green**	.25	.20	❑❑❑❑❑
475 _____				
	1-1/2¢ **yellow brown**	2.00	.20	❑❑❑❑❑
476 _____				
	2¢ **carmine red** Type I	.25	.20	❑❑❑❑❑
476A _____				
	2¢ **carmine red** Type II	300.00	15.00	❑❑❑❑❑
477 _____				
	3¢ **reddish violet**	.55	.20	❑❑❑❑❑

441

442

463 Type 1 (left); Type II (right)

463 Type II

	UnFVF	UseFVF	
478 _____			
4¢ **yellow brown**	2.75	.20	☐☐☐☐☐
479 _____			
5¢ **blue**	2.25	.20	☐☐☐☐☐
480 _____			
6¢ **orange**	2.25	.20	☐☐☐☐☐
481 _____			
7¢ **black**	2.25	.20	☐☐☐☐☐
482 _____			
8¢ **yellow olive**	2.25	.20	☐☐☐☐☐
483 _____			
9¢ **red**	2.00	.20	☐☐☐☐☐
484 _____			
10¢ **orange yellow**	4.00	.20	☐☐☐☐☐
485 _____			
11¢ **turquoise green**	2.75	.20	☐☐☐☐☐
486 _____			
12¢ **brown purple**	6.00	.20	☐☐☐☐☐
487 _____			
13¢ **yellow green**	2.25	.20	☐☐☐☐☐
488 _____			
14¢ **blue**	4.00	.50	☐☐☐☐☐
489 _____			
15¢ **gray black**	8.00	.20	☐☐☐☐☐
490 _____ **1931. Rotary Press Issue**			
17¢ **black**	5.50	.20	☐☐☐☐☐
491 _____			
20¢ **carmine rose**	9.50	.20	☐☐☐☐☐
492 _____			
25¢ **green**	11.00	.20	☐☐☐☐☐
493 _____			
30¢ **olive brown**	17.50	.20	☐☐☐☐☐
494 _____			
50¢ **lilac**	42.50	.20	☐☐☐☐☐
495 _____ **1929. Kansas and Nebraska Overprints Issue**			
1¢ **green**	2.00	1.50	☐☐☐☐☐
496 _____			
1-1/2¢ **yellow brown**	3.00	2.25	☐☐☐☐☐
497 _____			
2¢ **carmine red**	3.00	1.00	☐☐☐☐☐
498 _____			
3¢ **reddish violet**	15.00	11.00	☐☐☐☐☐
499 _____			
4¢ **yellow brown**	15.00	8.50	☐☐☐☐☐
500 _____			
5¢ **blue**	12.50	9.00	☐☐☐☐☐
501 _____			
6¢ **orange**	25.00	15.00	☐☐☐☐☐
502 _____			
7¢ **black**	25.00	20.00	☐☐☐☐☐
503 _____			
8¢ **yellow olive**	70.00	60.00	☐☐☐☐☐
504 _____			
9¢ **salmon**	12.50	10.00	☐☐☐☐☐

		UnFVF	UseFVF	

505 _____
  10¢ orange yellow   20.00   12.50 ☐☐☐☐☐
506 _____
  1¢ green   2.25   2.00 ☐☐☐☐☐
507 _____
  1-1/2¢ yellow brown   2.25   2.00 ☐☐☐☐☐
508 _____
  2¢ carmine red   2.25   1.00 ☐☐☐☐☐
509 _____
  3¢ reddish violet   11.00   8.00 ☐☐☐☐☐
510 _____
  4¢ yellow brown   15.00   10.00 ☐☐☐☐☐
511 _____
  5¢ blue   12.50   11.50 ☐☐☐☐☐
512 _____
  6¢ orange   35.00   17.50 ☐☐☐☐☐
513 _____
  7¢ black   18.50   12.50 ☐☐☐☐☐
514 _____
  8¢ yellow olive   25.00   17.50 ☐☐☐☐☐
515 _____
  9¢ salmon   30.00   22.50 ☐☐☐☐☐
516 _____
  10¢ orange yellow   85.00   17.50 ☐☐☐☐☐
517 _____ **1930-32. Warren G. Harding New Design Issue**
  1-1/2¢ yellow brown   .25   .20 ☐☐☐☐☐
518 _____ **1930-32. George Washington Issue**
  3¢ reddish violet   .25   .20 ☐☐☐☐☐
519 _____ **1930-32. William H. Taft Issue**
  4¢ yellow brown   .90   .20 ☐☐☐☐☐
520 _____ **1930-32. Warren G. Harding New Design Coil Issue**
  1-1/2¢ yellow brown   1.50   .20 ☐☐☐☐☐
521 _____ **1930-32. George Washington Coil Issue**
  3¢ reddish violet   1.75   .20 ☐☐☐☐☐
522 _____ **1930-32. William H. Taft Coil Issue**
  4¢ yellow brown   2.75   .75 ☐☐☐☐☐

495-505   502   503   506-516   514

516   517, 520   518, 521, 523   519, 522   520 Line Pair

		UnFVF	UseFVF

523 _____ **1930-32. George Washington Coil Issue**

3¢   **reddish violet** — 1.00   .75 ☐☐☐☐☐

524 _____ **1938. Benjamin Franklin Issue**

1/2¢ **red orange** — .25   .20 ☐☐☐☐☐

525 _____ **1938. George Washington Issue**

1¢   **green** — .25   .20 ☐☐☐☐☐

526 _____ **1938. Martha Washington Issue**

1-1/2¢ **yellow brown** — .25   .20 ☐☐☐☐☐

NOTE: No. 526z was produced circa 1955 as a result of experiments conducted by Pitney-Bowes for the Post Office Department. A single copy is known in collectors' hands.

527 _____ **1938. John Adams Issue**

2¢   **rose** — .25   .20 ☐☐☐☐☐

528 _____ **1938. Thomas Jefferson Issue**

3¢   **violet** — .25   .20 ☐☐☐☐☐

529 _____ **1938. James Madison Issue**

4¢   **bright purple** — 1.15   .20 ☐☐☐☐☐

530 _____ **1938. White House Issue**

4-1/2¢ **gray** — .25   .20 ☐☐☐☐☐

531 _____ **1938. James Monroe Issue**

5¢   **light blue** — .25   .20 ☐☐☐☐☐

532 _____ **1938. John Quincy Adams Issue**

6¢   **orange** — .35   .20 ☐☐☐☐☐

533 _____ **1938. Andrew Jackson Issue**

7¢   **sepia** — .45   .20 ☐☐☐☐☐

534 _____ **1938. Martin Van Buren Issue**

8¢   **olive green** — .45   .20 ☐☐☐☐☐

535 _____ **1938. William Henry Harrison Issue**

9¢   **rose pink** — .50   .20 ☐☐☐☐☐

536 _____ **1938. John Tyler Issue**

10¢   **Venetian red** — .45   .20 ☐☐☐☐☐

537 _____ **1938. James Knox Polk Issue**

11¢   **cobalt** — .75   .20 ☐☐☐☐☐

538 _____ **1938. Zachary Taylor Issue**

12¢ **light reddish violet** — 1.40   .20 ☐☐☐☐☐

539 _____ **1938. Millard Fillmore Issue**

13¢ **blue green** — 2.25   .20 ☐☐☐☐☐

540 _____ **1938. Franklin Pierce Issue**

14¢ **blue** — 1.15   .20 ☐☐☐☐☐

541 _____ **1938. James Buchanan Issue**

15¢ **slate** — .65   .20 ☐☐☐☐☐

542 _____ **1938. Abraham Lincoln Issue**

16¢ **black** — 1.25   .60 ☐☐☐☐☐

543 _____ **1938. Andrew Johnson Issue**

17¢ **rose red** — 1.25   .20 ☐☐☐☐☐

544 _____ **1938. Ulysses S. Grant Issue**

18¢ **brown carmine** — 2.25   .25 ☐☐☐☐☐

545 _____ **1938. Rutherford B. Hayes Issue**

19¢ **light reddish violet** — 2.00   .60 ☐☐☐☐☐

546 _____ **1938. James A. Garfield Issue**

20¢ **blue green** — 1.25   .20 ☐☐☐☐☐

547 _____ **1938. Chester A. Arthur Issue**

21¢ **slate blue** — 2.25   .20 ☐☐☐☐☐

548 _____ **1938. Grover Cleveland Issue**

22¢ **vermilion** — 1.50   .75 ☐☐☐☐☐

524

525, 556, 565

526, 557, 566

527, 558, 567

528, 559, 568

529, 560

530, 561

531, 562

532, 563

533

534

535

536, 564

537

538

539

540

541

542

543

544

545

546

547

548

549

550

551

552

553

	UnFVF	UseFVF

549 _____ **1938. Benjamin Harrison Issue**
24¢ **gray green**   4.25   .35 ☐☐☐☐☐
550 _____ **1938. William McKinley Issue**
25¢ **claret**   1.20   .20 ☐☐☐☐☐
551 _____ **1938. Theodore Roosevelt Issue**
30¢ **deep ultramarine**   5.00   .20 ☐☐☐☐☐
552 _____ **1938. William Howard Taft Issue**
50¢ **light red violet**   8.50   .20 ☐☐☐☐☐

NOTE: Flat plate printing, perforated 11.

553 _____ **1938. Woodrow Wilson Issue**
$1   **dark purple and black**   10.00   .20 ☐☐☐☐☐

NOTE: 553a is printed on pre-gummed, whiter and thicker paper. It was printed on "dry" paper; No. 553 was printed on pre-dampened paper.

554 _____ **1938. Warren G. Harding Issue**
$2   **green and black**   27.50 4.75 ☐☐☐☐☐
555 _____ **1938. Calvin Coolidge Issue**
$5   **carmine and black**   115.00 4.50 ☐☐☐☐☐
556 _____ **1939. Presidential Coil Issue**
1¢   **green**   .25   .20 ☐☐☐☐☐
557 _____
1-1/2¢ **yellow brown**   .20   .25 ☐☐☐☐☐
558 _____
2¢   **rose**   .25   .20 ☐☐☐☐☐
559 _____
3¢   **violet**   .25   .20 ☐☐☐☐☐
560 _____
4¢   **bright purple**   7.50   .75 ☐☐☐☐☐
561 _____
4-1/2¢ **gray**   .75   .50 ☐☐☐☐☐
562 _____
5¢   **bright blue**   6.00   .50 ☐☐☐☐☐
563 _____
6¢   **orange**   1.25   .50 ☐☐☐☐☐
564 _____
10¢ **Venetian red**   12.50 1.25 ☐☐☐☐☐
565 _____ **1939. Presidential Coil Issue**
1¢   **green**   .75   .25 ☐☐☐☐☐
566 _____
1-1/2¢ **yellow brown**   1.50   .75 ☐☐☐☐☐
567 _____
2¢   **rose**   2.50   .75 ☐☐☐☐☐

	MNHVF	UseVF

568 _____
3¢   **violet**   2.25   .75 ☐☐☐☐☐
569 _____ **1955. Benjamin Franklin Issue**
1/2¢ **vermilion** wet print   .25   .20 ☐☐☐☐☐
570 _____ **1954. George Washington Issue**
1¢   **dull green** wet print   .25   .20 ☐☐☐☐☐
571 _____ **1956. Mount Vernon Issue**
1-1/2¢ **brown carmine** dry print   .25   .20 ☐☐☐☐☐
572 _____ **1954. Thomas Jefferson Issue**
2¢   **rose** dry print   .25   .20 ☐☐☐☐☐

NOTE: Silkote paper was used for only 50,000 stamps. Silkote varieties need expertization.

	MNHVF	UseVF

573 _____ **1954. Statue of Liberty Issue**

3¢ **violet** wet print .25 .20 ☐☐☐☐☐

NOTE: Type I tagging: mat tagging. The four separate mats used did not cover the entire sheet of 400 stamps and certain untagged areas help to identify this variety. See expanded definition in the catalog introduction.

NOTE: Type II tagging: roll tagging. Continuously surfaced rolls replaced the previously used tagging mats. Only the plate number selvage margin is partially tagged, and the plate number blocks have one untagged margin.

NOTE: Type III tagging: curved metal plate tagging. Sheet margins are almost fully tagged but a "hot line" of intense phosphor-tagging or untagged narrow gap, 1mm or less in width, can appear on stamps from any position in the pane.

574 _____ **1954. Abraham Lincoln Issue**

4¢ **magenta** wet print .25 .20 ☐☐☐☐☐

575 _____ **1954. James Monroe Issue**

5¢ **blue** dry print .25 .20 ☐☐☐☐☐

576 _____ **1955. Theodore Roosevelt Issue**

6¢ **rose red** wet print .25 .20 ☐☐☐☐☐

577 _____ **1956. Woodrow Wilson Issue**

7¢ **carmine red** dry print .25 .20 ☐☐☐☐☐

578 _____ **1954. Statue of Liberty Issue**

8¢ **deep blue & carmine** .25 .20 ☐☐☐☐☐

NOTE: This stamp was produced on both flat-bed and rotary presses. See also 591 for Type II.

579 _____ **1956. The Alamo Issue**

9¢ **rose lilac** dry print .25 .20 ☐☐☐☐☐

580 _____ **1956. Independence Hall Issue**

10¢ **brown purple** dry print .25 .20 ☐☐☐☐☐

581 _____ **1956. Monticello Issue**

20¢ **bright blue** dry print .50 .20 ☐☐☐☐☐

582 _____ **1955. Robert E. Lee Issue**

30¢ **black** wet print 1.50 .25 ☐☐☐☐☐

554

555

569

570, 587

571

572, 588

573, 589

574, 590

575

576

577

578

579

580

581

	MNHVF	UseVF

583 _____ **1955. John Marshall Issue**

40¢ **brown carmine** wet print   2.75   .25 ❑❑❑❑❑

584 _____ **1955. Susan B. Anthony Issue**

50¢ **red violet** wet print   2.00   .20 ❑❑❑❑❑

585 _____ **1955. Patrick Henry Issue**

$1 **dark lilac** wet print   7.00   .20 ❑❑❑❑❑

586 _____ **1956. Alexander Hamilton Issue**

$5 **black** dry print   70.00   6.50 ❑❑❑❑❑

587 _____ **1954. George Washington Issue**

1¢ **dull green** wet print   .45   .25 ❑❑❑❑❑

588 _____ **1954. Thomas Jefferson Issue**

2¢ **rose** wet print   .25   .20 ❑❑❑❑❑

589 _____ **1954. Statue of Liberty Issue**

3¢ **purple** wet print, large holes   .25   .20 ❑❑❑❑❑

NOTE: No. 589psz1, the so-called "Look Coil," was prepared for Look magazine in coil rolls of 3,000 subjects. All but 99,000 of this issue were affixed to outgoing mail and return addressed envelopes on an automatic labeling machine at Des Moines, Iowa. The earliest known use was Dec. 29, 1966. The common usage was in combination with a 2¢ Jefferson coil (No. 588). The paper on which the stamps were printed is plain, without fluorescent content, and tagging is uniform and brilliant. A special printing was issued, in coils of 500 subjects, to satisfy collector demands (No. 589psz1). The original printing had a sharper, more well-defined design. The reprint has more intense shade of purple ink. The philatelic examples were on slightly fluorescent paper, the tagging was less intense and on some coils a tagging plate flaw repeats every 24th stamp, both as a "Hot" line and as an untagged line.

590 _____ **1958. Abraham Lincoln Issue**

4¢ **bright purple** wet print (Bureau precancel only)   29.00   1.00 ❑❑❑❑❑

591 _____ **1958. Statue of Liberty Issue**

8¢ **deep blue & carmine**   .25   .20 ❑❑❑❑❑

592 _____ **1958. John Jay Issue**

15¢ **brown purple** dry print   .75   .20 ❑❑❑❑❑

593 _____ **1958. Paul Revere Issue**

25¢ **deep blue green**   1.50   .20 ❑❑❑❑❑

594 _____ **1959. Bunker Hill Monument Issue**

2-1/2¢ **slate blue** dry print   .25   .20 ❑❑❑❑❑

595 _____ **1959. Hermitage Issue**

4-1/2¢ **blue green** dry print   .25   .20 ❑❑❑❑❑

596 _____ **1959. Benjamin Harrison Issue**

12¢ **carmine red** dry print   .30   .20 ❑❑❑❑❑

NOTE: Type IIa tagging: wide roll tagging. All margins are fully tagged.

597 _____ **1959. Hermitage Coil Issue**

4-1/2¢ **blue green** large holes   2.00   1.25 ❑❑❑❑❑

598 _____ **1959. Bunker Hill Monument Coil Issue**

2-1/2¢ **slate blue** large holes.   .25   .20 ❑❑❑❑❑

599 _____ **1960. Palace of the Governors**

1-1/4¢ **turquoise blue**.   .25   .20 ❑❑❑❑❑

600 _____ **1960. Palace of the Governors Coil Issue**

1-1/4¢ **turquoise blue** large holes   15.00   .25 ❑❑❑❑❑

601 _____ **1961. Statue of Liberty Issue**

11¢ **carmine red & blue**   .30   .20 ❑❑❑❑❑

NOTE: Type OP tagging: Used on multicolor stamps previously designated to be printed on Giori presses.

602 _____ **1961. John J. Pershing Issue**

8¢ **brown**   .25   .20 ❑❑❑❑❑

NOTE: There is disagreement concerning whether No. 602 is actually part of the Liberty Series. Although printed within the same period, it does not match the design characteristics of other stamps in the series.

603 _____ **1962. Evergreen Wreath and Burning Candles Issue**

4¢ **green & red**   .25   .20 ❑❑❑❑❑

604 _____ **1962. George Washington Issue**

5¢ **gray blue**   .25   .20 ❑❑❑❑❑

		MNHVF	UseVF	
605 _____	**1962. George Washington Coil Issue**			
5¢ gray blue		.25	.20 ☐☐☐☐☐
606 _____	**1963. U.S. Flag and White House Issue**			
5¢ blue & red		.25	.20 ☐☐☐☐☐
607 _____	**1963. Andrew Jackson Issue**			
1¢ green		.25	.20 ☐☐☐☐☐
608 _____	**1963. Andrew Jackson Coil Issue**			
1¢ green		.25	.20 ☐☐☐☐☐
609 _____	**1963. Christmas Tree and White House**			
5¢ dark blue, indigo & red		.25	.20 ☐☐☐☐☐
610 _____	**1964. Holiday Evergreens Issue**			
5¢ Holly		.25	.20 ☐☐☐☐☐
611 _____				
5¢ Mistletoe		.25	.20 ☐☐☐☐☐
612 _____				
5¢ Poinsettia		.25	.20 ☐☐☐☐☐

582

583

584

585

586

591

592

593, 614

594, 598

595, 597

596

599, 600

601

602

603

604, 605

606

607, 608

609

	MNHVF	UseVF

613 _____

5¢ **Conifer sprig**	.25	.20 ❑❑❑❑❑

614 _____   **1965. Paul Revere Coil Issue**

25¢ **deep blue green** small holes	.45	.25 ❑❑❑❑❑

615 _____   **1965. Angel Gabriel Issue**

5¢ **red, green & yellow**	.25	.20 ❑❑❑❑❑

616 _____   **1968. Thomas Jefferson Issue**

1¢ **green** tagged Type II or III	.25	.20 ❑❑❑❑❑

617 _____   **1967. Albert Gallatin Issue**

1-1/4¢ **light green**	.25	.20 ❑❑❑❑❑

618 _____   **1966. Frank Lloyd Wright Issue**

2¢ **blue** tagged Type II or III	.25	.20 ❑❑❑❑❑

619 _____   **1967. Francis Parkman Issue**

3¢ **purple** tagged Type II	.25	.20 ❑❑❑❑❑

620 _____   **1965. Abraham Lincoln Issue**

4¢ **black**	.25	.20 ❑❑❑❑❑

621 _____   **1965. George Washington Issue**

5¢ **deep blue**	.25	.20 ❑❑❑❑❑

622 _____   **1966. Franklin D. Roosevelt Issue**

6¢ **black brown**	.25	.20 ❑❑❑❑❑

623 _____   **1966. Albert Einstein Issue**

8¢ **violet**	.25	.20 ❑❑❑❑❑

624 _____   **1967. Andrew Jackson Issue**

10¢ **lavender** tagged Type II or III	.25	.20 ❑❑❑❑❑

624A _____   **1968. Henry Ford Issue**

12¢ **black** tagged Type II	.25	.20 ❑❑❑❑❑

625 _____   **1967. John F. Kennedy Issue**

13¢ **brown** tagged Type II or III	.25	.20 ❑❑❑❑❑

626 _____   **1968. Oliver Wendell Holmes Issue**

15¢ **maroon** design Type I, tagged Type III	.25	.20 ❑❑❑❑❑

NOTE: Type I: crosshatching on tie complete and strong; bottom of necktie just touches coat. Type II: crosshatching on tie (lines running upper left to lower right) very faint; necktie does not touch coat. Type III (only known on booklet pane) overall design smaller and "15¢" closer to head.

626A _____

15¢ **maroon** design Type II, tagged	.50	.20 ❑❑❑❑❑

626B _____

15¢ **maroon** design Type III, perforated 10	.25	.20 ❑❑❑❑❑

627 _____   **1967. George C. Marshall Issue**

20¢ **olive brown**	.35	.20 ❑❑❑❑❑

628 _____   **1967. Frederick Douglass Issue**

25¢ **maroon**	.50	.20 ❑❑❑❑❑

629 _____   **1968. John Dewey Issue**

30¢ **purple**	.55	.25 ❑❑❑❑❑

630 _____   **1968. Thomas Paine Issue**

40¢ **dark blue**	.75	.25 ❑❑❑❑❑

631 _____   **1968. Lucy Stone Issue**

50¢ **maroon**	1.00	.25 ❑❑❑❑❑

632 _____   **1967. Eugene O'Neill Issue**

$1 **dark purple**	2.25	.50 ❑❑❑❑❑

633 _____   **1966. John Bassett Moore Issue**

$5 **dark gray**	10.00	3.00 ❑❑❑❑❑

634 _____   **1968. Thomas Jefferson Coil Issue**

1¢ **green** tagged	.25	.20 ❑❑❑❑❑

635 _____   **1966. Abraham Lincoln Coil Issue**

4¢ **black** tagged Type II	.25	.20 ❑❑❑❑❑

610-613

615

616, 634

617

618

619, 693

620, 635

621, 636

622

623

624

624A

625

626, 721, 721A

627

628

629

630

631

632, 672

633

644

(637), 638

645

646, 747A

647, 650, 654

	MNHVF	UseVF

636 _____ **1966. George Washington Coil Issue**

5¢ **deep blue** tagged Type II · .25 · .20 ☐☐☐☐☐

637 _____ **1968. Franklin D. Roosevelt Coil Issue**

6¢ **black brown** tagged · .25 · .20 ☐☐☐☐☐

638 _____ **1967. Franklin D. Roosevelt Coil Issue**

6¢ **black brown** tagged · .25 · .20 ☐☐☐☐☐

NOTE: Nos. 639-643 are not assigned.

644 _____ **1966. Traditional Christmas Issue**

5¢ **multicolored** · .25 · .20 ☐☐☐☐☐

645 _____ **1967. Traditional Christmas Issue**

5¢ **multicolored** · .25 · .20 ☐☐☐☐☐

646 _____ **1967. George Washington Issue**

5¢ **deep blue** tagged, shiny gum · .25 · .20 ☐☐☐☐☐

647 _____ **1968. Flag Over White House Issue**

6¢ **dark blue, green & red** tagged Type OP · .25 · .20 ☐☐☐☐☐

648 _____ **1968. Serviceman's Airlift Issue**

$1 **multicolored** · 3.00 · 2.00 ☐☐☐☐☐

649 _____ **1968. Traditional Christmas Issue**

6¢ **multicolored** tagged Type B · .25 · .20 ☐☐☐☐☐

NOTE: Type B tagging: Billet or bar-like shapes designed to register within the limits of a single stamp. Untagged areas surround the design and were intended to register with the perforations.

650 _____ **1969. Flag Over White House Coil Stamp Issue**

6¢ **dark blue, green & red** tagged · .25 · .20 ☐☐☐☐☐

651 _____ **1969. Contemporary Christmas Issue**

6¢ **multicolored** tagged · .25 · .20 ☐☐☐☐☐

NOTE: Experimental precanceled stamps were sold for use by the public, imprinted, "ATLANTA, GA," "BALTIMORE, MD," "MEMPHIS, TN," and "NEW HAVEN, CT."

652 _____ **1970. Dwight D. Eisenhower Issue**

6¢ **blue** tagged Type II · .25 · .20 ☐☐☐☐☐

653 _____ **1970. Dwight D. Eisenhower Coil Issue**

6¢ **blue** tagged · .25 · .20 ☐☐☐☐☐

654 _____ **1970. Flag Over White House Issue**

6¢ **dark blue, green & red** tagged Type B · .25 · .20 ☐☐☐☐☐

655 _____ **1970. Contemporary Christmas Issue**

6¢ **multicolored** tagged · .25 · .20 ☐☐☐☐☐

656 _____

6¢ **multicolored** tagged · .25 · .20 ☐☐☐☐☐

657 _____

6¢ **multicolored** tagged · .25 · .20 ☐☐☐☐☐

658 _____

6¢ **multicolored** tagged · .25 · .20 ☐☐☐☐☐

659 _____ **1970. Traditional Christmas Issue**

6¢ **multicolored** tagged design Type I · .25 · .20 ☐☐☐☐☐

NOTE: Type I has a slightly blurry impression and no gum breaker ridges. Type II has a shiny surfaced paper, sharper impression, and both horizontal and vertical gum breaker ridges. Type I precancel is gray black; Type II precancel is intense black.

660 _____ **1971. Ernie Pyle Issue**

16¢ **brown** tagged · .30 · .20 ☐☐☐☐☐

661 _____ **1971. Flag Over White House Issue**

8¢ **dark blue, red & slate green** tagged Type B · .25 · .20 ☐☐☐☐☐

662 _____ **1971. Flag Over White House Coil Issue**

8¢ **dark blue, red & slate green** tagged Type B · .20 · .20 ☐☐☐☐☐

663 _____ **1971. Dwight D. Eisenhower Issue**

8¢ **black, blue gray & red** tagged Type OP · .25 · .20 ☐☐☐☐☐

	MNHVF	UseVF

663A _____ **1971. Dwight D. Eisenhower Booklet Issue**

8¢ **reddish brown** tagged Type II, in booklet form only, or III, in booklet form
only in shiny gum. .25 .20 ☐☐☐☐☐

NOTE: All these booklet stamps have 1 or 2 straight edges.

664 _____ **1971. Dwight D. Eisenhower Coil Issue**

8¢ **reddish brown** tagged .25 .20 ☐☐☐☐☐

665 _____ **1971. U.S. Postal Service Issue**

8¢ **multicolored** tagged .25 .20 ☐☐☐☐☐

666 _____ **1971. Contemporary Christmas Issue**

8¢ **multicolored** tagged .25 .20 ☐☐☐☐☐

667 _____ **1971. Traditional Christmas Issue**

8¢ **multicolored** tagged .25 .20 ☐☐☐☐☐

668 _____ **1972. Fiorello H. LaGuardia Issue**

14¢ **dark brown** tagged .25 .20 ☐☐☐☐☐

669 _____ **1972. Benjamin Franklin Issue**

7¢ **light blue** shiny gum, tagged .25 .20 ☐☐☐☐☐

649

648

651

652, 653

659

660

661, 662

655-658

663

663A, 664

665

666

667

668

669

	MNHVF	UseVF	

670 _____ **1972. Contemporary Christmas Issue**
  8¢ **multicolored** tagged   .25   .20 ☐☐☐☐☐
671 _____ **1972. Traditional Christmas Issue**
  8¢ **multicolored** tagged   .25   .20 ☐☐☐☐☐
672 _____ **1973. Eugene O'Neill Coil Issue**
  $1 **dark purple** tagged   2.00   .75 ☐☐☐☐☐
673 _____ **1973. Amadeo P. Giannini Issue**
  21¢ **banknote green** tagged   .40   .25 ☐☐☐☐☐
674 _____ **1973. Traditional Christmas Issue**
  8¢ **multicolored** tagged   .25   .20 ☐☐☐☐☐
675 _____ **1973. Contemporary Christmas Issue**
  8¢ **multicolored** tagged   .25   .20 ☐☐☐☐☐
676 _____ **1973. Crossed Flags Issue**
  10¢ **red & blue** tagged   .25   .20 ☐☐☐☐☐
677 _____ **1973. Crossed Flags Coil Issue**
  10¢ **red & blue** tagged   .40   .25 ☐☐☐☐☐

NOTE: The lines on this issue, which can occur every 4 stamps, are usually incomplete. Full, complete lines sell for a premium.

678 _____ **1973. Jefferson Memorial Issue**
  10¢ **blue** tagged, Type II or III   .25   .20 ☐☐☐☐☐
679 _____ **1973. Jefferson Memorial Coil Issue**
  10¢ **blue** tagged   .25   .20 ☐☐☐☐☐
680 _____ **1974. ZIP Code Issue**
  10¢ **multicolored** tagged with small rectangle in center of stamp .25   .20 ☐☐☐☐☐
681 _____ **1974. Elizabeth Blackwell Issue**
  18¢ **purple** tagged   .30   .25 ☐☐☐☐☐
682 _____ **1974. Swinging Bell Coil Issue**
  6.3¢ **brick red** tagged   .25   .20 ☐☐☐☐☐
683 _____ **1974. Contemporary Christmas Issue**
  10¢ **multicolored** tagged   .25   .20 ☐☐☐☐☐
684 _____ **1974. Dove of Peace Issue**
  10¢ **multicolored** self-adhesive   .25   .20 ☐☐☐☐☐

NOTE: Two types of rouletting were used on backing paper.

685 _____ **1974. Traditional Christmas Issue**
  10¢ **multicolored** tagged   .25   .20 ☐☐☐☐☐
686 _____ **1975. Contemporary Christmas Issue**
  10¢ **multicolored** tagged   .30   .20 ☐☐☐☐☐
686A _____
  10¢ **multicolored** tagged   .30   .20 ☐☐☐☐☐
686B _____
  10¢ **multicolored** tagged   .60   .20 ☐☐☐☐☐
687 _____ **1975. Traditional Christmas Issue**
  10¢ **multicolored** tagged   .30   .20 ☐☐☐☐☐
688 _____ **1975. Capitol Dome Issue**
  9¢ **green** on gray paper, tagged   .25   .20 ☐☐☐☐☐
689 _____ **1975. Colonial Printing Press Issue**
  11¢ **orange** on gray paper, tagged   .25   .20 ☐☐☐☐☐
690 _____ **1975. Flag over Independence Hall Issue**
  13¢ **dark blue & red** tagged   .25   .20 ☐☐☐☐☐
691 _____ **1975. Eagle and Shield Issue**
  13¢ **multicolored** tagged with eagle-shape untagged area   .25   .20 ☐☐☐☐☐
691A _____
  13¢ **multicolored** perforated 11 (L-perforation)   40.00   15.00 ☐☐☐☐☐

670

671

673

674

675

676, 677

678, 679

680

681

682

683

684

685

686

687

688, 697, 702, 702A

689

690, 694, 782

691

692

693

694

695, 696

697

	MNHVF	UseVF

692 _____ **1975. Old North Church Issue**
24¢ **red** on blue paper, tagged .50 .25 ☐☐☐☐☐
693 _____ **1975. Francis Parkman Coil Issue**
3¢ **purple** tagged, shiny gum .25 .20 ☐☐☐☐☐
694 _____ **1975. Flag over Independence Hall Coil Issue**
13¢ **dark blue & red** tagged .25 .20 ☐☐☐☐☐
695 _____ **1975. Liberty Bell Issue**
13¢ **brown** from booklet panes only, tagged .25 .20 ☐☐☐☐☐
696 _____ **1975. Liberty Bell Coil Issue**
13¢ **brown** shiny gum, tagged .25 .20 ☐☐☐☐☐
697 _____ **1976. Capitol Dome Coil Issue**
9¢ **green** on gray paper, shiny gum, tagged .25 .20 ☐☐☐☐☐
698 _____ **1976. American Eagle and Drum Coil Issue**
7.9¢ **red** on canary paper, shiny gum, tagged .25 .20 ☐☐☐☐☐
699 _____ **1976. Contemporary Christmas Issue**
13¢ **multicolored** overall tagged .40 .25 ☐☐☐☐☐
699A _____
13¢ **multicolored** block tagged .40 .25 ☐☐☐☐☐
700 _____ **1976. Traditional Christmas Issue**
13¢ **multicolored** tagged .40 .25 ☐☐☐☐☐
701 _____ **1976. Saxhorns Issue**
7.7¢ **brown** on canary paper, tagged .25 .20 ☐☐☐☐☐
702 _____ **1977. Capitol Dome Booklet Issue**
9¢ **green** tagged, perforated 11 x 10 1/2 1.00 .20 ☐☐☐☐☐
702A _____
9¢ **green** tagged 35.00 22.50 ☐☐☐☐☐
703 _____ **1977. Flag over Capitol Booklet Issue**
13¢ **red & blue** tagged .25 .20 ☐☐☐☐☐
703A _____ **1977. Flag over Capitol Issue**
13¢ **red & blue** tagged .75 .50 ☐☐☐☐☐
704 _____ **1977. Rural Mail Box Issue**
13¢ **multicolored** tagged .40 .20 ☐☐☐☐☐
705 _____ **1977. Washington Kneeling At Prayer Issue**
13¢ **multicolored** tagged .40 .20 ☐☐☐☐☐

NOTE: The multicolor Combination Press issue (No. 705) has "floating" plate numbers, a set of five numbers sand-wiched between two or three blanks, so that on a plate strip of 20 there are five numbers and five blanks, six numbers and four blanks, seven numbers and three blanks or eight numbers and two blanks. There are no ZIP or Mail Early slogans.

NOTE: Nos. 706-707 are not assigned.
708 _____ **1977. Contemplation of Justice Issue**
10¢ **purple** on gray paper, shiny gum, tagged .25 .20 ☐☐☐☐☐
709 _____ **1977. Contemplation of Justice Coil Issue**
10¢ **purple** on gray paper, tagged .25 .20 ☐☐☐☐☐
710 _____ **1977. Quill Pen and Inkwell Issue**
1¢ **blue** on green paper, tagged .25 .20 ☐☐☐☐☐
711 _____ **1977. Symbols of Speech Issue**
2¢ **brown** on green paper, shiny gum, tagged .25 .20 ☐☐☐☐☐
711A _____ **1981. Symbols of Speech Issue**
2¢ **brown** on cream paper, matte gum, tagged .25 .20 ☐☐☐☐☐
712 _____ **1977. Ballot Box Issue**
3¢ **olive** on green paper, shiny gum, tagged .25 .20 ☐☐☐☐☐
713 _____ **1977. Reading and Learning Issue**
4¢ **maroon** on cream paper, tagged .25 .20 ☐☐☐☐☐
714 _____ **1978. Indian Head Penny Issue**
13¢ **brown & blue** on tan paper, tagged .25 .20 ☐☐☐☐☐

698

699, 699A

700

701

702, 702A, 703, 703A

704

705

708, 709

710, 742

711, 711A

712

713

714

715, 716

716

717

718-720

722, 722A, 723

724

725

726

727

728

729

	MNHVF	UseVF

715 _____   1978. Statue of Liberty Issue
16¢ **blue** tagged   .30   .20 ⬚⬚⬚⬚⬚

716 _____   1978. Statue of Liberty Coil Issue
16¢ **blue** overall tagged   .35   .20 ⬚⬚⬚⬚⬚

716A _____
16¢ **multicolored** block tagged, B Press (design slightly narrower than 716,
no joint line)   —   — ⬚⬚⬚⬚⬚

717 _____   1978. Sandy Hook Lighthouse Issue
29¢ **blue** on blue paper, shiny gum, tagged   .50   .65 ⬚⬚⬚⬚⬚

718 _____   1978. "A" Stamp Issue
15¢ **orange** perforated 11, tagged   .30   .25 ⬚⬚⬚⬚⬚

718A _____   1978. "A" Stamp Issue
15¢ **orange** perforated 11 1/4, tagged   .30   .25 ⬚⬚⬚⬚⬚

719 _____   1978. "A" Booklet Stamp Issue
15¢ **orange** tagged   .25   .20 ⬚⬚⬚⬚⬚

720 _____   1978. "A" Stamp Coil Issue
15¢ **orange** tagged   .25   .15 ⬚⬚⬚⬚⬚

721 _____   1978. Oliver Wendell Holmes Issue
15¢ **maroon** Type I, tagged   .25   .20 ⬚⬚⬚⬚⬚

721A _____
15¢ **maroon** Type II matte gum, tagged   .25   .20 ⬚⬚⬚⬚⬚

NOTE: For booklet pane issued the same date see No. 626B.

722 _____   1978. American Flag Issue
15¢ **red, blue & gray** perforated 11, tagged   .30   .20 ⬚⬚⬚⬚⬚

722A _____   1978. American Flag Booklet Issue
15¢ **red, blue & gray** booklet stamp, perforated 11 x 10 1/2, tagged .35   .20 ⬚⬚⬚⬚⬚

723 _____   1978. American Flag Coil Issue
15¢ **red, blue & gray**   .40   .20 ⬚⬚⬚⬚⬚

724 _____   1978. American Roses Booklet Issue
15¢ **orange, red & green** tagged   .25   .20 ⬚⬚⬚⬚⬚

725 _____   1978. Steinway Grand Piano Coil Issue
8.4¢ **blue** on canary paper, shiny gum, tagged   .25   .20 ⬚⬚⬚⬚⬚

726 _____   1978. Blockhouse Issue
28¢ **brown** on blue paper, tagged, shiny gum   .50   .20 ⬚⬚⬚⬚⬚

727 _____   1978. Contemporary Christmas Issue
15¢ **multicolored** tagged   .40   .20 ⬚⬚⬚⬚⬚

728 _____   1978. Madonna and Child with Cherubim Issue
15¢ **multicolored** tagged   .40   .20 ⬚⬚⬚⬚⬚

729 _____   1978. Kerosene Table Lamp Issue
$2 **multicolored** tagged   3.50   1.00 ⬚⬚⬚⬚⬚

730 _____   1979. Rush Lamp and Candle Holder Issue
$1 **multicolored** tagged   2.00   .25 ⬚⬚⬚⬚⬚

731 _____   1979. Railroad Conductor's Lantern Issue
$5 **multicolored** tagged   8.50   2.25 ⬚⬚⬚⬚⬚

732 _____   1979. Country Schoolhouse Issue
30¢ **green** on blue paper, tagged   1.00   .30 ⬚⬚⬚⬚⬚

733 _____   1979. Iron "Betty" Lamp Issue
50¢ **black, orange & tan** tagged   1.00   .20 ⬚⬚⬚⬚⬚

734 _____   1979. Santa Claus Christmas Tree Ornament Issue
15¢ **multicolored** tagged   .40   .20 ⬚⬚⬚⬚⬚

735 _____   1979. Traditional Christmas Issue
15¢ **multicolored** tagged   .40   .20 ⬚⬚⬚⬚⬚

736 _____   1979. Standard Six-string Guitar Coil Issue
3.1¢ **brown** on canary paper, tagged   .25   .20 ⬚⬚⬚⬚⬚

	MNHVF	UseVF

737 _____ **1980. Historic Windmills Issue**
15¢ **Virginia, brown** on yellow paper, tagged   .30   .20 ☐☐☐☐☐
738 _____
15¢ **Rhode Island, brown** on yellow paper, tagged   .30   .20 ☐☐☐☐☐
739 _____
15¢ **Massachusetts, brown,** on yellow paper, tagged   .30   .20 ☐☐☐☐☐
740 _____
15¢ **Illinois, brown** on yellow paper, tagged   .30   .20 ☐☐☐☐☐
741 _____
15¢ **Texas, brown** on yellow paper, tagged   .30   .20 ☐☐☐☐☐
742 _____ **1980. Quill Pen and Inkwell Coil Issue**
1¢ **blue** on green paper, shiny gum, tagged   .25   .20 ☐☐☐☐☐
743 _____ **1980. Dolley Madison Issue**
15¢ **red brown & sepia** tagged   .40   .20 ☐☐☐☐☐
744 _____ **1980. Weaver Manufactured Violins Coil Issue**
3.5¢ **purple** on yellow paper, tagged   .25   .20 ☐☐☐☐☐
745 _____ **1980. Contemporary Christmas Issue**
15¢ **multicolored** tagged   .50   .20 ☐☐☐☐☐
746 _____ **1980. Traditional Christmas Issue**
15¢ **multicolored** tagged   .50   .20 ☐☐☐☐☐
747 _____ **1980. Sequoyah Issue**
19¢ **brown** overall tagged   .30   .20 ☐☐☐☐☐
747A _____ **1980. Washington Coil Issue**
5¢ **deep blue** tagged   .25   .20 ☐☐☐☐☐
748 _____ **1981. Non-Denominated "B" Stamp Issue**
18¢ **purple** tagged   .30   .20 ☐☐☐☐☐

730

731

732

733

734

735

736

737-741

743

744

745

746

747

	MNHVF	UseVF

749 _____ **1981. Non-Denominated "B" Booklet Issue**

18¢ **purple** tagged .30 .20 ❑❑❑❑❑

750 _____ **1981. Non-Denominated "B" Coil Issue**

18¢ **purple** tagged .40 .20 ❑❑❑❑❑

751 _____ **1981. Freedom Of Conscience Issue**

12¢ **brown** on beige paper, tagged .25 .20 ❑❑❑❑❑

NOTE: **U.S. Postal Service Plate-Numbering Change** In response to collector complaints that its plate-numbering system resulted in many inconvenient and costly blocks of 10, 12 and 20 stamps, the USPS in January 1981 instituted a new plate number arrangement. Under the new system, most sheets were to contain a single plate number consisting of one (for monocolor stamps) to six digits, each digit representing a given printing plate and color. Thus, under this system, most plate blocks returned to blocks of four.

NOTE: Booklet panes hereafter also contain a plate number in the selvage.

NOTE: In coils, a plate number was incorporated into some stamps in the roll, at various intervals between stamps, depending on press used.

752 _____ **1981. Freedom of Conscience Coil Issue**

12¢ **red brown** on beige paper, tagged .25 .20 ❑❑❑❑❑

753 _____ **1981. America The Beautiful Issue**

18¢ **multicolored** tagged .30 .20 ❑❑❑❑❑

754 _____ **1981. America The Beautiful Issue**

18¢ **multicolored** tagged .30 .20 ❑❑❑❑❑

755 _____ **1981. America The Beautiful Combination Booklet**

6¢ **blue** tagged .55 .25 ❑❑❑❑❑

756 _____

18¢ **multicolored** tagged .30 .20 ❑❑❑❑❑

757 _____ **1981. George Mason Issue**

18¢ **blue** overall tagged .30 .20 ❑❑❑❑❑

758 _____ **1981. Wildlife Booklet Issue**

18¢ **Bighorn sheep, brown,** tagged .50 .20 ❑❑❑❑❑

759 _____

18¢ **Puma, brown,** tagged .50 .20 ❑❑❑❑❑

760 _____

18¢ **Harbor seal, brown,** tagged .50 .20 ❑❑❑❑❑

761 _____

18¢ **Bison, brown,** tagged .50 .20 ❑❑❑❑❑

762 _____

18¢ **Brown bear, brown,** tagged .50 .20 ❑❑❑❑❑

763 _____

18¢ **Polar bear, brown,** tagged .50 .20 ❑❑❑❑❑

764 _____

18¢ **Elk (Wapiti), brown,** tagged .50 .20 ❑❑❑❑❑

765 _____

18¢ **Moose, brown,** tagged .50 .20 ❑❑❑❑❑

766 _____

18¢ **White-tailed deer, brown,** tagged .50 .20 ❑❑❑❑❑

767 _____

18¢ **Pronghorn antelope, brown,** tagged .50 .20 ❑❑❑❑❑

768 _____ **1981. Surrey Issue**

18¢ **brown** tagged .35 .20 ❑❑❑❑❑

769 _____ **1981. Rachel Carson Issue**

17¢ **green** overall tagged .30 .20 ❑❑❑❑❑

770 _____ **1981. Charles R. Drew Issue**

35¢ **gray** overall tagged .50 .25 ❑❑❑❑❑

NOTE: Note: Plate blocks from plates 3 & 4 carry a premium.

771 _____ **1981. Electric Auto Issue**

17¢ **blue** tagged .35 .20 ❑❑❑❑❑

	MNHVF	UseVF

772 _____ **1981. Non-Denominated "C" Issue**
20¢ **brown** tagged   .35   .20 ☐☐☐☐☐
773 _____ **1981. Non-Denominated "C" Booklet Pane Issue**
20¢ **brown** tagged   .50   .20 ☐☐☐☐☐
774 _____ **1981. Non-Denominated "C" Coil Issue**
20¢ **brown** tagged   .60   .20 ☐☐☐☐☐
775 _____ **1981. Christmas Issue**
20¢ **multicolored** tagged   .50   .20 ☐☐☐☐☐
776 _____
20¢ **multicolored** tagged   .50   .20 ☐☐☐☐☐
777 _____ **1981. Fire Pumper Issue**
20¢ **red** tagged   .40   .20 ☐☐☐☐☐
778 _____ **1981. Mail Wagon Issue**
9.3¢ **dark red** tagged   .25   .20 ☐☐☐☐☐
779 _____ **1981. Flag Over Supreme Court Issue**
20¢ **black, dark blue & red** perforated 11, tagged   .35   .20 ☐☐☐☐☐

748-750

751, 752

753

754

755, 756

757

768

769

770

771

758-767

775

772-774

	MNHVF	UseVF

779A _____
20¢ **black, dark blue & red** perforated 11 1/4, tagged — .35 — .20 ☐☐☐☐☐

780 _____ **1981. Flag Over Supreme Court Coil Issue**
20¢ **black, dark blue & red** tagged — .35 — .20 ☐☐☐☐☐

781 _____ **1981. Flag Over Supreme Court Issue**
20¢ **black, dark red & blue** tagged — .35 — .20 ☐☐☐☐☐

782 _____ **1981. Flag Over Independence Hall Issue**
13¢ **dark blue & red** block tagged — .60 — .25 ☐☐☐☐☐

783 _____ **1982. Bighorn Sheep Issue**
20¢ **blue** Type I, overall tagged — .50 — .20 ☐☐☐☐☐

783A _____
20¢ **blue** Type II, block tagged, 18 1/2mm wide. — .50 — .20 ☐☐☐☐☐

NOTE: Type I: is 18 3/4mm wide, Type II: is 18 1/2mm wide.

784 _____ **1982. Ralph Bunche Issue**
20¢ **maroon** overall tagged — .35 — .20 ☐☐☐☐☐

785 _____ **1982. Crazy Horse Issue**
13¢ **light maroon** overall tagged — .35 — .20 ☐☐☐☐☐

786 _____ **1982. Robert Millikan Issue**
37¢ **blue** overall tagged — .60 — .20 ☐☐☐☐☐

787 _____ **1982. High Wheeler Bicycle Issue**
5.9¢ **blue** tagged — .25 — .20 ☐☐☐☐☐

788 _____ **1982. Hansom Cab Issue**
10.9¢ **purple** tagged — .25 — .20 ☐☐☐☐☐

789 _____ **1982. Consumer Education Issue**
20¢ **blue** tagged — .50 — .20 ☐☐☐☐☐

790 _____ **1982. Locomotive Issue**
2¢ **black** tagged — .25 — .20 ☐☐☐☐☐

NOTE: (For similar design with "2 USA" see No. 873.)

791 _____ **1982. Stagecoach Issue**
4¢ **brown** tagged — .25 — .20 ☐☐☐☐☐

NOTE: For similar design with "Stagecoach 1890s" measuring 17mm long. see No. 868.

792 _____ **1982. Christmas Issue**
20¢ **Sledding, multicolored,** tagged — .35 — .20 ☐☐☐☐☐

793 _____
20¢ **Building snowman, multicolored,** tagged — .35 — .20 ☐☐☐☐☐

794 _____
20¢ **Skating, multicolored,** tagged — .35 — .20 ☐☐☐☐☐

795 _____
20¢ **Decorating tree, multicolored,** tagged — .35 — .20 ☐☐☐☐☐

796 _____ **1982. Traditional Christmas Issue**
20¢ **multicolored** tagged — .35 — .20 ☐☐☐☐☐

797 _____ **1982. Kitten and Puppy Issue**
13¢ **multicolored** tagged — .35 — .20 ☐☐☐☐☐

798 _____ **1982. Igor Stravinsky Issue**
2¢ **brown** overall tagged — .25 — .20 ☐☐☐☐☐

799 _____ **1983. Sleigh Issue**
5.2¢ **red** tagged — .25 — .20 ☐☐☐☐☐

800 _____ **1983. Handcar Issue**
3¢ **green** tagged — .25 — .20 ☐☐☐☐☐

801 _____ **1983. Carl Schurz Issue**
4¢ **purple** overall tagged — .20 — .20 ☐☐☐☐☐

802 _____ **1983. Thomas H. Gallaudet Issue**
20¢ **green** overall tagged — .40 — .20 ☐☐☐☐☐

803 _____ **1983. Pearl Buck Issue**
5¢ **red brown** overall tagged — .20 — .20 ☐☐☐☐☐

776

777

778

779-781

782

783, 783A

784

785

786

787

788

789

790

791

792-795

796

797

801

798

799

800

802

803

804

805

	MNHVF	UseVF	

804 _____ **1983. Henry Clay Issue**

3¢   **olive** overall tagged   .20   .20 ☐☐☐☐☐

805 _____ **1983. Express Mail Issue**

$9.35 **multicolored** tagged   25.00   20.00 ☐☐☐☐☐

806 _____ **1983. Omnibus Issue**

1¢   **purple** tagged   .20   .20 ☐☐☐☐☐

NOTE: For similar design with "1 USA" see No. 867.

807 _____ **1983. Dorothea Dix Issue**

1¢   **black** tagged (small block) perforated 11 1/4   .20   .20 ☐☐☐☐☐

807A _____

1¢   **black** tagged (small block) perforated 10 3/4   .20   .20 ☐☐☐☐☐

808 _____ **1983. Motorcycle Issue**

5¢   **dark green** tagged   .25   .20 ☐☐☐☐☐

809 _____ **1983. Christmas Issue**

20¢ **multicolored** tagged   .35   .20 ☐☐☐☐☐

810 _____

20¢ **multicolored** tagged   .35   .20 ☐☐☐☐☐

811 _____ **1984. Harry S. Truman Issue**

20¢ **black** tagged (small block)   .35   .20 ☐☐☐☐☐

NOTE: (See also No. 904.)

812 _____ **1984. Railroad Caboose Issue**

11¢ **red** tagged   .25   .20 ☐☐☐☐☐

813 _____ **1984. Lillian Gilbreth Issue**

40¢ **green,** tagged (small block) perforated 11   .60   .20 ☐☐☐☐☐

813A _____

40¢ **green** tagged (large block) perforated 11 1/4 (1987)   .60   .20 ☐☐☐☐☐

814 _____ **1984. Baby Buggy Issue**

7.4¢ **brown** tagged   .25   .20 ☐☐☐☐☐

815 _____ **1984. Richard Russell Issue**

10¢ **blue** tagged (small block)   .25   .20 ☐☐☐☐☐

NOTE: Imperforate printer's waste is known to exist, and in one case was used as postage.

816 _____ **1984. Frank C. Laubach Issue**

30¢ **green** tagged (small block) perforated 11   .75   .20 ☐☐☐☐☐

816A _____

30¢ **green** tagged (large block) perforated 11 1/4   .75   .20 ☐☐☐☐☐

817 _____ **1984. Christmas Issue**

20¢ **multicolored** tagged   .25   .20 ☐☐☐☐☐

818 _____

20¢ **multicolored** tagged   .25   .20 ☐☐☐☐☐

819 _____ **1985. Abraham Baldwin Issue**

7¢   **red** tagged (small block)   .25   .20 ☐☐☐☐☐

820 _____ **1985. Non-Denominated "D" Issue**

22¢ **green** tagged   .45   .20 ☐☐☐☐☐

821 _____ **1985. Non-Denominated "D" Coil Issue**

22¢ **green** tagged perforated 11   .60   .20 ☐☐☐☐☐

822 _____ **1985. Non-Denominated "D" Rate Booklet Issue**

22¢ **green** tagged   .40   .20 ☐☐☐☐☐

823 _____ **1985. Alden Partridge Issue**

11¢ **blue** overall tagged   .25   .20 ☐☐☐☐☐

824 _____ **1985. Chester W. Nimitz Issue**

50¢ **brown** overall tagged, perforated 11, shiny gum   .90   .20 ☐☐☐☐☐

824A _____

50¢ **brown** tagged (large block) perforated 11 1/4, matte gum   .90   .20 ☐☐☐☐☐

	MNHVF	UseVF

825 _____ **1985. Grenville Clark Issue**
39¢ **purple** tagged (small block) perforated 11 — .75 — .20 ☐☐☐☐☐
825A _____
39¢ **purple** tagged (large block), perforated 11 1/4 — .75 — .20 ☐☐☐☐☐
826 _____ **1985. Sinclair Lewis Issue**
14¢ **gray** tagged (small block) — .25 — .20 ☐☐☐☐☐
827 _____ **1985. Iceboat Issue**
14¢ **blue** Type I, overall tagged — .25 — .20 ☐☐☐☐☐
827A _____
14¢ **blue** Type II, block tagged — .25 — .20 ☐☐☐☐☐
NOTE: Type I is 17 1/2 mm wide with overall tagging. Type II is 17 1/4 mm wide with block tagging.
828 _____ **1985. Flag over the Capitol Issue**
22¢ **black, blue, & red** tagged — .35 — .20 ☐☐☐☐☐
829 _____ **1985. Flag Over the U.S. Capitol Coil Issue**
22¢ **black, blue, & red** tagged — .40 — .20 ☐☐☐☐☐
NOTE: For similar design with "T" at bottom, see No. 876.

806 807 808 809 810
811 812 813 814 815
816, 816A 817 818 819 820-822
823 824, 824A 825, 825A 826 827, 827A

	MNHVF	UseVF

830 _____ **1985. Flag Over the Capitol Booklet Issue**

22¢ **black, blue, & red** tagged   .40   .20 ☐☐☐☐☐

NOTE: Issued for use in vending machines, and was available with one or two panes.

831 _____ **1985. Stanley Steamer Issue**

12¢ **blue** Type I, tagged   .25   .20 ☐☐☐☐☐

831A _____

12¢ **blue** Type II, untagged (Bureau precancel: "PRESORTED FIRST-CLASS")   .25   .20 ☐☐☐☐☐

NOTE: Type I: "Stanley Steamer 1909" is 18mm long;

NOTE: Type II: "Stanley Steamer 1909" is 17 1/2 mm long.

832 _____ **1985. Seashell Booklet Issue**

22¢ **Frilled dogwinkle, black & brown** tagged   .35   .20 ☐☐☐☐☐

833 _____

22¢ **Reticulated helmet, black & multicolored** tagged   .35   .20 ☐☐☐☐☐

834 _____

22¢ **New England neptune, black & brown,** tagged   .35   .20 ☐☐☐☐☐

835 _____

22¢ **Calico scallop, black & purple** tagged   .35   .20 ☐☐☐☐☐

836 _____

22¢ **Lightning whelk, multicolored,** tagged   .35   .20 ☐☐☐☐☐

NOTE: Mis-registered tagging is common on this issue.

837 _____ **1985. Oil Wagon Issue**

10.1¢ **blue** tagged   .25   .20 ☐☐☐☐☐

838 _____ **1985. Pushcart Issue**

12.5¢ **olive** tagged   .25   .20 ☐☐☐☐☐

839 _____ **1985. John J. Audubon Issue**

22¢ **blue** tagged (small block) perforated 11   .40   .20 ☐☐☐☐☐

839A _____

22¢ **blue** tagged (large block) perforated 11 1/4   .40   .20 ☐☐☐☐☐

840 _____ **1985. Express Mail Issue**

$10.75 **multicolored** Type I, tagged   15.00   9.00 ☐☐☐☐☐

NOTE: Type I: overall dull appearance, "$10.75" appears grainy. Type II: more intense colors, "$10.75" smoother, much less grainy.

841 _____ **1985. Tricycle Issue**

6¢ **brown** tagged   .25   .20 ☐☐☐☐☐

842 _____ **1985. Sylvanus Thayer Issue**

9¢ **green** tagged (small block)   .25   .20 ☐☐☐☐☐

843 _____ **1985. School Bus Issue**

3.4¢ **green** tagged   .20   .20 ☐☐☐☐☐

844 _____ **1985. Stutz Bearcat Issue**

11¢ **green** tagged   .25   .20 ☐☐☐☐☐

845 _____ **1985. Ambulance Issue**

8.3¢ **green** Type I, tagged   .20   .20 ☐☐☐☐☐

845A _____

8.3¢ **green** Type II, untagged (Bureau precancel: "Blk. Rt./CAR-RT/SORT")   .20   .20 ☐☐☐☐☐

NOTE: Type I: "Ambulance 1860s" is 18 1/2mm long. Type II: "Ambulance 1860s" is 18mm long.

846 _____ **1985. Buckboard Issue**

4.9¢ **brown** tagged   .25   .20 ☐☐☐☐☐

847 _____ **1985. Henry Knox Issue**

8¢ **olive** overall tagged   .25   .20 ☐☐☐☐☐

848 _____ **1985. Walter Lippmann Issue**

6¢ **orange** tagged (large block)   .25   .20 ☐☐☐☐☐

849 _____ **1985. Envelope Stamp Issue**

21.1¢ **multicolored** tagged   .35   .20 ☐☐☐☐☐

NOTE: Some precanceled stamps are known with light tagging.

828, 829, 876

830

831, 831A

Frilled Dogwinkle

Oil Wagon 1890s
10.1 USA

837

Pushcart 1880s
12.5
USA

838

Reticulated Helmet

USA 22
New England Neptune

840

John J. Audubon
USA 22

839, 839A

Tricycle 1880s
6 USA

841

USA 22
Calico Scallop

Sylvanus Thayer
USA 9

842

School Bus 1920s
3.4 USA

843

Stutz Bearcat 1933
11 USA

844

Ambulance 1860s
8.3 USA

845, 845A

Lightning Whelk

832-836

Buckboard 1880s
USA
4.9

846

Henry Knox
USA 8

847

Walter Lippmann
6 USA

848

USA 21.1
ZIP+4

849

Season's Greetings USA22

850

CHRISTMAS
USA 22
Luca della Robbia, Detroit Institute of Arts

851

18
USA

852

USA 25
Jack London

853, 888, 889

		MNHVF	UseVF

850 _____ **1985. Contemporary Christmas Issue**

22¢ **multicolored** tagged — .35 — .20 ☐☐☐☐☐

851 _____ **1985. Traditional Christmas Issue**

22¢ **multicolored** tagged — .35 — .20 ☐☐☐☐☐

852 _____ **1985. George Washington & Monument Issue**

18¢ **multicolored** tagged — .35 — .20 ☐☐☐☐☐

NOTE: Some precanceled stamps are known with light tagging.

853 _____ **1986. Jack London Issue**

25¢ **blue** tagged (large block) perforated 11 — .45 — .20 ☐☐☐☐☐

NOTE: For booklet panes of 10 and 6, see Nos. 888-889.

854 _____ **1986. Hugo L. Black Issue**

5¢ **deep olive green** tagged (large block) — .25 — .20 ☐☐☐☐☐

855 _____ **1986. William Jennings Bryan Issue**

$2 **purple** tagged (large block) — 3.25 — .75 ☐☐☐☐☐

856 _____ **1986. Belva Ann Lockwood Issue**

17¢ **blue green** tagged (large block) — .35 — .20 ☐☐☐☐☐

857 _____ **1986. Margaret Mitchell Issue**

1¢ **brown** tagged (large block) — .25 — .20 ☐☐☐☐☐

858 _____ **1986. Father Flanagan Issue**

4¢ **purple** tagged (large block) — .25 — .20 ☐☐☐☐☐

859 _____ **1986. Dog Sled Issue**

17¢ **blue** tagged — .30 — .20 ☐☐☐☐☐

860 _____ **1986. John Harvard Issue**

56¢ **crimson** tagged (large block) — 1.10 — .20 ☐☐☐☐☐

861 _____ **1986. Paul Dudley White Issue**

3¢ **blue** tagged (large block), matte gum — .25 — .20 ☐☐☐☐☐

862 _____ **1986. Bernard Revel Issue**

$1 **blue** tagged (large block) — 2.00 — .25 ☐☐☐☐☐

863 _____ **1986. Christmas Issue**

22¢ **multicolored** tagged — .50 — .20 ☐☐☐☐☐

864 _____

22¢ **multicolored** tagged — .50 — .20 ☐☐☐☐☐

865 _____ **1986. Star Route Truck Issue**

5.5¢ **maroon** tagged — .25 — .20 ☐☐☐☐☐

866 _____ **1986. Bread Wagon Issue**

25¢ **orange brown** tagged, plates 2, 3, 4 — .40 — .20 ☐☐☐☐☐

867 _____ **1986. Omnibus Issue**

1¢ **violet** tagged — .25 — .20 ☐☐☐☐☐

NOTE: (For similar design with "USA 1¢" see No. 806)

868 _____ **1986. Stagecoach Issue**

4¢ **red brown** block tagged — .25 — .20 ☐☐☐☐☐

869 _____ **1987. Tow Truck Issue**

8.5¢ **dark gray** tagged — .50 — .20 ☐☐☐☐☐

870 _____ **1987. Tractor Issue**

7.1¢ **dark red** tagged — .25 — .20 ☐☐☐☐☐

871 _____ **1987. Julia Ward Howe Issue**

14¢ **red** tagged (large block) — .25 — .20 ☐☐☐☐☐

872 _____ **1987. Mary Lyon Issue**

2¢ **blue** tagged (large block) — .25 — .20 ☐☐☐☐☐

873 _____ **1987. Locomotive Issue**

2¢ **black** tagged — .25 — .20 ☐☐☐☐☐

NOTE: (For similar design with "USA 2¢" see No. 790.)

874 _____ **1987. Canal Boat Issue**

10¢ **sky blue** block tagged matte gum — .25 — .20 ☐☐☐☐☐

	MNHVF	UseVF

875 _____ **1987. Flag With Fireworks Issue**

22¢ **multicolored** tagged .35 .20 ☐☐☐☐☐

876 _____ **1987. Flag Over Capitol Coil Issue**

22¢ **black, blue, & red** with "T" at bottom .40 .20 ☐☐☐☐☐

877 _____ **1987. Red Cloud Issue**

10¢ **carmine red** tagged (large block) .25 .20 ☐☐☐☐☐

878 _____ **1987. Bret Harte Issue**

$5 **Venetian red** tagged (large block) 8.00 2.00 ☐☐☐☐☐

879 _____ **1987. Milk Wagon Issue**

5¢ **charcoal** tagged .25 .20 ☐☐☐☐☐

854	855	856	857	858
Hugo L. Black 5 USA	Bryan $2 USA William Jennings	Belva Ann Lockwood USA 17	Margaret Mitchell USA 1	Father Flanagan USA 4

859	860	861	862	863
Dog Sled 1920s 17 USA	John Harvard USA 56	Paul Dudley White MD USA 3	Bernard Revel USA $1	USA 22 GREETINGS

864	865	866	867	868
CHRISTMAS 22 USA Perugino, National Gallery	Star Route Truck 5.5 USA 1910s	Bread Wagon 1880s 25 USA	Omnibus 1880s 1 USA	Stagecoach 1890s USA 4c

869	870	871	872	873
Tow Truck 1920s 8.5 USA	Tractor 1920s 7.1 USA	14 USA Julia Ward Howe	Mary Lyon USA 2	Locomotive 1870s 2 USA

874	875	877	878	879
Canal Boat 1880s 10 USA	22 USA	Red Cloud 10 USA	Bret Harte USA $5	Milk Wagon 1900s 5 USA

	MNHVF	UseVF

880 _____ **1987. Racing Car Issue**
17.5¢ **blue violet** tagged .30 .20 ☐☐☐☐☐
881 _____ **1987. Christmas Issue**
22¢ **multicolored** tagged .50 .20 ☐☐☐☐☐
882 _____
22¢ **multicolored** tagged .50 .20 ☐☐☐☐☐
883 _____ **1988. Conestoga Wagon Coil Issue**
3¢ **dark lilac purple** tagged .25 .20 ☐☐☐☐☐
884 _____ **1988. Non-Denominated "E" Issue**
28¢ **multicolored** tagged .50 .20 ☐☐☐☐☐
885 _____ **1988. Non-Denominated "E" Coil Issue**
25¢ **multicolored** tagged .50 .20 ☐☐☐☐☐
886 _____ **1988. Non-Denominated "E" Booklet Issue**
25¢ **multicolored** tagged .50 .20 ☐☐☐☐☐
887 _____ **1988. Pheasant Booklet Issue**
25¢ **multicolored** tagged .50 .20 ☐☐☐☐☐
NOTE: Fully imperforate panes were cut from printer's waste.
888 _____ **1988. Jack London Booklet Issue**
25¢ **blue** tagged (large block) perforated 11 .45 .20 ☐☐☐☐☐
889 _____
25¢ **blue** tagged, perforated 10 .50 .20 ☐☐☐☐☐
890 _____ **1988. Flags With Clouds Issue**
25¢ **multicolored** tagged .35 .20 ☐☐☐☐☐
890A _____ **1988. Flags With Clouds Booklet Issue**
25¢ **multicolored** tagged .50 .20 ☐☐☐☐☐
891 _____ **1988. Flag Over Yosemite Issue**
25¢ **multicolored** tagged .40 .20 ☐☐☐☐☐
892 _____ **1988. Owl and Grosbeak Issue**
25¢ **multicolored** tagged .40 .20 ☐☐☐☐☐
893 _____
25¢ **multicolored** tagged .40 .20 ☐☐☐☐☐
894 _____ **1988. Buffalo Bill Cody Issue**
15¢ **maroon** tagged (large block) .30 .20 ☐☐☐☐☐
895 _____ **1988. Harvey Cushing Issue**
45¢ **blue** tagged (large block) 1.00 .20 ☐☐☐☐☐
NOTE: Nos. 896 and 897 are not assigned.
898 _____ **1988. Popcorn Wagon Issue**
16.7¢ **dark rose** (Bureau-printed service indicator "Bulk Rate") .35 .20 ☐☐☐☐☐
899 _____ **1988. Tugboat Issue**
15¢ **purple** block tagged .30 .20 ☐☐☐☐☐
900 _____ **1988. Coal Car Issue**
13.2¢ **dark green** (Bureau-printed red service indicator "Bulk Rate") .30 .20 ☐☐☐☐☐
901 _____ **1988. Wheel Chair Issue**
8.4¢ **dark violet** (Bureau-printed red service indicator: "Non-profit") .30 .20 ☐☐☐☐☐
902 _____ **1988. Railroad Mail Car Issue**
21¢ **green** (Bureau-printed red service indicator "Presorted First-Class") .35 .20 ☐☐☐☐☐
903 _____ **1988. Carreta Issue**
7.6¢ **brown** Bureau-printed red service indicator: "Nonprofit" .25 .20 ☐☐☐☐☐
904 _____ **1988. Harry S. Truman Issue**
20¢ **black** tagged (large block), matte gum .35 .20 ☐☐☐☐☐
NOTE: (See also No. 811)
905 _____ **1988. Honeybee Issue**
25¢ **multicolored** tagged .40 .20 ☐☐☐☐☐
906 _____ **1988. Elevator Issue**
5.3¢ **black** (Bureau-printed red service indicator: "Nonprofit/Carrier Route Sort") .25 .20 ☐☐☐☐☐

	MNHVF	UseVF

907 _____ **1988. Fire Engine Issue**
20.5¢ **red** (Bureau-printed black service indicator: "ZIP+4 Presort") — .35 — .20 ☐☐☐☐☐

908 _____ **1988. Eagle and Moon Issue**
$8.75 **multicolored** tagged — 25.00 — ☐☐☐☐☐

909 _____ **1988. Christmas Issue**
25¢ **multicolored,** tagged — .40 — .20 ☐☐☐☐☐

910 _____ **1988. Madonna And Child by Botticelli Issue**
25¢ **multicolored** tagged — .40 — .20 ☐☐☐☐☐

911 _____ **1988. Chester Carlson Issue**
21¢ **blue violet** tagged (large block) — .35 — .20 ☐☐☐☐☐

880

881

882

883

884-886

887

890, 890A

891

892

893

894

895

898

899

900

901

902

903

905

906

907

908

909

910

	MNHVF	UseVF

912 _____ 1988. Tandem Bicycle Issue

24.1¢ **deep blue violet** (Bureau-printed red service indicator: "ZIP+4")   .40   .20 ☐☐☐☐☐

913 _____ 1988. Cable Car Issue

20¢ **dark violet,** block tagged   .35   .20 ☐☐☐☐☐

914 _____ 1988. Police Patrol Wagon Issue

13¢ **black** (Bureau-printed red service indicator: "Presorted First-Class")   .30   .20 ☐☐☐☐☐

915 _____ 1988. Mary Cassatt Issue

23¢ **purple** tagged (large block)   .45   .20 ☐☐☐☐☐

916 _____ 1988. H.H. "Hap" Arnold Issue

65¢ **dark blue** tagged (large block)   1.25   .20 ☐☐☐☐☐

NOTE: No. 917 not assigned.

918 _____ 1989. Johns Hopkins Issue

$1   **blackish blue** tagged (large block), matte gum   2.00   .30 ☐☐☐☐☐

919 _____ 1989. Sitting Bull Issue

28¢ **green** tagged (large block)   .50   .20 ☐☐☐☐☐

920 _____ 1989. Sleigh with Gifts Issue

25¢ **multicolored** tagged   .40   .20 ☐☐☐☐☐

921 _____ 1989. Sleigh with Gifts Booklet Issue

25¢ **multicolored** booklet stamp, tagged   .40   .20 ☐☐☐☐☐

922 _____ 1989. The Dream of St. Alexandria Issue

25¢ **multicolored** tagged   .40   .20 ☐☐☐☐☐

NOTE: No. 923 is not assigned.

924 _____ 1989. Eagle and Shield Self-Adhesive Issue

25¢ **multicolored** tagged   .40   .20 ☐☐☐☐☐

NOTE: No. 925 is not assigned.

926 _____ 1990. Beach Umbrella Issue

15¢ **multicolored** booklet stamp, tagged   .30   .20 ☐☐☐☐☐

927 _____ 1990. Luis Muñoz Marin Issue

5¢   **dark rose,** overall tagged   .25   .20 ☐☐☐☐☐

928 _____ 1990. Seaplane Issue

$1   **dark blue & red** overall tagged, matte gum   1.75   .50 ☐☐☐☐☐

929 _____ 1990. Flag Issue for Automatic Teller Machines

25¢ **red & dark blue** tagged   .50   .50 ☐☐☐☐☐

930 _____ 1990. Bobcat Issue

$2   **multicolored** tagged   4.00   1.25 ☐☐☐☐☐

931 _____ 1990. Circus Wagon Issue

5¢   **carmine red** tagged   .25   .20 ☐☐☐☐☐

NOTE: For stamps of this design inscribed "USA 5¢" see No. 1007 (gravure) or No. 1077 (intaglio).

932 _____ 1990. Claire Lee Chennault Issue

40¢ **dark blue** overall tagged, matte gum   .75   .20 ☐☐☐☐☐

933 _____ 1990. Contemporary Christmas Issue

25¢ *Perforated 11* **multicolored** tagged   .40   .20 ☐☐☐☐☐

NOTE: Perforated 11 1/2 x 11

934 _____

25¢ **multicolored** booklet stamp, tagged   .40   .20 ☐☐☐☐☐

935 _____ 1990. Madonna and Child Issue

25¢ **multicolored** tagged   .40   .20 ☐☐☐☐☐

936 _____

25¢ **multicolored** booklet stamp, tagged   .40   .20 ☐☐☐☐☐

NOTE: The booklet version has a much heavier shading in the Madonna's veil where it meets the right frame line.

937 _____ 1991. "F" (Flower) Non-Denominated Issue

29¢ **multicolored** tagged   .50   .20 ☐☐☐☐☐

938 _____ 1991. "F" (Flower) Non-Denominated Booklet Issue

29¢ **multicolored** booklet stamp, tagged   .50   .20 ☐☐☐☐☐

	MNHVF	UseVF

939 _____ **1991. "F" (Flower) Non-Denominated Booklet Issue**
  29¢ **multicolored** booklet stamp, printed by KCS Industries, tagged .50 .20 ☐☐☐☐☐

940 _____ **1991. "F" (Flower) Non-Denominated Coil Issue**
  29¢ **multicolored** tagged .60 .20 ☐☐☐☐☐

941 _____ **1991. Non-Denominated 4¢ Make-Up Issue**
  4¢ **bister & carmine** .25 .20 ☐☐☐☐☐

942 _____ **1991. "F" Non-Denominated ATM Flag Issue**
  29¢ **black, dark blue & red** tagged .50 .20 ☐☐☐☐☐

943 _____ **1991. Steam Carriage Issue**
  4¢ **maroon** tagged .25 .20 ☐☐☐☐☐

911   912   913   914   915

916   918   919   920, 921   922

924   926   927   928   929

930   931   932   933, 934   935, 936

937-940   941   942   943   944

	MNHVF	UseVF

944 _____ 1991. Fawn Issue

19¢ multicolored tagged — .35 — .20 ☐☐☐☐☐

945 _____ 1991. Flag Over Mount Rushmore

29¢ red, blue, & maroon tagged — .50 — .20 ☐☐☐☐☐

945A _____

29¢ red, blue & brown color change "Toledo Brown" (error), tagged — 5.00 — — ☐☐☐☐☐

NOTE: For gravure version of this design, see No. 963.

946 _____ 1991. Dennis Chavez Issue

35¢ black phosphored paper mottled tagging — .75 — .20 ☐☐☐☐☐

947 _____ 1991. Flower Issue

29¢ multicolored tagged, perforated 11 — .40 — .20 ☐☐☐☐☐

947A _____ 1991. Flower Issue

29¢ multicolored tagged, perforated 12 1/2 x 13 — .40 — .20 ☐☐☐☐☐

948 _____ 1991. Flower Booklet Issue

29¢ multicolored booklet stamp, tagged, perforated 11 — .40 — .20 ☐☐☐☐☐

NOTE: For coil version of the Flower Issue, see Nos. 966 and 982.

949 _____ 1991. Lunch Wagon Issue

23¢ blue tagged, matte gum — .50 — .20 ☐☐☐☐☐

950 _____ 1991. Wood Duck Issue

29¢ multicolored booklet stamp, black inscription (B.E.P.), tagged — .75 — .20 ☐☐☐☐☐

951 _____ 1991. Wood Duck Issue

29¢ multicolored booklet stamp, red inscription (KCS Industries), tagged — 1.00 — .20 ☐☐☐☐☐

952 _____ 1991. U.S. Flag with Olympic Rings Issue

29¢ multicolored booklet stamp, tagged — .75 — .20 ☐☐☐☐☐

953 _____ 1991. Hot Air Balloon Issue

19¢ multicolored booklet stamp, tagged — .30 — .20 ☐☐☐☐☐

954 _____ 1991. Tractor Trailer Issue

10¢ green (Bureau-printed gray service indicator: "Additional Presort Postage Paid") — .25 — .20 ☐☐☐☐☐

NOTE: For version with service indicator in black, see No. 1042.

955 _____ 1991. Canoe Issue

5¢ brown (printed gray service indicator: "Additional Nonprofit Postage Paid") — .25 — .20 ☐☐☐☐☐

NOTE: For gravure version of No. 955 in red, see No. 979.

956 _____ 1991. Flags on Parade Issue

29¢ multicolored tagged — .50 — .20 ☐☐☐☐☐

957 _____ 1991. Hubert H. Humphrey Issue

52¢ purple phosphored paper (solid tagging), matte gum — 1.50 — .20 ☐☐☐☐☐

958 _____ 1991. Eagle and Olympic Rings Issue

$9.95 multicolored tagged — 15.00 — 7.50 ☐☐☐☐☐

959 _____ 1991. American Kestrel Issue

1¢ multicolored — .25 — .20 ☐☐☐☐☐

NOTE: For versions inscribed "USA 1¢", see No. 1079 (sheet) and No. 1115 (Coil).

960 _____ 1991. Bluebird Issue

3¢ Eastern bluebird — .25 — .20 ☐☐☐☐☐

961 _____ 1991. Cardinal Issue

30¢ multicolored on phosphored paper — .45 — .20 ☐☐☐☐☐

962 _____ 1991. Statue of Liberty Torch Issue

29¢ black, gold & green tagged, die cut — .60 — .30 ☐☐☐☐☐

963 _____ 1991. Flag Over Mount Rushmore Coil Issue

29¢ blue, red & brown tagged — .50 — .25 ☐☐☐☐☐

NOTE: For intaglio version of the same design, see No. 945.

964 _____ 1991. Eagle and Olympic Rings Issue

$2.90 multicolored tagged — 5.00 — 2.75 ☐☐☐☐☐

965 _____ 1991. Fishing Boat Coil Issue

19¢ multicolored Type I, tagged — .40 — .20 ☐☐☐☐☐

NOTE: Imperforates in this design came from printer's waste. For version with one loop of rope tying boat to piling, see No. 1044.

945, 945A   946   947, 947A, 948, 962   949   950, 951

952   953   954   955   956

957   958   959   960

961   962   963   964

965   966   967

969   971, 972, 972A   973   970

	MNHVF	UseVF

966 _____ 1991. Flower Coil Issue

29¢ **multicolored** tagged · .75 · .20 ☐☐☐☐☐

967 _____ 1991. Eagle Over Coastline, Olympic Rings Issue

$14 **multicolored** tagged · 30.00 · 17.50 ☐☐☐☐☐

NOTE: No. 968 is not assigned.

969 _____ 1991. U.S. Flag Issue

23¢ **red & blue** printed service indicator: "Presorted First-Class" · .65 · .20 ☐☐☐☐☐

970 _____ 1991. USPS Olympic Sponsor Issue

$1 **multicolored** tagged · 2.75 · .75 ☐☐☐☐☐

971 _____ 1991. Santa Descending a Chimney Issue

29¢ **multicolored** tagged · .45 · .20 ☐☐☐☐☐

972 _____ 1991. Santa Booklet Issue

29¢ **multicolored** booklet stamp, Type I, tagged · .45 · .20 ☐☐☐☐☐

972A _____

29¢ **multicolored** booklet stamp, Type II, tagged · .45 · .20 ☐☐☐☐☐

NOTE: Type I has an extra vertical line of brick in the top row of bricks at left; Type II is missing that vertical line of brick.

973 _____

29¢ **multicolored** booklet stamp, tagged · .45 · .20 ☐☐☐☐☐

974 _____

29¢ **multicolored** booklet stamp, tagged · .45 · .20 ☐☐☐☐☐

975 _____

29¢ **multicolored** booklet stamp, tagged · .45 · .20 ☐☐☐☐☐

976 _____

29¢ **multicolored** booklet stamp, tagged · .45 · .20 ☐☐☐☐☐

977 _____ 1991. Traditional Christmas Issue

29¢ **multicolored** tagged · .45 · .20 ☐☐☐☐☐

NOTE: No. 978 is not assigned.

979 _____ 1991. Canoe Issue

5¢ **red** (printed service indicator: "Additional Nonprofit Postage Paid") · .25 · .20 ☐☐☐☐☐

NOTE: For intaglio version in brown, see No. 955.

980 _____ 1991. Eagle and Shield Non-Denominated Issue

10¢ **multicolored** (printed service indicator: "Bulk Rate") · .25 · .20 ☐☐☐☐☐

NOTE: See Nos. 1011 and 1012 for similar stamps printed by the Bureau of Engraving and Printing, and Stamp Venturers.

981 _____ 1992. Wendell L. Willkie Issue

75¢ **maroon** phosphored paper (solid tagging), matte gum · 1.25 · .50 ☐☐☐☐☐

982 _____ 1992. Flower Perforated Coil Issue

29¢ **multicolored** tagged · .75 · .20 ☐☐☐☐☐

983 _____ 1992. Earl Warren Issue

29¢ **blue** phosphored paper (mottled tagging) · .50 · .20 ☐☐☐☐☐

984 _____ 1992. Flag Over White House Issue

29¢ **blue & red** tagged, phosphored paper · .50 · .20 ☐☐☐☐☐

985 _____ 1992. USA Issue

23¢ **multicolored** (printed service indicator: "Presorted First-Class") · .50 · .20 ☐☐☐☐☐

NOTE: See Nos. 994 and 1010 for similar stamps printed by the Bureau of Engraving and Printing and by Stamp Venturers.

986 _____ 1992. ECA GARD Variable Denominated Issue

red & blue variable rate, denomination (.01 to 9.99) printed in black, phosphored paper (solid tagging) matte gum · 1.50 · .50 ☐☐☐☐☐

NOTE: For narrow, tall format, see No. 1040.

987 _____ 1992. Pledge of Allegiance Issue

29¢ **multicolored** black inscription, booklet stamp, tagged · .75 · .20 ☐☐☐☐☐

NOTE: For version with red inscription see No. 1008.

988 _____ 1992. Eagle and Shield Self-Adhesive Issue

29¢ **multicolored** red inscription, tagged · .45 · .30 ☐☐☐☐☐

NOTE: No. 989 is not assigned.

	MNHVF	UseVF

990 _____
29¢ **multicolored** green inscription, tagged .45 .30 ☐☐☐☐☐
NOTE: No. 991 is not assigned.

992 _____
29¢ **multicolored** brown inscription, tagged .45 .30 ☐☐☐☐☐
NOTE: No. 993 is not assigned.

994 _____ **1992. "USA" Issue**
23¢ **multicolored** printed service indicator: "Presorted First-Class," shiny gum .50 .20 ☐☐☐☐☐
NOTE: In this version, "23" is 7mm long. See Nos. 985 and 1010 for versions printed by the American Bank Note Co. or by Stamp Venturers.

995 _____ **1992. Contemporary Christmas Issue**
29¢ **Locomotive multicolored,** tagged .45 .20 ☐☐☐☐☐

996 _____
29¢ **Pony & rider multicolored,** tagged .45 .20 ☐☐☐☐☐

997 _____
29¢ **Fire engine multicolored,** tagged .45 .20 ☐☐☐☐☐

998 _____
29¢ **Steamship multicolored,** tagged .45 .20 ☐☐☐☐☐

974

975

976

Christmas 1991 USA

977

Canoe 1800s
Additional Nonprofit
Postage Paid
USA 05

979

Bulk Rate USA

980

Wendell Willkie 1892-1944
75 USA Statesman

981

29 USA

982

Earl Warren Chief Justice of the U.S.
USA 29

983

The White House 1792 1992
29 USA

984

USA
Presorted First-Class

985

USA
* 0 • 29

986

USA 29
I pledge allegiance...

987, 1008

USA 29

988, 990, 992

USA
Presorted First-Class 23

994

29 USA
GREETINGS

29 USA
GREETINGS

29 USA
GREETINGS

29 USA
GREETINGS

995, 999, 1005 (upper left)
996, 1000 (upper right)
997, 1001 (lower left)
998, 1002 (lower right)

CHRISTMAS
29 USA
Bellini c. 1490 National Gallery

1003

29 USA
GREETINGS

1005

	MNHVF	UseVF

999 _____ **1992. Contemporary Booklet Issue**

29¢ **Locomotive multicolored,** booklet single .45 .20 ☐☐☐☐☐

1000 _____

29¢ **Pony & rider multicolored,** booklet single .45 .20 ☐☐☐☐☐

1001 _____

29¢ **Fire engine multicolored,** booklet single .45 .20 ☐☐☐☐☐

1002 _____

29¢ **Steamship multicolored,** booklet single .45 .20 ☐☐☐☐☐

1003 _____ **1992. Traditional Christmas Issue**

29¢ **multicolored** tagged .45 .20 ☐☐☐☐☐

NOTE: No. 1004 is not assigned.

1005 _____ **1992. Contemporary Christmas Self-Adhesive ATM Issue**

29¢ **multicolored** tagged .75 .20 ☐☐☐☐☐

1006 _____ **1992. Pumpkinseed Sunfish Issue**

45¢ **multicolored** tagged 1.00 .20 ☐☐☐☐☐

1007 _____ **1992. Circus Wagon Issue**

5¢ **red** untagged .25 .20 ☐☐☐☐☐

NOTE: For intaglio stamps of this design see No. 931 ("05 USA") and No. 1077 ("USA 5¢").

1008 _____ **1993. Pledge of Allegiance Issue**

29¢ **multicolored** red inscription, tagged .75 .20 ☐☐☐☐☐

NOTE: For similar stamp with black inscription see No. 987.

1009 _____ **1993. Thomas Jefferson Issue**

29¢ **indigo** phosphored paper (solid tagging) .50 .30 ☐☐☐☐☐

1010 _____ **1993. USA Issue**

23¢ **multicolored** printed service indicator: "Presorted First-Class" .75 .20 ☐☐☐☐☐

NOTE: In this version, "23" is 8 1/2mm long. See No. 985 and No. 994 for versions printed by the American Bank Note Co. and by the Bureau of Engraving and Printing.

1011 _____ **1993. Eagle and Shield Non-Denominated Issue**

10¢ **multicolored** (B.E.P.) .30 .20 ☐☐☐☐☐

1012 _____

10¢ **multicolored** (Stamp Venturers) .30 .20 ☐☐☐☐☐

NOTE: See No. 980 for similar design printed by the American Bank Note Co.

1013 _____ **1993. Futuristic Space Shuttle Issue**

$2.90 **multicolored** 6.50 2.50 ☐☐☐☐☐

1014 _____ **1993. Red Squirrel Issue**

29¢ **multicolored** from booklet or coil, tagged .50 .20 ☐☐☐☐☐

NOTE: No. 1015 is not assigned.

1016 _____ **1993. Rose Issue**

29¢ **multicolored** from booklet or coil, tagged .50 .20 ☐☐☐☐☐

NOTE: No. 1017 is not assigned.

1018 _____ **1993. African Violet Booklet Issue**

29¢ **multicolored** from booklet, tagged .75 .20 ☐☐☐☐☐

1019 _____ **1993. Contemporary Christmas Issue**

29¢ **Jack-in-the-box,** tagged .50 .20 ☐☐☐☐☐

1020 _____

29¢ **Reindeer,** tagged .50 .20 ☐☐☐☐☐

1021 _____

29¢ **Snowman,** tagged .50 .20 ☐☐☐☐☐

1022 _____

29¢ **Toy soldier,** tagged .50 .20 ☐☐☐☐☐

1023 _____

29¢ **Jack-in-the-box,** tagged .50 .20 ☐☐☐☐☐

1024 _____

29¢ **Reindeer,** tagged .50 .20 ☐☐☐☐☐

1025 _____

29¢ **Snowman,** tagged .50 .20 ☐☐☐☐☐

	MNHVF	UseVF

1026 _____
   29¢ **Toy soldier,** tagged (single) .... .50 .20 ☐☐☐☐☐
1027 _____ **1993. Traditional Christmas Issue**
   29¢ **multicolored** tagged .... .50 .20 ☐☐☐☐☐
1028 _____
   29¢ **multicolored** booklet single, tagged .... .50 .20 ☐☐☐☐☐
1029 _____ **1993. Contemporary Christmas Self-adhesive Issue**
   29¢ **Jack-in-the-box,** tagged .... .50 .20 ☐☐☐☐☐
1030 _____
   29¢ **Reindeer,** tagged .... .50 .20 ☐☐☐☐☐
1031 _____
   29¢ **Snowman,** tagged .... .50 .20 ☐☐☐☐☐
1032 _____
   29¢ **Toy soldier,** tagged .... .50 .20 ☐☐☐☐☐
NOTE: Nos. 1033-1036 are not assigned.
1037 _____ **1993. Snowman ATM Pane Issue**
   29¢ **multicolored,** tagged .... .75 .25 ☐☐☐☐☐

NOTE: Although the placement is different, the Snowmen depicted on Nos. 1021 and 1031 have three buttons and seven snowflakes beneath the nose. No. 1025 has two buttons and five snowflakes beneath the nose.

USA 45
Pumpkinseed Sunfish
1006

Thomas Jefferson
USA 29
1009

USA Bulk Rate
1011, 1012

USA $2.90
1013

29 USA
1014

USA 29
1016

Greetings 29 USA · 29 USA
Greetings · Greetings 29 USA
29 USA

1019, 1023, 1029
(upper left)
1020, 1024, 1030
(upper right)
1021, 1025, 1031
(lower left)
1022, 1026, 1032
(lower right)

African Violet USA 29
1018

CHRISTMAS
29 USA
*Giovanni Battista Cima, c.1497
North Carolina Museum of Art*
1027, 1028

Greetings 29 USA
1037

USA 29
1038

29 USA
1039

USA $0.32
1040

POSTAGE
$1 One Dollar
1041

Tractor Trailer
Additional Presort 1930s
Postage Paid
USA 10
1042

	MNHVF	UseVF

1038 _____ **1993. Pine Cone Issue**

29¢ **multicolored** from booklet or coil, tagged — .50 — .20 ☐☐☐☐☐

1039 _____ **1994. Eagle Issue**

29¢ **red, cream & blue** from booklet or coil, tagged — .50 — .20 ☐☐☐☐☐

1040 _____ **1994. Postage and Mail Center (PMC) Issue**

(variable rate) red and blue, denomination 20¢-$99.99 printed in black, phosphored paper — 1.50 — .50 ☐☐☐☐☐

1041 _____ **1994. Surrender of Burgoyne at Saratoga Issue**

$1 **dark blue** tagged — 2.00 — .75 ☐☐☐☐☐

1042 _____ **1994. Tractor Trailer Issue**

10¢ **green** Bureau-printed service indicator (in gray): "Additional Presort Postage Paid" — .25 — .20 ☐☐☐☐☐

1043 _____ **1994. Statue of Liberty Issue**

29¢ **multicolored** from booklet or coil, tagged — .50 — .20 ☐☐☐☐☐

1044 _____ **1994. Fishing Boat Issue**

19¢ **multicolored** tagged — .50 — .20 ☐☐☐☐☐

1045 _____ **1994. Moon Landing Issue**

$9.95 **multicolored** tagged — 25.00 — 10.00 ☐☐☐☐☐

1046 _____ **1994. Washington and Jackson Issue**

$5 **dark green** tagged — 10.00 — 3.75 ☐☐☐☐☐

1047 _____ **1994. Contemporary Christmas Issue**

29¢ **multicolored** from sheet or booklet, tagged — .50 — .20 ☐☐☐☐☐

1048 _____ **1994. Traditional Christmas Issue**

29¢ **multicolored** shiny gum, tagged — .50 — .20 ☐☐☐☐☐

1049 _____

29¢ **multicolored** from booklet, tagged — .50 — .20 ☐☐☐☐☐

1050 _____ **1994. Contemporary Santa Claus Booklet Issue**

29¢ **multicolored** from booklet or coil, tagged — .50 — .20 ☐☐☐☐☐

1051 _____ **1994. Cardinal in Snow ATM Issue**

29¢ **multicolored** tagged — .50 — .20 ☐☐☐☐☐

1052 _____ **1994. Virginia Apgar Issue**

29¢ **brown** phosphored paper grainy tagging — .50 — .20 ☐☐☐☐☐

1053 _____ **1994. Postage and Mail Center (PMC) Issue**

(variable rate) red & blue, denomination (.01-9.99) printed in black phosphored paper, (mottled tagging), shiny gum — .75 — .50 ☐☐☐☐☐

1054 _____ **1994. Black "G" Sheet Issue**

32¢ **red, blue, gray & black** tagged — .50 — .20 ☐☐☐☐☐

1055 _____ **1994. Red "G" Sheet Issue**

(32¢) **red, blue, gray & black** tagged — .75 — .20 ☐☐☐☐☐

1056 _____ **1994. Black "G" Booklet Issue**

(32¢) **red, blue, gray & black** tagged — .50 — .20 ☐☐☐☐☐

1057 _____ **1994. Blue "G" Booklet Issue**

(32¢) **red, blue, gray & black** tagged — .50 — .20 ☐☐☐☐☐

1058 _____ **1994. Red "G" Booklet Issue**

(32¢) **red, blue, gray & black** tagged — .50 — .20 ☐☐☐☐☐

1059 _____ **1994. Black "G" Coil Issue**

(32¢) **red, blue, gray & black** tagged — .50 — .20 ☐☐☐☐☐

1060 _____ **1994. Blue "G" Coil Issue**

(32¢) **red, blue, gray & black** tagged — .50 — .20 ☐☐☐☐☐

1061 _____ **1994. Red "G" Coil Issue**

(32¢) **red, blue, gray & black** tagged — .50 — .20 ☐☐☐☐☐

1061A _____ **1994. Red "G" Coil Issue**

(32¢) **red, blue, gray & black** tagged — .50 — .20 ☐☐☐☐☐

1062 _____ **1994. "G" Self-Adhesive Issue**

(32¢) **red, dark blue, light blue, gray & black,** from booklet or coil, tagged — 1.00 — .35 ☐☐☐☐☐

	MNHVF	UseVF

1063 _____ **1994. "G" Self-Adhesive ATM Issue**

(32¢) **red, blue & black** tagged .... 1.00 .35 ☐☐☐☐☐

1064 _____ **1994. "G" First-Class Presort Rate Issue**

(25¢) **red, dark blue, gray, black & light blue** .... .50 .20 ☐☐☐☐☐

1065 _____ **1994. Black "G" Postcard Rate Issue**

(20¢) **red, blue, gray, yellow & black** tagged .... .50 .20 ☐☐☐☐☐

1066 _____ **1994. Red "G" Postcard Rate Issue**

(20¢) **red, blue, gray, yellow & black,** tagged .... .50 .20 ☐☐☐☐☐

1067 _____ **1994. Non-Denominated "Make-Up" Rate Issue**

(3¢) **red, bright blue & tan** .... .20 .20 ☐☐☐☐☐

1068 _____ **1994. Non-Denominated "Make-Up" Rate**

(3¢) **red, dark blue & tan** .... .20 .20 ☐☐☐☐☐

1069 _____ **1995. "G" Nonprofit Presort Coil Issue**

(5¢) **green & multicolored** untagged .... .25 .20 ☐☐☐☐☐

NOTE: First-day covers received a Dec. 13, 1994, cancellation although these stamps were not yet available on that date.

1070 _____ **1995. Butte and "Nonprofit Organization" Issue**

(5¢) **yellow, blue & red** untagged .... .25 .20 ☐☐☐☐☐

1043

1044

1045

1046

1047

1048, 1049

1050

1054-1063

1051

1052

1053

1064

1065, 1066

1067, 1068

1069

1070

	MNHVF	UseVF

1071 _____ 1995. Car Hood and "Bulk Rate" Issue

(10¢) **black, brown & red brown** untagged .30 .20 ▢▢▢▢▢

1072 _____ 1995. Tail Fin Presorted First-Class Coil Issue

(15¢) **yellow orange & multicolored** untagged .40 .30 ▢▢▢▢▢

1073 _____ 1995. Tail Fin Presorted First-Class Coil Issue

15¢ **buff & multicolored** untagged .40 .30 ▢▢▢▢▢

1074 _____ 1995. Juke Box Presorted First-Class Coil Issue

25¢ **dark red, yellow green & multicolored,** untagged .65 .40 ▢▢▢▢▢

1075 _____ 1995. Juke Box "Presorted First-Class" Coil Issue

25¢ **orange red, bright yellow green & multicolored** untagged .65 .40 ▢▢▢▢▢

1076 _____ 1995. Flag Over Field ATM Issue

32¢ **multicolored** tagged 1.00 .30 ▢▢▢▢▢

1077 _____ 1995. Circus Wagon Issue

5¢ **red** untagged .25 .20 ▢▢▢▢▢

NOTE: For intaglio & gravure versions of this design inscribed "05 USA" see Nos. 931 & 1007.

1078 _____ 1995. Flag Over Porch Self-Adhesive Booklet Issue

32¢ **multicolored** from booklet or coil, phosphored paper, large "1995" .70 .20 ▢▢▢▢▢

1079 _____ 1995. American Kestrel Issue

1¢ **multicolored** tagged .25 .20 ▢▢▢▢▢

NOTE: For version inscribed "USA 01" see No. 959. For coil see No. 1115.

1080 _____ 1995. Flag Over Porch Issue

32¢ **multicolored** tagged .60 .20 ▢▢▢▢▢

1081 _____ 1995. Flag Over Porch Booklet Issue

32¢ **multicolored** tagged .80 .20 ▢▢▢▢▢

1082 _____ 1995. Flag Over Porch Coil Issue

32¢ **multicolored** tagged, red "1995" .50 .20 ▢▢▢▢▢

1083 _____ 1995. Flag Over Porch Coil Issue

32¢ **multicolored** tagged, blue "1995" .75 .20 ▢▢▢▢▢

1084 _____ 1995. Pink Rose Issue

32¢ **pink, green & black** from booklet or coil, phosphored .80 .30 ▢▢▢▢▢

1085 _____ 1995. Ferryboat Issue

32¢ **deep blue** phosphored paper .65 .20 ▢▢▢▢▢

1086 _____ 1995. Cog Railway Issue

20¢ **green** phosphored paper .40 .20 ▢▢▢▢▢

1087 _____ 1995. Blue Jay Issue

20¢ **multicolored** phosphored paper .45 .20 ▢▢▢▢▢

1088 _____ 1995. Space Shuttle Challenger Issue

$3 **multicolored** phosphored paper 6.00 3.00 ▢▢▢▢▢

1089 _____ 1995. Peaches and Pear Issue

32¢ **multicolored** phosphored paper .75 .20 ▢▢▢▢▢

1090 _____

32¢ **multicolored** phosphored paper .75 .20 ▢▢▢▢▢

1091 _____ 1995. Peaches and Pear Self-Adhesive Issue

32¢ **multicolored** phosphored paper .85 .30 ▢▢▢▢▢

1091A _____ 1995. Peaches and Pear Self-Adhesive Coil Issue

32¢ **multicolored** .85 .30 ▢▢▢▢▢

1092 _____ 1995. Peaches and Pear Self-Adhesive Issue

32¢ **multicolored** phosphored paper .85 .30 ▢▢▢▢▢

1092A _____ 1995. Peaches and Pear Self-Adhesive Coil Issue

32¢ **multicolored** .85 .30 ▢▢▢▢▢

1093 _____ 1995. Alice Hamilton Issue

55¢ **green** phosphored paper, grainy tagging 1.10 .20 ▢▢▢▢▢

1094 _____ 1995. Space Shuttle Endeavor Issue

$10.75 **multicolored** phosphored paper 21.00 8.00 ▢▢▢▢▢

	MNHVF	UseVF

1095 _____ **1995. Alice Paul Issue**
78¢ **purple** phosphored paper, solid tagging — 1.75 — .25 ☐☐☐☐☐

1096 _____ **1995. Milton S. Hershey Issue**
32¢ **chocolate brown** phosphored paper, solid tagging — .65 — .20 ☐☐☐☐☐

1097 _____ **1995. Eddie Rickenbacker Issue**
60¢ **multicolored** phosphored paper — .75 — .20 ☐☐☐☐☐

1098 _____ **1995. Contemporary Christmas Issue**
32¢ **Santa on rooftop,** phosphored paper — .60 — .20 ☐☐☐☐☐

1099 _____
32¢ **Child and jumping jack,** phosphored paper — .60 — .20 ☐☐☐☐☐

1071

1072

1073, 1133

1074-75, 1134, 1153

1076

1077

1078, 1080-83

1079

1084

1085

1086

1087, 1135-36

1088

1089, 1091, 1091A (left)
1090, 1092, 1092A (right)

1093

1094

1095

1098, 1102, 1106
(upper left)
1099, 1103, 1107
(upper right)
1100, 1104, 1108
(lower left)
1101, 1105, 1109
(lower right) →

1096

1097, 1250

	MNHVF	UseVF

1100 _____

32¢ **Child and tree,** phosphored paper   .60   .20 ☐☐☐☐☐

1101 _____

32¢ **Santa in workshop,** phosphored paper   .60   .20 ☐☐☐☐☐

1102 _____ **1995. Contemporary Christmas Coil Issue**

32¢ **Santa on rooftop,** phosphored paper   .60   .20 ☐☐☐☐☐

1103 _____

32¢ **Child and jumping jack,** phosphored paper   .60   .20 ☐☐☐☐☐

1104 _____

32¢ **Child and tree,** phosphored paper   .60   .20 ☐☐☐☐☐

1105 _____

32¢ **Santa in workshop,** phosphored paper   .60   .20 ☐☐☐☐☐

1106 _____ **1995. Contemporary Christmas Booklet Issue**

32¢ **multicolored** phosphored paper   .60   .20 ☐☐☐☐☐

1107 _____

32¢ **multicolored** phosphored paper   .60   .20 ☐☐☐☐☐

1108 _____

32¢ **multicolored** phosphored paper   .60   .20 ☐☐☐☐☐

1109 _____

32¢ **multicolored** phosphored paper   .60   .20 ☐☐☐☐☐

1110 _____ **1995. Midnight Angel Christmas Booklet Issue**

32¢ **multicolored** phosphored paper   .60   .20 ☐☐☐☐☐

1110A _____ **1995. Midnight Angel Christmas Coil Issue**

32¢ **multicolored** phosphored paper   .75   .45 ☐☐☐☐☐

1111 _____ **1995. Contemporary Christmas Booklet ATM Issue**

32¢ **multicolored** phosphored lacquer on surface of stamps   .75   .45 ☐☐☐☐☐

1112 _____ **1995. Traditional Christmas Issue**

32¢ **multicolored** phosphored paper, perforated 11 1/4   .75   .20 ☐☐☐☐☐

1113 _____

32¢ **multicolored** phosphored paper, perforated 9 3/4 x 11   .75   .20 ☐☐☐☐☐

1114 _____ **1995. Ruth Benedict Issue**

45¢ **carmine** phosphored paper, mottled tagging   1.00   .25 ☐☐☐☐☐

1115 _____ **1996. American Kestrel Issue**

1¢ **multicolored** untagged   .25   .20 ☐☐☐☐☐

NOTE: For sheet version see No. 1079. For version inscribed "USA 01" see No. 959.

1116 _____ **1996. Flag Over Porch Issue**

32¢ **multicolored** phosphored paper   .75   .30 ☐☐☐☐☐

1117 _____ **1996. Unisys Variable Denomination Issue**

32¢ **red & blue** denomination (.20 to $20.00) printed in black, tagged   .95   .50 ☐☐☐☐☐

1118 _____ **1996. Red-headed Woodpecker Issue**

2¢ **multicolored** untagged   .25   .20 ☐☐☐☐☐

1119 _____ **1996. Space Shuttle Challenger Issue**

$3 **multicolored** phosphored paper   6.00   3.00 ☐☐☐☐☐

1120 _____ **1996. Jacqueline Cochran Issue**

50¢ **multicolored** phosphored paper   1.20   .40 ☐☐☐☐☐

1121 _____ **1996. Mountain Coil Issue**

5¢ **purple & multicolored** untagged   .25   .20 ☐☐☐☐☐

1122 _____ **1996. Mountain Coil Issue**

5¢ **blue & multicolored** untagged   .25   .20 ☐☐☐☐☐

1123 _____ **1996. Eastern Bluebird Issue**

3¢ **multicolored** untagged   .25   .20 ☐☐☐☐☐

1124 _____ **1996. Cal Farley Issue**

32¢ **green** phosphored paper, solid tagging   .65   .20 ☐☐☐☐☐

1125 _____ **1996. Flag Over Porch Booklet Stamp Issue**

32¢ **multicolored** phosphored paper   .75   .30 ☐☐☐☐☐

	MNHVF	UseVF

1126 _____ **1996. Flag Over Porch Coil Stamp Issue**
32¢ **multicolored** phosphored paper   1.00   .30 ☐☐☐☐☐

1127 _____ **1996. Flag Over Porch Coil Stamp Issue**
32¢ **multicolored** phosphored paper   1.50   .50 ☐☐☐☐☐

1128 _____ **1996. Flag Over Porch Coil Stamp Issue**
32¢ **multicolored** phosphored paper   .70   .20 ☐☐☐☐☐

NOTE: On this issue, stamps are spaced apart on the 10,000 stamp coil roll.

1129 _____ **1996. Eagle and Shield Non-Denominated Self-Adhesive Coil Issue**
10¢ **multicolored** untagged   .25   .20 ☐☐☐☐☐

1130 _____ **1996. Butte Coil Issue**
5¢ **yellow, blue & red** untagged   .25   .20 ☐☐☐☐☐

1131 _____ **1996. Mountains Coil Issue**
5¢ **purple & multicolored** untagged   .25   .20 ☐☐☐☐☐

1132 _____ **1996. Automobile Coil Issue**
10¢ **black, brown & red brown** untagged   .25   .20 ☐☐☐☐☐

1133 _____ **1996. Auto Tail Fin Coil Issue**
15¢ **buff & multicolored** untagged   .35   .30 ☐☐☐☐☐

1134 _____ **1996. Juke Box Coil Issue**
25¢ **orange red, bright yellow green & multicolored** untagged   .60   .30 ☐☐☐☐☐

1110, 1110A   1111

1112, 1113

1114   1115

1116   1117   1118   1119   1120

1121, 1122   1123   1124   1125-1128   1129   1130

1131   1132   1133   1134   1135, 1136

	MNHVF	UseVF	

1135 _____ **1996. Blue Jay Booklet Issue**

20¢ **multicolored** phosphored paper   .45   .25 ❑❑❑❑❑

1136 _____ **1996. Blue Jay Coil Issue**

20¢ **multicolored** phosphored paper   .40   .20 ❑❑❑❑❑

1137 _____ **1996. Contemporary Christmas Issue**

32¢ **Family at yule hearth,** phosphored paper   .60   .20 ❑❑❑❑❑

1138 _____

32¢ **Family trimming tree,** phosphored paper   .60   .20 ❑❑❑❑❑

1139 _____

32¢ **Dreaming of Santa,** phosphored paper   .60   .20 ❑❑❑❑❑

1140 _____

32¢ **Holiday shopping,** phosphored paper   .60   .20 ❑❑❑❑❑

1141 _____ **1996. Contemporary Self Adhesive Booklet Issue**

32¢ **Family at yule hearth,** phosphored paper   .60   .20 ❑❑❑❑❑

1142 _____

32¢ **Family trimming tree,** phosphored paper   .60   .20 ❑❑❑❑❑

1143 _____

32¢ **Dreaming of Santa,** phosphored paper   .60   .20 ❑❑❑❑❑

1144 _____

32¢ **Holiday shopping,** phosphored paper   .60   .20 ❑❑❑❑❑

1145 _____ **1996. Holiday Skaters Booklet ATM Issue**

32¢ **multicolored,** phosphored lacquer on surface of stamps   .75   .30 ❑❑❑❑❑

1146 _____ **1996. Traditional Christmas Issue**

32¢ **multicolored** phosphored paper, perforated 11 1/4   .70   .20 ❑❑❑❑❑

1147 _____

32¢ **multicolored** tagged, serpentine die cut   .95   .30 ❑❑❑❑❑

NOTE: No. 1148 is not assigned.

1149 _____ **1996. Yellow Rose Issue**

32¢ **yellow & multicolored** phosphored paper   .75   .25 ❑❑❑❑❑

1150 _____ **1997. Flag Over Porch Booklet Issue**

32¢ **multicolored** phosphored paper   .75   .30 ❑❑❑❑❑

1151 _____ **1997. Flag Over Porch Coil Issue**

32¢ **multicolored** phosphored paper   .75   .30 ❑❑❑❑❑

1152 _____ **1997. Mountain Coil Issue**

5¢ **purple & multicolored** untagged   .25   .20 ❑❑❑❑❑

1153 _____ **1997. Juke Box Coil Issue**

25¢ **multicolored** untagged   .60   .20 ❑❑❑❑❑

1154 _____ **1997. Statue of Liberty Issue**

32¢ **multicolored** phosphored paper   .75   .20 ❑❑❑❑❑

1155 _____ **1997. Citron and Insect Issue**

32¢ **multicolored** tagged   .75   .20 ❑❑❑❑❑

1156 _____ **1997. Flowering Pineapple Issue**

32¢ **multicolored** tagged   .75   .20 ❑❑❑❑❑

1157 _____ **1997. Citron and Insect Booklet Issue**

32¢ **multicolored** tagged   .75   .20 ❑❑❑❑❑

1158 _____ **1997. Flowering Pineapple Booklet Issue**

32¢ **multicolored** tagged   .75   .20 ❑❑❑❑❑

1159 _____ **1997. Citron and Insect Booklet Issue**

32¢ **multicolored** tagged   1.25   .50 ❑❑❑❑❑

1160 _____ **1997. Flowering Pineapple Booklet Issue**

32¢ **multicolored** tagged   1.25   .50 ❑❑❑❑❑

NOTE: Nos. 1159-60, which are die cut on all four sides, have a single irregular large serration near the middle of the right side created by die cutting.

1137, 1141
(upper left)
1138, 1142
(upper right)
1139, 1143
(lower left)
1140, 1144
(lower right)

1145

1146, 1147

1149, 1163

1150-1151

1152

1153

1154

1155

1156

1157, 1159

1158, 1160

1161

1162

1163

1164

1166, 1167

American Holly 32 USA

1165

Henry R. Luce
EDITOR

1168

MARS PATHFINDER
JULY 4, 1997
Mars Rover Sojourner
$3.00 USA

1169

1170, 1177

1171

1172, 1173, 1248

	MNHVF	UseVF

1161 _____ **1997. Juke Box Issue**

25¢ **multicolored** untagged | .60 | .20 ☐☐☐☐☐

1162 _____ **1997. Flag Over Porch Issue**

32¢ **multicolored** tagged | .60 | .20 ☐☐☐☐☐

1163 _____ **1997. Rose Issue**

32¢ **yellow & multicolored** tagged | .65 | .20 ☐☐☐☐☐

1164 _____ **1997. Christmas Issue**

32¢ **multicolored** tagged (single) | .50 | .20 ☐☐☐☐☐

1165 _____

32¢ **multicolored** tagged (single) | .50 | .20 ☐☐☐☐☐

1166 _____ **1997. Mars Pathfinder Issue**

$3 **multicolored** tagged *(15,000,000 printed)* | 4.50 | 2.50 ☐☐☐☐☐

1167 _____ **1998. Mars Pathfinder Press Sheet Issue**

$3 **multicolored** tagged (single) | 15.00 | — ☐☐☐☐☐

1168 _____ **1998. Henry R. Luce Issue**

32¢ **lake** phosphored paper grainy tagging | .50 | .20 ☐☐☐☐☐

1169 _____ **1998. Swamp Coil Issue**

5¢ **multicolored** | .25 | .20 ☐☐☐☐☐

1169A _____ **1998. Swamp Self-Adhesive Coil Issue**

5¢ **multicolored** | .20 | .20 ☐☐☐☐☐

1170 _____ **1998. Diner Non-Denominated Coil Issue**

25¢ **multicolored** tagged | .40 | .20 ☐☐☐☐☐

1171 _____ **1998. Lila and De Witt Wallace Issue**

32¢ **blue** phosphored paper solid tagging | .50 | .20 ☐☐☐☐☐

1172 _____ **1998. Ring-necked Pheasant Coil Issue**

20¢ **multicolored** tagged | .40 | .20 ☐☐☐☐☐

1173 _____ **1998. Ring-necked Pheasant Booklet Issue**

20¢ **multicolored** tagged (single) | .40 | .20 ☐☐☐☐☐

1174 _____ **1998. Red Fox Issue**

$1 **multicolored** tagged | 1.50 | .75 ☐☐☐☐☐

1175 _____ **1998. Bicycle Coil Issue**

10¢ **multicolored** untagged | .30 | .20 ☐☐☐☐☐

1176 _____ **1998. Bicycle Self-Adhesive Coil Issue**

10¢ **multicolored** untagged | .30 | .20 ☐☐☐☐☐

1177 _____ **1998. Diner Coil Issue**

25¢ **multicolored** untagged | .30 | .20 ☐☐☐☐☐

1178 _____ **1998. Traditional Christmas Issue**

32¢ **multicolored** | .50 | .20 ☐☐☐☐☐

1179 _____ **1998. Contemporary Christmas Issue**

32¢ **Traditional wreath,** tagged | .50 | .20 ☐☐☐☐☐

1180 _____

32¢ **Colonial wreath,** tagged | .50 | .20 ☐☐☐☐☐

1181 _____

32¢ **Chili wreath,** tagged | .50 | .20 ☐☐☐☐☐

1182 _____

32¢ **Tropical wreath,** tagged | .50 | .20 ☐☐☐☐☐

1183 _____ **1998. Contemporary Christmas Booklet Issue**

32¢ **Traditional wreath** | .50 | .20 ☐☐☐☐☐

1184 _____

32¢ **Colonial wreath** | .50 | .20 ☐☐☐☐☐

1185 _____

32¢ **Chili wreath** | .50 | .20 ☐☐☐☐☐

1186 _____

32¢ **Tropical wreath** | .50 | .20 ☐☐☐☐☐

	MNHVF	UseVF	

1187 _____

32¢ **Traditional wreath**   .50   .20 ☐☐☐☐☐

1188 _____

32¢ **Colonial wreath**   .50   .20 ☐☐☐☐☐

1189 _____

32¢ **Chili wreath**   .50   .20 ☐☐☐☐☐

1190 _____

32¢ **Tropical wreath**   .50   .20 ☐☐☐☐☐

1191 _____   **1998. "H" Make-Up Rate, USA White Issue**

1¢ **multicolored**   .25   .20 ☐☐☐☐☐

1192 _____   **1998. "H" Make-Up Rate, USA Light Blue Issue**

1¢ **multicolored**   .25   .20 ☐☐☐☐☐

1193 _____   **1998. Hat "H" First-Class Issue**

33¢ **multicolored** tagged   .50   .20 ☐☐☐☐☐

1194 _____   **1998. Hat "H" First-Class Coil Issue**

33¢ **multicolored** tagged   .50   .20 ☐☐☐☐☐

1195 _____   **1998. Hat "H" First-Class Booklet Issue**

33¢ **multicolored** tagged   .50   .20 ☐☐☐☐☐

1174

1175, 1176

1178

GREETINGS 32 USA   GREETINGS 32 USA
GREETINGS 32 USA   GREETINGS 32 USA

1179, 1183, 1187
(upper left)
1180, 1184, 1188
(upper right)
1181, 1185, 1189
(lower left)
1182, 1186, 1190
(lower right)

1191

1192

1193-1197

1198, 1199

1200

1201

1202

1203

1206, 1207, 1208
1209, 1210, 1211, 1212

1213

	MNHVF	UseVF	

1196 _____

33¢ **multicolored** tagged — .50 — .20 ☐☐☐☐☐

1197 _____ **1998. Hat "H" First-Class Coil Issue**

33¢ **multicolored** tagged — .50 — .20 ☐☐☐☐☐

1198 _____ **1998. Uncle Sam Issue**

22¢ **multicolored** tagged — .50 — .20 ☐☐☐☐☐

1199 _____ **1998. Uncle Sam Coil Issue**

22¢ **multicolored** tagged — .50 — .20 ☐☐☐☐☐

1200 _____ **1998. Mary Breckinridge Issue**

77¢ **blue** phosphored paper, solid tagging — 1.00 — .20 ☐☐☐☐☐

1201 _____ **1998. Shuttle Landing Issue**

$3.20 **multicolored** tagged — 4.00 — 2.75 ☐☐☐☐☐

1202 _____ **1998. Shuttle Piggyback Transport Issue**

$11.75 **multicolored** tagged — 14.00 — 8.00 ☐☐☐☐☐

1203 _____ **1998. Hat "H" First-Class ATM Vending Issue**

33¢ **multicolored** — .50 — .20 ☐☐☐☐☐

1204 _____ **1998. Eagle and Shield Coil Issue**

10¢ **multicolored** — .20 — .20 ☐☐☐☐☐

NOTE: See U.S. Nos. 980 ("Bulk Rate USA"), 1011 and 1012 ("USA Bulk Rate") and 1129 ("USA Bulk Rate").

1205 _____ **1998. Eagle and Shield Coil Issue**

10¢ **multicolored** — .20 — .20 ☐☐☐☐☐

1206 _____ **1999. Flag and Skyscrapers Issue**

33¢ **multicolored** — .50 — .20 ☐☐☐☐☐

1207 _____ **1999. Flag and Skyscrapers Coil Issue**

33¢ **multicolored** — .50 — .20 ☐☐☐☐☐

1208 _____ **1999. Flag and Skyscrapers Coil Issue**

33¢ **multicolored** — .50 — .20 ☐☐☐☐☐

1209 _____ **1999. Flag and Skyscrapers Coil Issue**

33¢ **multicolored** — .50 — .20 ☐☐☐☐☐

1210 _____ **1999. Flag and Skyscrapers Issue**

33¢ **multicolored** — .50 — .20 ☐☐☐☐☐

1211 _____ **1999. Flag and Skyscrapers Issue**

33¢ **multicolored** — .60 — .20 ☐☐☐☐☐

1212 _____ **1999. Flag and Skyscrapers Issue**

33¢ **multicolored** — .60 — .20 ☐☐☐☐☐

1213 _____ **1999. Flag in Classroom Issue**

33¢ **multicolored** — .50 — .20 ☐☐☐☐☐

1214 _____ **1999. Fruit Berries Issue**

33¢ Blueberries — .50 — .20 ☐☐☐☐☐

1215 _____

33¢ Raspberries — .50 — .20 ☐☐☐☐☐

1216 _____

33¢ Strawberries — .50 — .20 ☐☐☐☐☐

1217 _____

33¢ Blackberries — .50 — .20 ☐☐☐☐☐

1218 _____ **1999. Fruit Berries Issue**

33¢ Blueberries — .50 — .20 ☐☐☐☐☐

1219 _____

33¢ Strawberries — .50 — .20 ☐☐☐☐☐

1220 _____

33¢ Raspberries — .50 — .20 ☐☐☐☐☐

1221 _____

33¢ Blackberries — .50 — .20 ☐☐☐☐☐

1222 _____ **1999. Fruit Berries Coil Issue**

33¢ Blackberries — .50 — .20 ☐☐☐☐☐

	MNHVF	UseVF	

1223 _____
  33¢ Strawberries   .50   .20 ☐☐☐☐☐
1224 _____
  33¢ Blueberries   .50   .20 ☐☐☐☐☐
1225 _____
  33¢ Raspberries   .50   .20 ☐☐☐☐☐
1226 _____ **1999. Niagara Falls Issue**
  48¢ multicolored   1.00   .20 ☐☐☐☐☐
1227 _____ **1999. Red-headed Woodpecker Issue**
  2¢ multicolored   .20   .20 ☐☐☐☐☐
1228 _____ **1999. Justin S. Morrill Issue**
  55¢ black   1.00   .20 ☐☐☐☐☐
1229 _____ **1999. American Kestrel Coil Issue**
  1¢ multicolored   .20   .20 ☐☐☐☐☐
1230 _____ **1999. Rio Grande Issue**
  40¢ multicolored   .75   .20 ☐☐☐☐☐
1231 _____ **1999. Billy Mitchell Issue**
  55¢ multicolored   1.00   .40 ☐☐☐☐☐

1214-1217, 1251-1254

1218-1221

1222-1225

1226

1227

1228

1229, 1247

1232, 1255

	MNHVF	UseVF	

1232 _____ **1999. Coral Pink Rose Issue**

33¢ **multicolored**   .50   .20 □□□□□

1233 _____ **1999. Uncle Sam Issue**

22¢ **multicolored**   .50   .20 □□□□□

1234 _____ **1999. Madonna and Child Issue**

33¢ **multicolored**   .50   .20 □□□□□

1235 _____ **1999. Greetings Reindeer Issue**

33¢ **red** background   .50   .20 □□□□□

1236 _____

33¢ **blue** background   .50   .20 □□□□□

1237 _____

33¢ **violet** background   .50   .20 □□□□□

1238 _____

33¢ **green** background   .50   .20 □□□□□

1239 _____ **1999. Greetings Reindeer Booklet Issue**

33¢ **red** background   .50   .20 □□□□□

1240 _____

33¢ **blue** background   .50   .20 □□□□□

1241 _____

33¢ **violet** background   .50   .20 □□□□□

1242 _____

33¢ **green** background   .50   .20 □□□□□

1243 _____ **1999. Greetings Reindeer Vending Booklet Issue**

33¢ **red** background   .50   .20 □□□□□

1244 _____

33¢ **blue** background   .50   .20 □□□□□

1245 _____

33¢ **violet** background   .50   .20 □□□□□

1246 _____

33¢ **green** background   .50   .20 □□□□□

1230

1233

1231

1234

1235-1238, 1239-1242, 1243-1246

		MNHVF	UseVF	

1247 _____ **1999. American Kestrel Issue**

  1¢ multicolored   .20   .20 ☐☐☐☐☐

1248 _____ **1999. Ring-necked Pheasant Booklet Issue**

  20¢ multicolored   .40   .20 ☐☐☐☐☐

1249 _____ **2000. Grand Canyon Issue**

  60¢ multicolored   1.20   .30 ☐☐☐☐☐

1250 _____ **2000. Eddie Rickenbacker Issue**

  60¢ multicolored   1.20   .30 ☐☐☐☐☐

1251 _____ **2000. Fruit Berries Issue**

  33¢ multicolored   .60   .20 ☐☐☐☐☐

1252 _____

  33¢ multicolored   .60   .20 ☐☐☐☐☐

1253 _____

  33¢ multicolored   .60   .20 ☐☐☐☐☐

1254 _____

  33¢ multicolored   .60   .20 ☐☐☐☐☐

1255 _____ **2000. Coral Pink Rose Issue**

  33¢ multicolored   .60   .20 ☐☐☐☐☐

1256 _____ **2000. Fruit Berries Vertical Coil Issue**

  33¢ multicolored   .60   .20 ☐☐☐☐☐

1257 _____

  33¢ multicolored   .60   .20 ☐☐☐☐☐

1258 _____

  33¢ multicolored   .60   .20 ☐☐☐☐☐

1259 _____

  33¢ multicolored   .60   .20 ☐☐☐☐☐

1260 _____ **2000. Joseph W. Stillwell Issue**

  10¢ multicolored   .20   .20 ☐☐☐☐☐

1261 _____ **2000. Claude Pepper Issue**

  33¢ multicolored   .50   .20 ☐☐☐☐☐

1262 _____ **2000. The New York Public Library Lion Issue**

  10¢ multicolored   .20   .20 ☐☐☐☐☐

1263 _____ **2000. Blue Kestrel Issue**

  1¢ multicolored   .20   .20 ☐☐☐☐☐

1249

1250

1256-1259

1260

1261

		MNHVF	UseVF	

1264 _____   **2000. Farm Flag Issue**
34¢ **multicolored**   .50   .20 ☐☐☐☐☐

1265 _____   **2000. Farm Flag Issue**
34¢ **multicolored**   .50   .20 ☐☐☐☐☐

1266 _____   **2000. Farm Flag Issue**
34¢ **multicolored**   .50   .20 ☐☐☐☐☐

1267 _____   **2000. Statue of Liberty Issue**
34¢ **multicolored**   .50   .20 ☐☐☐☐☐

1268 _____   **2000. Statue of Liberty Issue**
34¢ **multicolored**   .50   .20 ☐☐☐☐☐

1269 _____   **2000. Statue of Liberty Issue**
34¢ **multicolored**   .50   .20 ☐☐☐☐☐

1270 _____   **2000. Flowers Coil Issue**
34¢ **multicolored**   .50   .20 ☐☐☐☐☐

1271 _____
34¢ **multicolored**   .50   .20 ☐☐☐☐☐

1272 _____
34¢ **multicolored**   .50   .20 ☐☐☐☐☐

1273 _____
34¢ **multicolored**   .50   .20 ☐☐☐☐☐

1274 _____   **2000. Flowers Booklet Issue**
34¢ **Longiflorum lily** purple background, 10 1/4 x 10 3/4   .50   .20 ☐☐☐☐☐

1275 _____
34¢ **Cymbidium orchid** tan, 10 1/4 x 10 3/4   .50   .20 ☐☐☐☐☐

1276 _____
34¢ **Freesia** green, 10 1/4 x 10 3/4   .50   .20 ☐☐☐☐☐

1277 _____
34¢ **Asian hybrid lily** red, 10 1/4 x 10 3/4   .50   .20 ☐☐☐☐☐

1278 _____
34¢ **Longiflorum lily** purple background, 11 1/2 x 11 3/4 .50   .20 ☐☐☐☐☐

1279 _____
34¢ **Cymbidium orchid** tan, 11 1/2 x 11 3/4   .50   .20 ☐☐☐☐☐

1280 _____
34¢ **Freesia** green, 11 1/2 x 11 3/4   .50   .20 ☐☐☐☐☐

1281 _____
34¢ **Asian hybrid lily** red, 11 1/2 x 11 3/4   .50   .20 ☐☐☐☐☐

1262

1263

1264-1266

1267-1269

1274-1277, 1278-1281

1270-1273

	UnFVF	UseFVF

COMMEMORATIVE ISSUES

CM1 _____ **1893. Columbian Issues**

		UnFVF	UseFVF
1¢	**deep blue** (449,195,550)	17.50	.35 ☐☐☐☐☐

CM2 _____

2¢	**dull purple** (1,464,588,750)	17.50	.20 ☐☐☐☐☐

NOTE: Imperforate 2¢ Columbians are from printer's waste.

CM3 _____

3¢	**deep bluish green** (11,501,250)	40.00	11.00 ☐☐☐☐☐

CM4 _____

4¢	**gray blue** (19,181,550)	60.00	5.50 ☐☐☐☐☐

CM5 _____

5¢	**brown** (35,248,250)	65.00	6.00 ☐☐☐☐☐

CM6 _____

6¢	**dark lilac** (4,707,550)	60.00	17.50 ☐☐☐☐☐

CM7 _____

8¢	**brown purple** (10,656,550)	50.00	7.00 ☐☐☐☐☐

CM8 _____

10¢	**black brown** (16,516,950)	95.00	5.50 ☐☐☐☐☐

CM9 _____

15¢	**deep bluish green** (1,576,950)	175.00	50.00 ☐☐☐☐☐

CM1

CM2

CM3

CM4

CM5

CM6

CM7

CM8

CM9

CM10

CM11

CM12

	UnFVF	UseFVF	

CM10 _____
| 30¢ **orange brown** (617,250) | 225.00 | 65.00 | ❑❑❑❑❑ |

CM11 _____
| 50¢ **slate black** (243,750) | 350.00 | 125.00 | ❑❑❑❑❑ |

CM12 _____
| $1 **Venetian red** (55,050) | 1,000.00 | 450.00 | ❑❑❑❑❑ |

CM13 _____
| $2 **brown red** (45,550) | 1,100.00 | 400.00 | ❑❑❑❑❑ |

CM14 _____
| $3 **bronze green** (27,650) | 1,700.00 | 725.00 | ❑❑❑❑❑ |

CM15 _____
| $4 **deep rose** (26,350) | 2,250.00 | 1,000.00 | ❑❑❑❑❑ |

CM16 _____
| $5 **black** (27,350) | 2,750.00 | 1,600.00 | ❑❑❑❑❑ |

NOTE: For stamps of these designs, but with "1992" instead of "1893" in the top-right corner see Nos. CM1456-61.

CM17 _____   **1898. Trans-Mississippi Issue**
| 1¢ **green** (70,993,400) | 22.50 | 4.75 | ❑❑❑❑❑ |

CM18 _____
| 2¢ **brown red** (159,720,800) | 19.00 | 1.25 | ❑❑❑❑❑ |

CM19 _____
| 4¢ **orange red** (94,924,500) | 100.00 | 17.50 | ❑❑❑❑❑ |

CM20 _____
| 5¢ **deep blue** (7,694,180) | 100.00 | 17.50 | ❑❑❑❑❑ |

CM21 _____
| 8¢ **chocolate** (2,927,200) | 135.00 | 32.50 | ❑❑❑❑❑ |

CM22 _____
| 10¢ **violet black** (4,629,760) | 135.00 | 17.50 | ❑❑❑❑❑ |

CM23 _____
| 50¢ **bronze green** (530,400) | 450.00 | 130.00 | ❑❑❑❑❑ |

CM24 _____
| $1 **black** (56,900) | 950.00 | 400.00 | ❑❑❑❑❑ |

CM25 _____
| $2 **red brown** (56,200) | 2,700.00 | 700.00 | ❑❑❑❑❑ |

NOTE: For bicolor versions of the Trans-Mississippi Issue, see Nos. CM1985 and CM1986.

CM26 _____   **1901. Pan-American Issue**
| 1¢ **emerald & black** (91,401,500) | 15.00 | 2.75 | ❑❑❑❑❑ |

CM27 _____
| 2¢ **rose red & black** (209,759,700) | 15.00 | 1.00 | ❑❑❑❑❑ |

CM28 _____
| 4¢ **orange brown & black** (5,737,100) | 70.00 | 12.50 | ❑❑❑❑❑ |

CM29 _____
| 5¢ **gray blue & black** (7,201,300) | 75.00 | 12.50 | ❑❑❑❑❑ |

CM30 _____
| 8¢ **chocolate & black** (4,921,700) | 100.00 | 45.00 | ❑❑❑❑❑ |

CM31 _____
| 10¢ **yellow brown & black** (5,043,700) | 140.00 | 22.50 | ❑❑❑❑❑ |

CM32 _____   **1904. Louisiana Purchase Exposition Issue**
| 1¢ **green** (79,779,200) | 20.00 | 3.50 | ❑❑❑❑❑ |

CM33 _____
| 2¢ **carmine** (192,732,400) | 19.00 | 1.25 | ❑❑❑❑❑ |

CM34 _____
| 3¢ **dark red violet** (4,542,600) | 60.00 | 25.00 | ❑❑❑❑❑ |

CM35 _____
| 5¢ **indigo** (6,926,700) | 75.00 | 17.50 | ❑❑❑❑❑ |

CM13

CM14

CM15

CM16

CM17

CM18

CM19

CM20

CM21

CM22

CM23

CM24

CM25

CM26

CM27

CM28

CM29

CM30

CM31

CM32

CM33

	UnFVF	UseFVF	

CM36 _____
   10¢ **red brown** (4,011,200) — 125.00 — 25.00 ☐☐☐☐☐

CM37 _____   **1907. Jamestown Issue**
   1¢   **deep bluish green** (77,728,794) — 17.50 — 3.00 ☐☐☐☐☐

CM38 _____
   2¢   **rose red** (149,497,994) — 22.50 — 2.75 ☐☐☐☐☐

CM39 _____
   5¢   **indigo** (7,980,594) — 85.00 — 22.50 ☐☐☐☐☐
   Perforated 12.

CM40 _____   **1909. Lincoln Memorial Centennial Issue**
   2¢   **carmine** (148,387,191) — 5.00 — 1.75 ☐☐☐☐☐
   Imperforate.

CM41 _____
   2¢   **carmine** (1,273,900) — 22.50 — 1,750.00 ☐☐☐☐☐
   Bluish gray paper, perforated 12 (Feb. 1909).

CM42 _____
   2¢   **carmine** (637,000) — 175.00 — 195.00 ☐☐☐☐☐

CM43 _____   **1909. Alaska-Yukon Issue**
   2¢   *Perforated 12.*
      carmine (152,887,311) — 7.00 — 1.50 ☐☐☐☐☐
   Imperforate.

CM44 _____
   2¢   **carmine** (525,400) — 30.00 — 22.50 ☐☐☐☐☐

CM45 _____   **1909. Hudson-Fulton Issue**
   2¢   **carmine** (72,634,631) — 10.00 — 3.50 ☐☐☐☐☐
   Imperforate.

CM46 _____
   2¢   **carmine** (216,480) — 35.00 — 22.50 ☐☐☐☐☐

CM47 _____   **1913-15. Panama-Pacific Issue**
   1¢   **green** (334,796,926) — 15.50 — 1.25 ☐☐☐☐☐

CM48 _____
   2¢   **rose red** (503,713,086) — 20.00 — .50 ☐☐☐☐☐

CM49 _____
   5¢   **blue** (29,088,726) — 75.00 — 9.00 ☐☐☐☐☐

CM50 _____
   10¢ **orange yellow** (16,968,365) — 125.00 — 20.00 ☐☐☐☐☐

CM51 _____
   10¢ **orange** (16,968,365) (Aug. 1913) — 200.00 — 15.00 ☐☐☐☐☐

CM52 _____   **1914-15. Panama-Pacific Issue**
   1¢   **green** — 22.00 — 5.25 ☐☐☐☐☐

CM53 _____
   2¢   **rose red** — 70.00 — 1.50 ☐☐☐☐☐

CM54 _____
   5¢   **blue** — 160.00 — 14.50 ☐☐☐☐☐

CM55 _____
   10¢ **orange** — 900.00 — 60.00 ☐☐☐☐☐

CM56 _____   **1919. Victory Issue**
   3¢   **dark lilac** (99,585,200) — 7.50 — 3.00 ☐☐☐☐☐

CM57 _____   **1920. Pilgrim Tercentenary Issue**
   1¢   **green** (137,978,207) — 3.50 — 2.50 ☐☐☐☐☐

CM58 _____
   2¢   **rose red** (196,037,327) — 5.25 — 1.75 ☐☐☐☐☐

	UnFVF	UseFVF	

CM59_____
5¢ **deep blue** (11,321,607)   35.00   12.50 ☐☐☐☐☐
Flat plate printing, perforated 11.
CM60_____ **1923. Harding Memorial Issue**
2¢ **black** (1,459,487,085)   .60   .20 ☐☐☐☐☐
Flat plate printing, imperforate.
CM61_____
2¢ **black** (770,000)   6.50   4.50 ☐☐☐☐☐
Rotary press printing, perforated 10.
CM62_____
2¢ **gray black** (99,950,300)   15.00   1.75 ☐☐☐☐☐
Rotary press printing, perforated 11.
CM63_____
2¢ **gray black**   30,000.00 ☐☐☐☐☐

CM34

CM35

CM36

CM37

CM38

CM39

CM40-42

CM43, CM44

CM45

CM47, CM52

CM48, CM53

CM49, CM54

CM50-51, CM55

CM56

CM57

		UnFVF	UseFVF	

CM64_____ **1924. Huguenot-Walloon Issue**
1¢ **green** (51,378,023)   2.75   2.75 ☐☐☐☐☐
CM65_____
2¢ **carmine red** (77,753,423)   5.00   2.00 ☐☐☐☐☐
CM66_____
5¢ **Prussian blue** (5,659,023)   27.50   14.00 ☐☐☐☐☐
CM67_____ **1925. Lexington-Concord Issue**
1¢ **green** (15,615,000)   2.75   2.50 ☐☐☐☐☐
CM68_____
2¢ **carmine red** (26,596,600)   5.00   3.50 ☐☐☐☐☐
CM69_____
5¢ **Prussian blue** (5,348,800)   25.00   14.00 ☐☐☐☐☐
CM70_____ **1925. Norse-American Issue**
2¢ **carmine & black** (9,104,983)   4.00   3.00 ☐☐☐☐☐
CM71_____
5¢ **indigo & black** (1,900,983)   15.00   12.50 ☐☐☐☐☐
CM72_____ **1926. Sesquicentennial Issue**
2¢ **carmine red** (307,731,900)   2.50   .50 ☐☐☐☐☐
CM73_____ **1926. Ericsson Memorial Issue**
5¢ **slate violet** (20,280,500)   6.00   2.50 ☐☐☐☐☐
CM74_____ **1926. White Plains Issue**
2¢ **carmine red** (40,639,485)   2.00   1.50 ☐☐☐☐☐
CM75_____ **1926. White Plains Philatelic Exhibition Issue**
2¢ **carmine red** (107,398)   400.00   425.00 ☐☐☐☐☐
CM76_____ **1927. Vermont Sesquicentennial Issue**
2¢ **carmine red** (39,974,900)   1.25   1.00 ☐☐☐☐☐
CM77_____ **1927. Burgoyne Campaign Issue**
2¢ **carmine red** (25,628,450)   3.50   2.25 ☐☐☐☐☐
CM78_____ **1928. Valley Forge Issue**
2¢ **carmine red** (101,330,328)   1.00   .50 ☐☐☐☐☐
CM79_____ **1928. Hawaiian Sesquicentennial Issue**
2¢ **carmine** (5,519,897)   4.50   4.50 ☐☐☐☐☐
CM80_____
5¢ **blue** (1,459,897)   12.50   12.50 ☐☐☐☐☐
CM81_____ **1928. Molly Pitcher Issue**
2¢ **carmine** (9,779,896)   1.00   1.25 ☐☐☐☐☐
CM82_____ **1928. Aeronautics Conference Issue**
2¢ **carmine red** (51,342,273)   1.25   1.00 ☐☐☐☐☐
CM83_____
5¢ **Prussian blue** (10,319,700)   5.00   3.00 ☐☐☐☐☐
CM84_____ **1929. George Rogers Clark Issue**
2¢ **carmine & black** (16,684,674)   .60   .50 ☐☐☐☐☐
Flat press, perforated 11.
CM85_____ **1929. Edison Commemorative Issue**
2¢ **carmine red** (31,679,200)   .75   .75 ☐☐☐☐☐
Rotary press, perforated 11 x 10 1/2.
CM86_____
2¢ **carmine red** (210,119,474)   .75   .25 ☐☐☐☐☐
Rotary press coil, perforated 10 vertically.
CM87_____
2¢ **carmine red** (133,530,000)   12.50   1.50 ☐☐☐☐☐
CM88_____ **1929. Sullivan Expedition Issue**
2¢ **carmine red** (51,451,880)   .75   .75 ☐☐☐☐☐
CM89_____ **1929. Battle of Fallen Timbers Issue**
2¢ **carmine red** (29,338,274)   .75   .75 ☐☐☐☐☐

CM58

CM59

CM60-63

CM64

CM65

CM66

CM67

CM68

CM69

CM70

CM71

CM72

CM73

CM74

CM76

CM77

CM78

CM79

CM75

	UnFVF	UseFVF	

CM90_____ **1929. Ohio River Canalization Issue**
2¢ **carmine red** (32,680,900) .50 .75 ☐☐☐☐☐

CM91_____ **1930. Massachusetts Bay Colony Issue**
2¢ **carmine red** (74,000,774) .75 .45 ☐☐☐☐☐

CM92_____ **1930. Carolina-Charleston Issue**
2¢ **carmine red** (25,215,574) 1.25 1.00 ☐☐☐☐☐

CM93_____ **1930. Braddock's Field Issue**
2¢ **carmine red** (25,609,470) 1.00 1.00 ☐☐☐☐☐

CM94_____ **1930. Von Steuben Issue**
2¢ **carmine red** (66,487,000) .50 .50 ☐☐☐☐☐

CM95_____ **1931. Pulaski Issue**
2¢ **carmine red** (96,559,400) .25 .20 ☐☐☐☐☐

CM96_____ **1931. Red Cross Issue**
2¢ **black & scarlet** (99,074,600) .25 .20 ☐☐☐☐☐

CM97_____ **1931. Yorktown Issue**
2¢ **carmine red & black** (25,006,400) .35 .20 ☐☐☐☐☐

CM98_____ **1932. Washington Bicentennial Issue**
1/2¢ **olive brown** (87,969,700). .25 .20 ☐☐☐☐☐

CM99_____
1¢ **yellow green** (1,265,555,100) .25 .20 ☐☐☐☐☐

CM100_____
1-1/2¢ **yellow brown** (304,926,800) .50 .20 ☐☐☐☐☐

CM101_____
2¢ **carmine red** (4,222,198,300) .25 .20 ☐☐☐☐☐

CM102_____
3¢ **slate purple** (456,198,500) .50 .20 ☐☐☐☐☐

CM103_____
4¢ **yellow brown** (151,201,300) .40 .20 ☐☐☐☐☐

CM104_____
5¢ **Prussian blue** (170,656,100) 1.75 .20 ☐☐☐☐☐

CM105_____
6¢ **orange** (111,739,400) 3.50 .20 ☐☐☐☐☐

CM106_____
7¢ **black** (83,257,400) .40 .20 ☐☐☐☐☐

CM107_____
8¢ **bister** (96,506,100) 3.00 .75 ☐☐☐☐☐

CM108_____
9¢ **salmom** (75,706,200) 2.50 .20 ☐☐☐☐☐

CM109_____
10¢ **orange yellow** (147,216,000) 12.50 .20 ☐☐☐☐☐

CM110_____ **1932. Olympic Winter Games Issue**
2¢ **carmine red** (51,102,800) .40 .25 ☐☐☐☐☐

CM111_____ **1932. Arbor Day Issue**
2¢ **carmine red** (100,869,300) .25 .20 ☐☐☐☐☐

CM112_____ **1932. Olympic Summer Games Issue**
3¢ **reddish violet** (168,885,300) 1.50 .20 ☐☐☐☐☐

CM113_____
5¢ **blue** (52,376,100) 2.25 .30 ☐☐☐☐☐

CM114_____ **1932. William Penn Issue**
3¢ **reddish violet** (49,949,000) .35 .25 ☐☐☐☐☐

CM115_____ **1933. Daniel Webster Issue**
3¢ **reddish violet** (49,538,500) .35 .40 ☐☐☐☐☐

CM116_____ **1933. Oglethorpe Issue**
3¢ **reddish violet** (61,719,200) .35 .25 ☐☐☐☐☐

CM80 ← CM81 CM82 →

CM83

CM84

CM85

CM88

CM89

CM90

CM91

CM92

CM93

CM94

CM95

CM96

CM97

CM98

CM99

CM100

CM101

CM102

CM103

CM104

CM105

CM106

CM107

		UnFVF	UseFVF

CM117_____ **1933. Newburgh Issue**

   3¢ **reddish violet** (73,382,400)   .25   .20 ❑❑❑❑❑

NOTE: For ungummed stamps (Farley Issue), see CM142.

CM118_____ **1933. Century of Progress Issue**

   1¢ **yellow green** (348,266,800)   .25   .20 ❑❑❑❑❑

CM119_____

   3¢ **reddish violet** (480,239,300)   .25   .20 ❑❑❑❑❑

CM120_____ **1933. Century of Progress Souvenir Sheets**

   1¢ **yellow green** (456,704)   35.00   32.50 ❑❑❑❑❑

CM121_____

   3¢ **reddish violet** (441,172)   30.00   27.50 ❑❑❑❑❑

NOTE: For ungummed stamps (Farley issue) see CM156 & CM157.

CM122_____ **1933. NRA Issue**

   3¢ **reddish violet** (1,978,707,300)   .25   .20 ❑❑❑❑❑

CM123_____ **1933. Byrd Antarctic Issue**

   3¢ **blue** (5,735,944)   .75   .60 ❑❑❑❑❑

NOTE: For ungummed stamps (Farley issue), see CM143.

CM124_____ **1933. Kosciuszko Issue**

   5¢ **blue** (45,137,700)   .75   .35 ❑❑❑❑❑

CM125_____ **1934. Byrd Souvenir Sheet**

   3¢ **blue** (811,404)   17.50   16.50 ❑❑❑❑❑

NOTE: For ungummed stamps (Farley issue), see CM158.

CM126_____ **1934. Maryland Tercentenary Issue**

   3¢ **carmine red** (46,258,300)   .25   .20 ❑❑❑❑❑
   Rotary press, perforated 11 x 10 1/2.

CM127_____ **1934. Mother's Day Issue**

   3¢ **reddish violet** (193,239,100)   .25   .20 ❑❑❑❑❑
   Flat press, perforated 11.

CM128_____

   3¢ **reddish violet** (15,432,200)   .25   .20 ❑❑❑❑❑

NOTE: For ungummed stamps (Farley issue), see CM144.

CM129_____ **1934. Wisconsin Tercentenary Issue**

   3¢ **reddish violet** (64,525,400)   .25   .20 ❑❑❑❑❑

NOTE: For ungummed stamps (Farley issue), see CM145.

CM130_____ **1934. National Parks Issue**

   1¢ **green** (84,896,350)   .25   .20 ❑❑❑❑❑

CM131_____

   2¢ **red** (74,400,200)   .25   .20 ❑❑❑❑❑

CM132_____

   3¢ **reddish violet** (95,089,000)   .25   .20 ❑❑❑❑❑

CM133_____

   4¢ **yellow brown** (19,178,650)   .50   .35 ❑❑❑❑❑

CM134_____

   5¢ **light blue** (30,980,100)   1.00   .75 ❑❑❑❑❑

CM135_____

   6¢ **blue** (16,923,350)   1.25   1.00 ❑❑❑❑❑

CM136_____

   7¢ **black** (15,988,250)   1.00   .75 ❑❑❑❑❑

CM137_____

   8¢ **gray green** (15,288,700)   2.00   1.75 ❑❑❑❑❑

CM138_____

   9¢ **orange red** (17,472,600)   2.00   .75 ❑❑❑❑❑

CM139_____

   10¢ **gray black** (18,874,300)   3.25   1.25 ❑❑❑❑❑

NOTE: For ungummed stamps, (Farley issue), see CM146-CM155.

CM108 CM109 CM110 CM111

CM112   CM113   CM114   CM115   CM116

CM117, CM142   CM118

CM119   CM122

CM120, CM156

BYRD ANTARCTIC EXPEDITION II

CM124

CM123, CM143

CM121, 157

CM125, CM158

	UnFVF	UseFVF

CM140_____   **1934. Trans-Mississippi Philatelic Exposition Issue**

1¢   **green,** sheet of 6 (793,551)   14.00   12.50 ☐☐☐☐☐

NOTE: For ungummed stamps, (Farley issue), see CM159.

CM141_____   **1934. American Philatelic Society Issue**

3¢   **reddish violet,** sheet of 6 (511,391)   40.00   30.00 ☐☐☐☐☐

NOTE: For ungummed stamps (Farley issue), see CM160.

CM142_____   **1935. Newburgh, Farley Issue**

3¢   **reddish violet** (3,274,556)   .25   .20 ☐☐☐☐☐

CM143_____   **1935. Byrd, Farley Issue**

3¢   **blue** (2,040,760)   .50   .45 ☐☐☐☐☐

CM144_____   **1935. Mother's Day, Farley Issue**

3¢   **reddish violet** (2,389,288)   .60   .60 ☐☐☐☐☐

CM145_____   **1935. Wisconsin, Farley Issue**

3¢   **reddish violet** (2,294,948)   .60   .60 ☐☐☐☐☐

CM146_____   **1935. National Parks, Farley Issue**

1¢   **green** (3,217,636)   .25   .20 ☐☐☐☐☐

CM147_____

2¢   **red** (2,746,640)   .25   .20 ☐☐☐☐☐

CM148_____

3¢   **reddish violet** (2,168,088)   .50   .45 ☐☐☐☐☐

CM149_____

4¢   **yellow brown** (1,822,684)   1.25   1.25 ☐☐☐☐☐

CM150_____

5¢   **light blue** (1,724,576)   1.75   1.75 ☐☐☐☐☐

CM151_____

6¢   **blue** (1,647,696)   2.25   2.25 ☐☐☐☐☐

CM152_____

7¢   **black** (1,682,948)   2.00   1.75 ☐☐☐☐☐

CM153_____

8¢   **gray green** (1,638,644)   2.00   2.00 ☐☐☐☐☐

CM154_____

9¢   **orange red** (1,625,224)   2.00   2.00 ☐☐☐☐☐

CM155_____

10¢ **gray black** (1,644,900)   4.00   3.50 ☐☐☐☐☐

CM156_____   **1935. Century of Progress Souvenir Sheet, Farley Issue**

1¢   **yellow green** (2,467,800)   22.50   22.50 ☐☐☐☐☐

CM157_____

3¢   **reddish violet** (2,147,856)   20.00   20.00 ☐☐☐☐☐

CM158_____   **1935. Byrd Souvenir Sheet, Farley Issue**

3¢   **blue** (1,603,200)   17.50   12.50 ☐☐☐☐☐

CM159_____   **1935. National Parks Souvenir Sheets, Farley Issue**

1¢   **green** (1,679,760)   10.00   9.00 ☐☐☐☐☐

CM160_____

3¢   **reddish violet** (1,295,520)   25.00   20.00 ☐☐☐☐☐

CM161_____   **1935. Airmail Special Delivery, Farley Issue**

16¢ **blue** (1,370,560)   2.75   2.50 ☐☐☐☐☐

CM162_____   **1935. Connecticut Tercentenary Issue**

3¢   **purple** (70,726,800)   .25   .20 ☐☐☐☐☐

NOTE: For imperforates, see No. CM168.

CM163_____   **1935. California-Pacific Issue**

3¢   **dark lilac** (100,839,600)   .25   .20 ☐☐☐☐☐

NOTE: For imperforates, see No. CM168.

CM164_____   **1935. Boulder Dam Issue**

3¢   **dark lilac** (73,610,650)   .25   .20 ☐☐☐☐☐

CM126

CM129, CM145

CM127-128, CM144

CM130, CM146

CM131, CM147

CM132, CM148

CM134, CM150

CM133, CM149

CM135, CM151

CM136, CM152

CM137, CM153

CM138, CM154

CM139, CM155

CM140, CM159

CM141, CM160

CM162

CM163

CM164

	UnFVF	UseFVF

CM165_____ **1935. Michigan Centennial Issue**

3¢ **dark lilac** (75,823,900)   .25   .20 ⬜⬜⬜⬜⬜

NOTE: For imperforates, see No. CM168.

CM166_____ **1936. Texas Centennial Issue**

3¢ **dark lilac** (124,324,500)   .25   .20 ⬜⬜⬜⬜⬜

NOTE: For imperforates, see No. CM168.

CM167_____ **1936. Rhode Island Tercentenary Issue**

3¢ **dull purple** (67,127,650)   .25   .20 ⬜⬜⬜⬜⬜

CM168_____ **1936. TIPEX Souvenir Sheet**

4x3¢ **reddish purple** (2,809,039)   2.75   2.50 ⬜⬜⬜⬜⬜

CM169_____ **1936. Arkansas Centennial Issue**

3¢ **dark lilac** (72,992,650)   .25   .20 ⬜⬜⬜⬜⬜

CM170_____ **1936. Oregon Territory Centennial Issue**

3¢ **dark lilac** (74,407,450)   .25   .20 ⬜⬜⬜⬜⬜

CM171_____ **1936. Susan B. Anthony Issue**

3¢ **reddish purple** (269,522,200)   .25   .20 ⬜⬜⬜⬜⬜

CM172_____ **1936-37. Army Issue**

1¢ **green** (105,196,150)   .25   .20 ⬜⬜⬜⬜⬜

CM173_____

2¢ **rose red** (93,848,500)   .25   .20 ⬜⬜⬜⬜⬜

CM174_____

3¢ **dull purple** (87,741,150)   .25   .20 ⬜⬜⬜⬜⬜

CM175_____

4¢ **slate** (35,794,150)   .50   .20 ⬜⬜⬜⬜⬜

CM176_____

5¢ **gray blue** (36,839,250)   .75   .20 ⬜⬜⬜⬜⬜

CM177_____ **1936-37. Navy Issue**

1¢ **green** (104,773,450)   .25   .20 ⬜⬜⬜⬜⬜

CM178_____

2¢ **rose red** (92,054,550)   .25   .20 ⬜⬜⬜⬜⬜

CM179_____

3¢ **dull purple** (93,291,650)   .25   .20 ⬜⬜⬜⬜⬜

CM180_____

4¢ **slate** (34,521,950)   .50   .20 ⬜⬜⬜⬜⬜

CM181_____

5¢ **gray blue** (36,819,050)   .75   .20 ⬜⬜⬜⬜⬜

CM182_____ **1937. Northwest Ordinance Issue of 1787**

3¢ **dull purple** (84,825,250)   .25   .20 ⬜⬜⬜⬜⬜

CM183_____ **1937. Virginia Dare Issue**

5¢ **light slate blue** (25,040,400)   .25   .20 ⬜⬜⬜⬜⬜

CM184_____ **1937. Society of Philatelic Americans Souvenir Sheet**

10¢ **blue green** (5,277,445)   .75   .65 ⬜⬜⬜⬜⬜

CM185_____ **1937. Constitution Sesquicentennial Issue**

3¢ **bright purple** (99,882,300)   .25   .20 ⬜⬜⬜⬜⬜

CM186_____ **1937. Hawaii Territory Issue**

3¢ **violet** (78,454,450)   .25   .20 ⬜⬜⬜⬜⬜

CM187_____ **1937. Alaska Territory Issue**

3¢ **violet** (77,004,200)   .25   .20 ⬜⬜⬜⬜⬜

CM188_____ **1937. Puerto Rico Territory Issue**

3¢ **light reddish violet** (81,292,450)   .25   .20 ⬜⬜⬜⬜⬜

CM189_____ **1937. Virgin Islands Issue**

3¢ **lilac** (76, 474,550)   .25   .20 ⬜⬜⬜⬜⬜

CM190_____ **1938. Constitution Ratification Issue**

3¢ **violet** (73,043,650)   .50   .20 ⬜⬜⬜⬜⬜

CM165

CM166 ←

CM167

CM168

CM169

CM170 →

CM171

CM172

CM173

CM174

CM175

CM176

CM177

CM178

CM179

CM180

CM181

CM182

CM183

		UnFVF	UseFVF

CM191_____   **1938. Swedes and Finns Issue**
3¢   **carmine purple** (58,564,368)   .25   .20 ☐☐☐☐☐

CM192_____   **1938. Northwest Territory Issue**
3¢   **light reddish violet** (65,939,500)   .25   .20 ☐☐☐☐☐

CM193_____   **1938. Iowa Territory Issue**
3¢   **violet** (47,064,300)   .25   .20 ☐☐☐☐☐

CM194_____   **1939. Golden Gate Exposition Issue**
3¢   **light reddish violet** (114,439,600)   .25   .20 ☐☐☐☐☐

CM195_____   **1939. New York World's Fair Issue**
3¢   **bluish violet** (101,699,550)   .25   .20 ☐☐☐☐☐

CM196_____   **1939. Washington Inauguration Issue**
3¢   **bright purple** (73,764,550)   .25   .20 ☐☐☐☐☐

CM197_____   **1939. Baseball Centennial Issue**
3¢   **violet** (81,269,600)   2.25   .20 ☐☐☐☐☐

CM198_____   **1939. Panama Canal Issue**
3¢   **deep reddish purple** (67,813,350)   .50   .20 ☐☐☐☐☐

CM199_____   **1939. Printing Tercentenary Issue**
3¢   **violet** (71,394,750)   .25   .20 ☐☐☐☐☐

CM200_____   **1939. Four States Issue**
3¢   **reddish purple** (66,835,000)   .25   .20 ☐☐☐☐☐

CM185

CM186

CM187

CM191

CM184

CM188

CM189

CM190

CM192

CM193

CM194

CM195

CM196

CM197

CM198

CM200

CM199

CM201

CM202

CM203

CM204

CM205

CM206

CM207

CM208

CM209

CM210

CM211

CM212

CM213

CM214

CM215

CM216

CM217

CM218

	MNHVF	UseVF	

CM201 _____   **1940. Famous Americans Series**

		MNHVF	UseVF	
1¢	**emerald** (56,348,320)	.25	.20	☐☐☐☐☐
CM202 _____				
2¢	**carmine** (53,177,110)	.25	.20	☐☐☐☐☐
CM203 _____				
3¢	**bright purple** (53,260,270)	.25	.20	☐☐☐☐☐
CM204 _____				
5¢	**gray blue** (22,104,950)	.40	.25	☐☐☐☐☐
CM205 _____				
10¢	**sepia** (13,201,270)	2.25	1.75	☐☐☐☐☐
CM206 _____				
1¢	**emerald** (51,603,580)	.25	.20	☐☐☐☐☐
CM207 _____				
2¢	**carmine** (52,100,510)	.25	.20	☐☐☐☐☐
CM208 _____				
3¢	**bright purple** (51,666,580)	.25	.20	☐☐☐☐☐
CM209 _____				
5¢	**gray blue** (22,207,780)	.45	.25	☐☐☐☐☐
CM210 _____				
10¢	**sepia** (11,835,530)	2.25	1.75	☐☐☐☐☐
CM211 _____				
1¢	**emerald** (52,471,160)	.25	.20	☐☐☐☐☐
CM212 _____				
2¢	**carmine** (52,366,440)	.25	.20	☐☐☐☐☐
CM213 _____				
3¢	**bright purple** (51,636,270)	.25	.20	☐☐☐☐☐
CM214 _____				
5¢	**gray blue** (20,729,030)	.40	.30	☐☐☐☐☐
CM215 _____				
10¢	**sepia** (14,125,580)	2.50	1.75	☐☐☐☐☐
CM216 _____				
1¢	**emerald** (59,409,000)	.25	.20	☐☐☐☐☐
CM217 _____				
2¢	**carmine** (57,888,600)	.25	.20	☐☐☐☐☐
CM218 _____				
3¢	**bright purple** (58,273,180)	.25	.20	☐☐☐☐☐
CM219 _____				
5¢	**gray blue** (23,779,000)	.50	.20	☐☐☐☐☐
CM220 _____				
10¢	**sepia** (15,112,580)	1.50	1.50	☐☐☐☐☐
CM221 _____				
1¢	**emerald** (57,322,790)	.25	.20	☐☐☐☐☐
CM222 _____				
2¢	**carmine** (58,281,580)	.25	.20	☐☐☐☐☐
CM223 _____				
3¢	**bright purple** (56,398,790)	.25	.20	☐☐☐☐☐
CM224 _____				
5¢	**gray blue** (21,147,000)	.75	.30	☐☐☐☐☐
CM225 _____				
10¢	**sepia** (13,328,000)	5.00	2.00	☐☐☐☐☐
CM226 _____				
1¢	**emerald** (54,389,510)	.25	.20	☐☐☐☐☐
CM227 _____				
2¢	**carmine** (53,636,580)	.25	.20	☐☐☐☐☐

CM219

CM220

CM221

CM222

CM223

CM224

CM225

CM226

CM227

CM228

CM229

CM230

CM231

CM232

CM233

CM234

CM235

CM236

CM237

CM238

CM239

CM240

CM241

CM242

CM243

CM244

CM245

	MNHVF	UseVF	

CM228 _____
| 3¢ **bright purple** (55,313,230) | .25 | .20 ⬜⬜⬜⬜⬜ |

CM229 _____
| 5¢ **gray blue** (21,720,580) | .75 | .30 ⬜⬜⬜⬜⬜ |

CM230 _____
| 10¢ **sepia** (13,600,580) | 2.00 | 1.75 ⬜⬜⬜⬜⬜ |

CM231 _____
| 1¢ **emerald** (47,599,580) | .25 | .20 ⬜⬜⬜⬜⬜ |

CM232 _____
| 2¢ **carmine** (53,766,510) | .25 | .20 ⬜⬜⬜⬜⬜ |

CM233 _____
| 3¢ **bright purple** (54,193,580) | .25 | .20 ⬜⬜⬜⬜⬜ |

CM234 _____
| 5¢ **gray blue** (20,264,580) | 1.25 | .50 ⬜⬜⬜⬜⬜ |

CM235 _____
| 10¢ **sepia** (13,726,580) | 15.00 | 3.25 ⬜⬜⬜⬜⬜ |

CM236 _____ **1940. Pony Express Issue**
| 3¢ **chestnut** (46,497,400) | .35 | .20 ⬜⬜⬜⬜⬜ |

CM237 _____ **1940. Pan-American Union Issue**
| 3¢ **lilac** (47,700,000) | .30 | .20 ⬜⬜⬜⬜⬜ |

CM238 _____ **1940. Idaho Statehood Issue**
| 3¢ **light reddish violet** (50,618,150) | .25 | .20 ⬜⬜⬜⬜⬜ |

CM239 _____ **1940. Wyoming Statehood Issue**
| 3¢ **purple brown** (50,034,400) | .25 | .20 ⬜⬜⬜⬜⬜ |

CM240 _____ **1940. Coronado Expedition Issue**
| 3¢ **reddish lilac** (60,943,700) | .25 | .20 ⬜⬜⬜⬜⬜ |

CM241 _____ **1940. National Defense Issue**
| 1¢ **emerald** (6,081,409,300) | .25 | .20 ⬜⬜⬜⬜⬜ |

CM242 _____
| 2¢ **rose** (5,211,708,200) | .25 | .20 ⬜⬜⬜⬜⬜ |

CM243 _____
| 3¢ **light reddish violet** (8,384,867,600) | .25 | .20 ⬜⬜⬜⬜⬜ |

CM244 _____ **1940. Thirteenth Amendment Issue**
| 3¢ **violet** (44,389,550) | .35 | .20 ⬜⬜⬜⬜⬜ |

CM245 _____ **1941. Vermont Statehood Issue**
| 3¢ **violet** (54,574,550) | .25 | .20 ⬜⬜⬜⬜⬜ |

CM246 _____ **1942. Kentucky Statehood Issue**
| 3¢ **reddish violet** (63,558,400) | .25 | .20 ⬜⬜⬜⬜⬜ |

CM247 _____ **1942. Win The War Issue**
| 3¢ **violet** (20,642,793,300) | .25 | .20 ⬜⬜⬜⬜⬜ |

CM248 _____ **1942. Chinese Commemorative Issue**
| 5¢ **Prussian blue** (21,272,800) | .60 | .30 ⬜⬜⬜⬜⬜ |

CM249 _____ **1943. Allied Nations Issue**
| 2¢ **carmine** (1,671,564,200) | .25 | .20 ⬜⬜⬜⬜⬜ |

CM250 _____ **1943. Four Freedoms Issue**
| 1¢ **emerald** (1,227,334,200) | .25 | .20 ⬜⬜⬜⬜⬜ |

CM251 _____ **1943-44. Overrun Countries Issue**
| 5¢ **slate, violet, scarlet & black** (19,999,646) | .25 | .20 ⬜⬜⬜⬜⬜ |

CM252 _____
| 5¢ **slate, violet, blue, scarlet & black** (19,999,646) | .25 | .20 ⬜⬜⬜⬜⬜ |

CM253 _____
| 5¢ **slate, violet, rose red, ultramarine & black** (19,999,616) | .25 | .20 ⬜⬜⬜⬜⬜ |

CM254 _____
| 5¢ **slate, violet, rose red, light blue & black** (19,999,646) | .25 | .20 ⬜⬜⬜⬜⬜ |

CM246

CM247

CM248

CM249

CM250

CM251

CM252

CM253

CM254

CM255

CM256

CM257

CM258

CM259

CM260

CM261

CM262

CM263

CM264

	MNHVF	UseVF

CM255_____
5¢ **slate, violet, scarlet, blue & black** (19,999,646)   .25   .20 ❑❑❑❑❑

CM256_____
5¢ **slate, violet, scarlet, greenish yellow & black** (19,999,646)   .25   .20 ❑❑❑❑❑

CM257_____
5¢ **slate, violet, blue, red & black** (19,999,648)   .25   .20 ❑❑❑❑❑

CM258_____
5¢ **slate, violet, pale light blue & black** (14,999,646)   .50   .20 ❑❑❑❑❑

CM259_____
5¢ **slate, violet, blue, rose red & black** (14,999,646)   .30   .20 ❑❑❑❑❑

CM260_____
5¢ **slate, violet, red & black** (14,999,646)   .30   .20 ❑❑❑❑❑

CM261_____
5¢ **slate, violet, red & black** (14,999,646)   .30   .20 ❑❑❑❑❑

CM262_____
5¢ **slate, violet, scarlet & black** (14,999,646)   .30   .20 ❑❑❑❑❑

CM263_____
5¢ **slate, violet, scarlet, bright blue & gray** (14,999,646)   .30   .20 ❑❑❑❑❑

CM264_____ **1944. Transcontinental Railroad Issue**
3¢ **violet** (61,303,000)   .30   .20 ❑❑❑❑❑

CM265_____ **1944. Steamship Issue**
3¢ **violet** (61,001,450)   .25   .20 ❑❑❑❑❑

CM266_____ **1944. Telegraph Centennial Issue**
3¢ **bright purple** (60,605,000)   .25   .20 ❑❑❑❑❑

CM267_____ **1944. Corregidor Issue**
3¢ **violet** (50,129,350)   .25   .20 ❑❑❑❑❑

CM268_____ **1944. Motion Picture Issue**
3¢ **violet** (53,479,400)   .25   .20 ❑❑❑❑❑

CM269_____ **1945. Florida Centennial Issue**
3¢ **bright purple** (61,617,350)   .25   .20 ❑❑❑❑❑

CM270_____ **1945. United Nations Conference Issue**
5¢ **ultramarine** (75,500,000)   .25   .20 ❑❑❑❑❑

CM271_____ **1945-46. Roosevelt Series**
1¢ **blue green** (128,140,000)   .25   .20 ❑❑❑❑❑

CM265

CM266

CM267

CM268

CM269

CM270

CM271

CM272

CM273

CM274

CM275 ←

CM276

CM277

CM278

CM279

CM280

CM281

CM282

CM283

CM284

CM285

CM286

CM287 ←

CM288

CM289

	MNHVF	UseVF

CM272_____
2¢ **carmine red** (67,255,000) .25 .20 ❏❏❏❏❏
CM273_____
3¢ **lilac** (138,870,000) .25 .20 ❏❏❏❏❏
CM274_____
5¢ **light blue** (76,455,400) .25 .20 ❏❏❏❏❏
CM275_____ **1945. Marine Commemorative**
3¢ **dark yellow green** (137,321,000) .25 .20 ❏❏❏❏❏
CM276_____ **1945. Army Commemorative**
3¢ **brown olive** (128,357,750) .25 .20 ❏❏❏❏❏
CM277_____ **1945. Navy Commemorative**
3¢ **blue** (138,863,000) .25 .20 ❏❏❏❏❏
CM278_____ **1945. Coast Guard Commemorative**
3¢ **blue green** (111,616,700) .25 .20 ❏❏❏❏❏
CM279_____ **1946. Merchant Marine Commemorative**
3¢ **blue green** (135,927,000) .25 .20 ❏❏❏❏❏
CM280_____ **1945. Alfred E. Smith Issue**
3¢ **dark lilac** (308,587,700) .25 .20 ❏❏❏❏❏
CM281_____ **1945. Texas Statehood Issue**
3¢ **Prussian blue** (170,640,000) .25 .20 ❏❏❏❏❏
CM282_____ **1946. Honorable Discharge Stamp**
3¢ **violet** (269,339,100) .25 .20 ❏❏❏❏❏
CM283_____ **1946. Tennessee Statehood Issue**
3¢ **violet** (132,274,500) .25 .20 ❏❏❏❏❏
CM284_____ **1946. Iowa Statehood Issue**
3¢ **Prussian blue** (132,430,000) .25 .20 ❏❏❏❏❏
CM285_____ **1946. Smithsonian Institution Issue**
3¢ **brown purple** (139,209,500) .25 .20 ❏❏❏❏❏
CM286_____ **1946. Kearny Expedition Issue**
3¢ **brown purple** (114,684,450) .25 .20 ❏❏❏❏❏
CM287_____ **1947. Thomas A. Edison Issue**
3¢ **bright purple** (156,540,510) .25 .20 ❏❏❏❏❏
CM288_____ **1947. Joseph Pulitzer Issue**
3¢ **dark lilac** (120,452,600) .25 .20 ❏❏❏❏❏
CM289_____ **1947. Postage Stamp Centenary Issue**
3¢ **blue** (127,104,300) .25 .20 ❏❏❏❏❏
CM290_____ **1947. CIPEX Souvenir Sheet**
15¢ **Complete sheet of 2 stamps** (10,299,600) .75 .65 ❏❏❏❏❏
CM291_____ **1947. The Doctors Issue**
3¢ **brown purple** (132,902,000) .25 .20 ❏❏❏❏❏
CM292_____ **1947. Utah Issue**
3¢ **violet** (131,968,000) .25 .20 ❏❏❏❏❏
CM293_____ **1947. U.S. Frigate Constitution Issue**
3¢ **blue green** (131,488,000) .25 .20 ❏❏❏❏❏
CM294_____ **1947. Everglades National Park Issue**
3¢ **emerald** (122,362,000) .25 .20 ❏❏❏❏❏
CM295_____ **1948. George Washington Carver Issue**
3¢ **bright purple** (121,548,000) .25 .20 ❏❏❏❏❏
CM296_____ **1948. California Gold Centennial Issue**
3¢ **violet** (131,109,500) .25 .20 ❏❏❏❏❏
CM297_____ **1948. Mississippi Territory Issue**
3¢ **brown purple** (122,650,500) .25 .20 ❏❏❏❏❏
CM298_____ **1948. Four Chaplains Issue**
3¢ **black** (121,953,500) .25 .20 ❏❏❏❏❏

CM290

CM291

CM292

CM293

CM294

CM295

CM296

CM297

CM298

CM299

CM300

CM301

CM302
→

CM303

CM304

CM305

	MNHVF	UseVF

CM299_____ **1948. Wisconsin Centennial Issue**
   3¢ **violet** (115,250,000)   .25   .20 ☐☐☐☐☐

CM300_____ **1948. Swedish Pioneers Issue**
   5¢ **blue** (64,198,500)   .25   .20 ☐☐☐☐☐

CM301_____ **1948. The Progress of Women Issue**
   3¢ **violet** (117,642,500)   .25   .20 ☐☐☐☐☐

CM302_____ **1948. William Allen White Issue**
   3¢ **bright purple** (77,649,000)   .25   .20 ☐☐☐☐☐

CM303_____ **1948. United States - Canada Friendship Issue**
   3¢ **blue** (113,474,500)   .25   .20 ☐☐☐☐☐

CM304_____ **1948. Francis Scott Key Issue**
   3¢ **carmine** (120,868,500)   .25   .20 ☐☐☐☐☐

CM305_____ **1948. American Youth Issue**
   3¢ **blue** (77,800,500)   .25   .20 ☐☐☐☐☐

CM306_____ **1948. Oregon Territory Issue**
   3¢ **Venetian red** (52,214,000)   .25   .20 ☐☐☐☐☐

CM307_____ **1948. Harlan Fiske Stone Issue**
   3¢ **bright purple** (53,958,100)   .25   .20 ☐☐☐☐☐

CM308_____ **1948. Palomar Mountain Observatory Issue**
   3¢ **blue** (61,120,010)   .25   .20 ☐☐☐☐☐

CM309_____ **1948. Clara Barton Issue**
   3¢ **carmine** (57,823,000)   .25   .20 ☐☐☐☐☐

CM310_____ **1948. Poultry Industry Centennial Issue**
   3¢ **sepia** (52,975,000)   .25   .20 ☐☐☐☐☐

CM311_____ **1948. Gold Star Mothers Issue**
   3¢ **yellow** (77,149,000)   .25   .20 ☐☐☐☐☐

CM312_____ **1948. Fort Kearny Issue**
   3¢ **violet** (58,332,000)   .25   .20 ☐☐☐☐☐

CM313_____ **1948. Volunteer Fireman Issue**
   3¢ **rose carmine** (56,228,000)   .25   .20 ☐☐☐☐☐

CM314_____ **1948. Indian Centennial Issue**
   3¢ **brown** (57,832,000)   .25   .20 ☐☐☐☐☐

CM315_____ **1948. Rough Riders Issue**
   3¢ **brown purple** (53,875,000)   .25   .20 ☐☐☐☐☐

CM316_____ **1948. Juliette Low Issue**
   3¢ **blue green** (63,834,000)   .25   .20 ☐☐☐☐☐

CM317_____ **1948. Will Rogers Issue**
   3¢ **bright purple** (67,162,200)   .25   .20 ☐☐☐☐☐

CM318_____ **1948. Fort Bliss Centennial Issue**
   3¢ **chestnut** (64,561,000)   .35   .20 ☐☐☐☐☐

CM319_____ **1948. Moina Michael Issue**
   3¢ **rose carmine** (64,079,500)   .25   .20 ☐☐☐☐☐

CM320_____ **1948. Gettysburg Address Issue**
   3¢ **light blue** (63,388,000)   .25   .20 ☐☐☐☐☐

CM321_____ **1948. American Turners Issue**
   3¢ **carmine** (62,285,000)   .25   .20 ☐☐☐☐☐

CM322_____ **1948. Joel Chandler Harris Issue**
   3¢ **bright purple** (57,492,610)   .25   .20 ☐☐☐☐☐

CM323_____ **1949. Minnesota Territory Issue**
   3¢ **blue green** (99,190,000)   .25   .20 ☐☐☐☐☐

CM324_____ **1949. Washington and Lee University Issue**
   3¢ **bright blue** (104,790,000)   .25   .20 ☐☐☐☐☐

CM325_____ **1949. Puerto Rico Election Issue**
   3¢ **dull green** (108,805,000)   .25   .20 ☐☐☐☐☐

CM306

CM307

CM308

CM309

CM310

CM311

CM312

CM313

CM314

CM315

CM316

CM317

CM318

CM319

CM320

CM321

CM322

CM323

CM324

CM325

CM326

		MNHVF	UseVF

CM326_____   **1949. Annapolis Tercentenary Issue**
3¢ **turquoise green** (107,340,000)   .25   .20 ⬚⬚⬚⬚⬚
CM327_____   **1949. GAR Issue**
3¢ **carmine** (117,020,000)   .25   .20 ⬚⬚⬚⬚⬚
CM328_____   **1949. Edgar Allan Poe Issue**
3¢ **bright purple** (122,633,000)   .25   .20 ⬚⬚⬚⬚⬚
CM329_____   **1950. American Bankers Association Issue**
3¢ **green** (130,960,000)   .25   .20 ⬚⬚⬚⬚⬚
CM330_____   **1950. Samuel Gompers Issue**
3¢ **bright purple** (128,478,000)   .25   .20 ⬚⬚⬚⬚⬚
CM331_____   **1950. National Capital Sesquicentennial Issue**
3¢ **light blue** (132,090,000)   .25   .20 ⬚⬚⬚⬚⬚
CM332_____
3¢ **dull green** (130,050,000)   .25   .20 ⬚⬚⬚⬚⬚
CM333_____
3¢ **bluish violet** (131,350,000)   .25   .20 ⬚⬚⬚⬚⬚
CM334_____
3¢ **bright purple** (129,980,000)   .25   .20 ⬚⬚⬚⬚⬚
CM335_____   **1950. Railroad Engineers Issue**
3¢ **brown purple** (122,315,000)   .25   .20 ⬚⬚⬚⬚⬚
CM336_____   **1950. Kansas City Centennial Issue**
3¢ **violet** (122,170,000)   .25   .20 ⬚⬚⬚⬚⬚
CM337_____   **1950. Boy Scout Issue**
3¢ **sepia** (131,635,000)   .25   .20 ⬚⬚⬚⬚⬚
CM338_____   **1950. Indiana Territory Sesquicentennial Issue**
3¢ **light blue** (121,860,000)   .25   .20 ⬚⬚⬚⬚⬚
CM339_____   **1950. California Statehood Centennial Issue**
3¢ **yellow** (121,120,000)   .25   .20 ⬚⬚⬚⬚⬚
CM340_____   **1951. Confederate Veterans Issue**
3¢ **gray** (119,120,000)   .25   .20 ⬚⬚⬚⬚⬚
CM341_____   **1951. Nevada Centennial Issue**
3¢ **light olive green** (112,125,000)   .25   .20 ⬚⬚⬚⬚⬚
CM342_____   **1952. Detroit Issue**
3¢ **light blue** (114,140,000)   .25   .20 ⬚⬚⬚⬚⬚
CM343_____   **1951. Colorado Statehood Issue**
3¢ **violet blue** (114,490,000)   .25   .20 ⬚⬚⬚⬚⬚
CM344_____   **1951. American Chemical Society Issue**
3¢ **brown purple** (117,200,000)   .25   .20 ⬚⬚⬚⬚⬚
CM345_____   **1951. Battle of Brooklyn Issue**
3¢ **violet** (16,130,000)   .25   .20 ⬚⬚⬚⬚⬚
CM346_____   **1952. Betsy Ross Issue**
3¢ **carmine red** (116,175,000)   .25   .20 ⬚⬚⬚⬚⬚
CM347_____   **1952. 4-H Club Issue**
3¢ **blue green** (115,945,000)   .25   .20 ⬚⬚⬚⬚⬚
CM348_____   **1952. American Railroads Issue**
3¢ **light blue** (112,540,000)   .25   .20 ⬚⬚⬚⬚⬚
CM349_____   **1952. AAA Issue**
3¢ **blue** (117,415,000)   .25   .20 ⬚⬚⬚⬚⬚
CM350_____   **1952. NATO Issue**
3¢ **violet** (2,899,580,000)   .25   .20 ⬚⬚⬚⬚⬚
CM351_____   **1952. Grand Coulee Dam Issue**
3¢ **blue green** (114,540,000)   .25   .20 ⬚⬚⬚⬚⬚
CM352_____   **1952. Lafayette Issue**
3¢ **bright blue** (113,135,000)   .25   .20 ⬚⬚⬚⬚⬚

CM327

CM328

CM329

CM330

CM331

CM332

CM333

CM334

CM335

CM336

CM337

CM338

CM339

CM340

CM341

CM342

CM343

CM344

CM345

	MNHVF	UseVF

CM353_____ 1952. Mount Rushmore Memorial Issue
3¢ **blue green** (116,255,000) — .25 — .20 ☐☐☐☐☐

CM354_____ 1952. Engineering Centennial Issue
3¢ **ultramarine** (113,860,000) — .25 — .20 ☐☐☐☐☐

CM355_____ 1952. Service Women Issue
3¢ **blue** (124,260,000) — .25 — .20 ☐☐☐☐☐

CM356_____ 1952. Gutenberg Bible Issue
3¢ **violet** (115,735,000) — .25 — .20 ☐☐☐☐☐

CM357_____ 1952. Newspaperboys of America Issue
3¢ **violet** (115,430,000) — .25 — .20 ☐☐☐☐☐

CM358_____ 1952. International Red Cross Issue
3¢ **ultramarine & scarlet** (136,220,000) — .25 — .20 ☐☐☐☐☐

CM359_____ 1953. National Guard Issue
3¢ **light blue** (114,894,600) — .25 — .20 ☐☐☐☐☐

CM360_____ 1953. Ohio Sesquicentennial Issue
3¢ **sepia** (117,706,000) — .25 — .20 ☐☐☐☐☐

CM361_____ 1953. Washington Territory Issue
3¢ **blue green** (114,190,000) — .25 — .20 ☐☐☐☐☐

CM362_____ 1953. Louisiana Purchase Issue
3¢ **brown purple** (113,990,000) — .25 — .20 ☐☐☐☐☐

CM363_____ 1953. Opening of Japan Issue
5¢ **blue green** (89,289,600) — .25 — .20 ☐☐☐☐☐

CM364_____ 1953. American Bar Association Issue
3¢ **light reddish violet** (114,865,000) — .25 — .20 ☐☐☐☐☐

CM365_____ 1953. Sagamore Hill Issue
3¢ **green** (115,780,000) — .25 — .20 ☐☐☐☐☐

CM346

CM347

CM348

CM349

CM350 ←

CM351

CM352

CM353 ←

CM354

CM355

CM356

CM357

CM358

CM359

CM360

CM361

CM362

CM363

CM364

CM365

CM366

CM367

CM368

CM369

CM370

CM371

CM372

	MNHVF	UseVF	

CM366_____ **1953. Future Farmers of America Issue**
3¢ bright blue (115,224,600) .25 .20 ☐☐☐☐☐

CM367_____ **1953. Trucking Industry Issue**
3¢ violet (123,709,600) .25 .20 ☐☐☐☐☐

CM368_____ **1953. General Patton Issue**
3¢ bluish violet (114,789,600) .25 .20 ☐☐☐☐☐

CM369_____ **1953. New York City Tercentenary Issue**
3¢ bright purple (115,759,600) .25 .20 ☐☐☐☐☐

CM370_____ **1953. Gadsden Purchase Issue**
3¢ Venetian red (115,759,600) .25 .20 ☐☐☐☐☐

CM371_____ **1953. Columbia University Issue**
3¢ cobalt blue (118,540,000) .25 .20 ☐☐☐☐☐

CM372_____ **1954. Nebraska Territorial Centennial Issue**
3¢ violet (115,810,000) .25 .20 ☐☐☐☐☐

CM373_____ **1954. Kansas Territorial Centennial Issue**
3¢ salmon (113,603,700) .25 .20 ☐☐☐☐☐

CM374_____ **1954. George Eastman Issue**
3¢ brown purple (121,100,000) .25 .20 ☐☐☐☐☐

CM375_____ **1954. Lewis and Clark Expedition Issue**
3¢ brown (116,078,150) .25 .20 ☐☐☐☐☐

CM376_____ **1955. Pennsylvania Academy of Fine Arts Issue**
3¢ brown purple (116,139,800) .25 .20 ☐☐☐☐☐

CM377_____ **1955. First Land-Grant College Issue**
3¢ emerald green (120,484,800) .25 .20 ☐☐☐☐☐

CM378_____ **1955. Rotary International Issue**
8¢ deep blue (53,854,750) .25 .20 ☐☐☐☐☐

CM379_____ **1955. The Armed Forces Reserve Issue**
3¢ bright purple (176,075,000) .25 .20 ☐☐☐☐☐

CM380_____ **1955. Old Man of the Mountains Issue**
3¢ blue green (125,944,400) .25 .20 ☐☐☐☐☐

CM381_____ **1955. Soo Locks Centennial Issue**
3¢ blue (122,284,600) .25 .20 ☐☐☐☐☐

CM382_____ **1955. Atoms for Peace Issue**
3¢ deep blue (133,638,850) .25 .20 ☐☐☐☐☐

CM383_____ **1955. Fort Ticonderoga Bicentennial Issue**
3¢ dark red brown (118,664,600) .25 .20 ☐☐☐☐☐

CM384_____ **1955. Andrew Mellon Issue**
3¢ carmine red (112,434,000) .25 .20 ☐☐☐☐☐

CM385_____ **1956. Franklin 250th Anniversary Issue**
3¢ carmine (129,384,550) .25 .20 ☐☐☐☐☐

CM386_____ **1956. Booker T. Washington Issue**
3¢ deep blue (121,184,600) .25 .20 ☐☐☐☐☐

CM387_____ **1956. FIPEX Issue**
3¢ violet (119,784,200) .25 .20 ☐☐☐☐☐

CM388_____ **1956. Fifth International Philatelic Exhibition (FIPEX) Souvenir Sheet**
11¢ Complete sheet of 2 stamps (9,802,025) 2.50 2.00 ☐☐☐☐☐

CM389_____ **1956. Wild Turkey Issue**
3¢ brown purple (123,159,400) .25 .20 ☐☐☐☐☐

CM390_____ **1956. Pronghorn Antelope Issue**
3¢ sepia (123,138,800) .25 .20 ☐☐☐☐☐

CM391_____ **1956. King Salmon Issue**
3¢ blue green (109,275,000) .25 .20 ☐☐☐☐☐

CM392_____ **1956. Pure Food and Drug Laws Issue**
3¢ blue green (112,932,200) .25 .20 ☐☐☐☐☐

CM373

CM374

CM375

← CM376

CM377

CM378

CM379

CM380 ←

CM381

CM382

CM384

CM383 ←

CM386 →

CM385 ←

CM387

CM388 →

CM389

	MNHVF	UseVF

CM393_____   **1956. Wheatland Issue**
3¢   **black brown** (125,475,000)   .25   .20 ☐☐☐☐☐

CM394_____   **1956. Labor Day Issue**
3¢   **deep blue** (117,855,000)   .25   .20 ☐☐☐☐☐

CM395_____   **1956. Nassau Hall Issue**
3¢   **black on orange** (122,100,00)   .25   .20 ☐☐☐☐☐

CM396_____   **1956. Devils Tower Issue**
3¢   **lilac** (118,180,000)   .25   .20 ☐☐☐☐☐

CM397_____   **1956. Children's Issue**
3¢   **blue** (100,975,000)   .25   .20 ☐☐☐☐☐

CM398_____   **1957. Alexander Hamilton Bicentennial Issue**
3¢   **rose red** (115,299,450)   .25   .20 ☐☐☐☐☐

CM399_____   **1957. Anti-Polio Issue**
3¢   **bright purple** (186,949,250)   .25   .20 ☐☐☐☐☐

CM400_____   **1957. Coast and Geodetic Survey Issue**
3¢   **deep blue** (115,235,000)   .25   .20 ☐☐☐☐☐

CM401_____   **1957. Architects of America Issue**
3¢   **rose lilac** (106,647,500)   .25   .20 ☐☐☐☐☐

CM402_____   **1957. Steel Industry in America Issue**
3¢   **bright blue** (112,010,000)   .25   .20 ☐☐☐☐☐

CM403_____   **1957. International Naval Review Issue**
3¢   **blue green** (118,399,600)   .25   .20 ☐☐☐☐☐

CM404_____   **1957. Oklahoma Statehood Issue**
3¢   **bright blue** (102,209,500)   .25   .20 ☐☐☐☐☐

CM405_____   **1957. Teachers of America Issue**
3¢   **brown purple** (103,045,000)   .25   .20 ☐☐☐☐☐

CM406_____   **1957. American Flag Issue**
4¢   **deep blue & carmine** (84,054,400)   .25   .20 ☐☐☐☐☐

CM407_____   **1957. Virginia of Sagadahock Issue**
3¢   **violet** (126,266,000)   .25   .20 ☐☐☐☐☐

CM408_____   **1957. Ramon Magsaysay Issue**
8¢   **scarlet, deep ultramarine & ocher** (39,489,600)   .25   .20 ☐☐☐☐☐

CM409_____   **1957. Lafayette Issue**
3¢   **brown purple** (122,990,000)   .25   .20 ☐☐☐☐☐

CM410_____   **1957. Whooping Crane Issue**
3¢   **gray blue, yellow & blue green** (174,372,800)   .25   .20 ☐☐☐☐☐

CM411_____   **1957. Flushing Remonstrance Issue**
3¢   **brown black** (114,365,000)   .25   .20 ☐☐☐☐☐

CM412_____   **1958. Garden and Horticultural Issue**
3¢   **dull green** (122,765,200)   .25   .20 ☐☐☐☐☐

CM413_____   **1958. Brussels Universal and International Exhibition Issue**
3¢   **brown purple** (113,660,200)   .25   .20 ☐☐☐☐☐

CM414_____   **1958. James Monroe Issue**
3¢   **violet** (120,196,580)   .25   .20 ☐☐☐☐☐

CM415_____   **1958. Minnesota Statehood Centennial Issue**
3¢   **emerald green** (120,805,200)   .25   .20 ☐☐☐☐☐

CM416_____   **1958. International Geophysical Year Issue**
3¢   **black & red** (125,815,200)   .25   .20 ☐☐☐☐☐

CM417_____   **1958. Gunston Hall Bicentennial Issue**
3¢   **dull green** (108,415,200)   .25   .20 ☐☐☐☐☐

CM418_____   **1958. Mackinac Straits Bridge Issue**
3¢   **turquoise blue** (107,195,200)   .25   .20 ☐☐☐☐☐

CM419_____   **1958. Simon Bolívar Issue**
4¢   **olive buff** (115,745,280)   .25   .20 ☐☐☐☐☐

CM390

CM393

CM396

CM399

CM402

CM391

CM392 →

← CM394

CM397

CM400

CM403

CM405

CM395

CM398

CM401

CM404

CM407

CM406

	MNHVF	UseVF

CM420_____   **1958. Simon Bolívar Issue**
8¢ **scarlet, deep ultramarine & deep ocher** (39,743,640)   .25   .20 ☐☐☐☐☐
CM421_____   **1958. Atlantic Cable Centennial Issue**
4¢ **red violet** (114,570,200)   .25   .20 ☐☐☐☐☐
CM422_____   **1958. Lincoln Douglas Debate Issue**
4¢ **brown** (114,860,200)   .25   .20 ☐☐☐☐☐
CM423_____   **1958. Lajos Kossuth Issue**
4¢ **dull green** (120,561,280)   .25   .20 ☐☐☐☐☐
CM424_____   **1958. Lajos Kossuth Issue**
8¢ **scarlet, deep ultramarine & deep ochre** (44,064,576)   .25   .20 ☐☐☐☐☐
CM425_____   **1958. Journalism and Freedom of the Press Issue**
4¢ **gray black** (118,390,200)   .25   .20 ☐☐☐☐☐
CM426_____   **1958. Overland Mail Centennial Issue**
4¢ **orange red** (125,770,200)   .25   .20 ☐☐☐☐☐
CM427_____   **1958. Noah Webster Bicentennial Issue**
4¢ **magenta** (114,114,280)   .25   .20 ☐☐☐☐☐
CM428_____   **1958. Forest Conservation Issue**
4¢ **deep green, yellow & brown** (156,600,200)   .25   .20 ☐☐☐☐☐
CM429_____   **1958. Fort Duquesne Bicentennial Issue**
4¢ **light blue** (124,200,200)   .25   .20 ☐☐☐☐☐
CM430_____   **1959. Lincoln Sesquicentennial Issue**
1¢ **deep green** (120,400,200)   .25   .20 ☐☐☐☐☐
CM431_____   **1959. Head of Lincoln Issue**
3¢ **deep plum** (91,160,200)   .25   .20 ☐☐☐☐☐
CM432_____   **1959. Lincoln Statue Issue**
4¢ **blue** (126,500,000)   .25   .20 ☐☐☐☐☐
CM433_____   **1959. Oregon Statehood Issue**
4¢ **blue green** (120,740,200)   .25   .20 ☐☐☐☐☐
CM434_____   **1959. José de San Martin Issue**
4¢ **blue** (113,623,280)   .25   .20 ☐☐☐☐☐
CM435_____
8¢ **carmine, blue & ocher** (45,569,088)   .25   .20 ☐☐☐☐☐
CM436_____   **1959. NATO Issue**
4¢ **blue** (122,493,280)   .25   .20 ☐☐☐☐☐
CM437_____   **1959. Arctic Explorations Issue**
4¢ **turquoise blue** (131,260,200)   .25   .20 ☐☐☐☐☐
CM438_____   **1959. Peace through Trade Issue**
8¢ **brown purple** (47,125,200)   .25   .20 ☐☐☐☐☐
CM439_____   **1959. Silver Centennial Issue**
4¢ **black** (123,105,000)   .25   .20 ☐☐☐☐☐
CM440_____   **1959. St. Lawrence Seaway Issue**
4¢ **blue & red** (126,105,050)   .25   .20 ☐☐☐☐☐
CM441_____   **1959. 49-Star Flag Issue**
4¢ **deep blue & carmine** (209,170,000)   .25   .20 ☐☐☐☐☐
CM442_____   **1959. Soil Conservation Issue**
4¢ **blue green & yellow orange** (120,835,000)   .25   .20 ☐☐☐☐☐
CM443_____   **1959. Petroleum Industry Centennial Issue**
4¢ **brown** (115,715,000)   .25   .20 ☐☐☐☐☐
CM444_____   **1959. Dental Health Issue**
4¢ **dark green** (118,445,000)   .25   .20 ☐☐☐☐☐
CM445_____   **1959. Ernst Reuter Issue**
4¢ **black** (111,685,000)   .25   .20 ☐☐☐☐☐
CM446_____   **1959. Ernst Reuter Issue**
8¢ **carmine, blue & ocher** (43,099,200)   .25   .20 ☐☐☐☐☐

CM408

CM409

CM410

CM411

CM412

CM413

CM414

CM415

CM416

CM417

CM418

CM419

CM420

CM421

CM422

CM423

CM424

CM425

CM426

CM427

CM429

CM428 ←

→ CM430

→ CM431

CM432

CM433

CM434 ←

CM435 ←

CM436 ←

CM437

CM438

CM439

CM440

CM441

CM442

CM443

CM444

CM445

CM446 ←

CM447

CM448

CM449

CM450

CM451

CM452

CM453

CM454

CM455

CM456

CM457

CM458

CM459

CM460

CM461

CM462

CM463

CM464

	MNHVF	UseVF

CM447_____ **1959. Ephraim McDowell Issue**
4¢ **brown purple** (115,444,000)   .25   .20 ☐☐☐☐☐

CM448_____ **1960. George Washington Issue**
4¢ **deep blue & carmine** (126,470,000)   .25   .20 ☐☐☐☐☐

CM449_____ **1960. Benjamin Franklin Issue**
4¢ **brown bister & emerald** (124,460,000)   .25   .20 ☐☐☐☐☐

CM450_____ **1960. Thomas Jefferson Issue**
4¢ **gray & scarlet** (115,445,000)   .25   .20 ☐☐☐☐☐

CM451_____ **1960. Francis Scott Key**
4¢ **carmine red & deep blue** (122,060,000)   .25   .20 ☐☐☐☐☐

CM452_____ **1960. Abraham Lincoln Issue**
4¢ **bright purple & green** (120,540,000)   .25   .20 ☐☐☐☐☐

CM453_____ **1960. Patrick Henry Issue**
4¢ **green & brown** (113,075,000)   .25   .20 ☐☐☐☐☐

CM454_____ **1960. Boy Scout Issue**
4¢ **red, deep blue & deep ocher** (139,325,000)   .25   .20 ☐☐☐☐☐

CM455_____ **1960. Winter Olympic Games Issue**
4¢ **turquoise blue** (124,445,000)   .25   .20 ☐☐☐☐☐

CM456_____ **1960. Tomas G. Masaryk Issue**
4¢ **blue** (113,792,000)   .25   .20 ☐☐☐☐☐

CM457_____
8¢ **carmine, deep blue & ocher** (44,215,200)   .25   .20 ☐☐☐☐☐

CM458_____ **1960. World Refugee Year Issue**
4¢ **gray black** (113,195,000)   .25   .20 ☐☐☐☐☐

CM459_____ **1960. Water Conservation Issue**
4¢ **blue, green & orange brown** (120,570,000)   .25   .20 ☐☐☐☐☐

CM460_____ **1960. SEATO Issue**
4¢ **blue** (115,353,000)   .25   .20 ☐☐☐☐☐

CM461_____ **1960. American Women Issue**
4¢ **violet** (111,080,000)   .25   .20 ☐☐☐☐☐

CM462_____ **1960. 50-Star Flag Issue**
4¢ **deep blue & scarlet** (153,025,000)   .25   .20 ☐☐☐☐☐

CM463_____ **1960. Pony Express Centenary Issue**
4¢ **sepia** (119,665,000)   .25   .20 ☐☐☐☐☐

CM464_____ **1960. Employ the Handicapped Issue**
4¢ **blue** (117,855,000)   .25   .20 ☐☐☐☐☐

CM465_____ **1960. Fifth World Forestry Congress Issue**
4¢ **blue green** (118,185,000)   .25   .20 ☐☐☐☐☐

CM466_____ **1960. Mexican Independence Issue**
4¢ **deep green & carmine red** (112,260,000)   .25   .20 ☐☐☐☐☐

CM467_____ **1960. United States of America-Japan Centennial Issue**
4¢ **light blue & carmine** (125,010,000)   .25   .20 ☐☐☐☐☐

CM468_____ **1960. Ignace Jan Paderewski Issue**
4¢ **blue** (119,798,000)   .25   .20 ☐☐☐☐☐

CM469_____
8¢ **red, blue & ocher** (42,696,000)   .25   .20 ☐☐☐☐☐

CM470_____ **1960. Robert A. Taft Issue**
4¢ **violet** (115,171,000)   .25   .20 ☐☐☐☐☐

CM471_____ **1960. Wheels of Freedom Issue**
4¢ **blue** (109,695,000)   .25   .20 ☐☐☐☐☐

CM472_____ **1960. Boys' Clubs of America Issue**
4¢ **deep blue, black & red** (123,690,000)   .25   .20 ☐☐☐☐☐

CM473_____ **1960. First Automated Post Office Issue**
4¢ **deep blue & scarlet** (127,970,000)   .25   .20 ☐☐☐☐☐

FIFTH WORLD FORESTRY CONGRESS
4¢ U.S.POSTAGE

CM465

MEXICAN INDEPENDENCE
1810 1960
4¢ JOINT ISSUE MEXICO-UNITED STATES U.S.POSTAGE

CM466

UNITED STATES & JAPAN
1860 1960 U.S. POSTAGE 4¢

CM467

CHAMPION OF LIBERTY
STATESMAN
UNITED STATES POSTAGE 4¢

CM468

CHAMPION OF LIBERTY
STATESMAN
UNITED STATES POSTAGE 8¢

CM469

UNITED STATES POSTAGE
ROBERT A.TAFT
4¢

CM470

WHEELS OF FREEDOM
UNITED STATES POSTAGE 4¢

CM471

BOYS' CLUBS OF AMERICA MOVEMENT
1860 · 1960
4¢ U.S. POSTAGE

CM472

U.S.POSTAGE
1960 PROVIDENCE,R.I.
4¢ FIRST AUTOMATED POST OFFICE IN THE UNITED STATES 4¢

CM473

CHAMPION OF LIBERTY
UNITED STATES POSTAGE 4¢

CM474

CHAMPION OF LIBERTY
UNITED STATES POSTAGE 8¢

CM475

1910 1960
CAMP FIRE GIRLS
UNITED STATES POSTAGE 4¢

CM476

CHAMPION OF LIBERTY
JOINT ITALIAN UNIFICATION 1860
GARIBALDI
UNITED STATES POSTAGE 4¢

CM477

CHAMPION OF LIBERTY
JOINT ITALIAN UNIFICATION 1860
GARIBALDI
UNITED STATES POSTAGE 8¢

CM478

UNITED STATES POSTAGE
WALTER F. GEORGE
4¢

CM479

UNITED STATES POSTAGE
JOHN FOSTER DULLES
4¢

CM480

UNITED STATES POSTAGE
ANDREW CARNEGIE
4¢

CM481

COMMUNICATIONS FOR PEACE
ECHO I
U·S·POSTAGE 4¢

CM482

CHAMPION OF LIBERTY
MAHATMA GANDHI
UNITED STATES POSTAGE 4¢

CM483

CHAMPION OF LIBERTY
MAHATMA GANDHI
UNITED STATES POSTAGE 8¢

CM484

RANGE CONSERVATION
THE TRAIL BOSS
UNITED STATES POSTAGE 4¢

CM485

	MNHVF	UseVF	

CM474_____ **1960. Baron Karl Gustaf Emil Mannerheim Issue**
4¢ **blue** (124,796,000) .25 .20 ☐☐☐☐☐

CM475_____
8¢ **red, blue & ocher** (42,076,800) .25 .20 ☐☐☐☐☐

CM476_____ **1960. Campfire Girls Issue**
4¢ **blue & red** (116,215,000) .25 .20 ☐☐☐☐☐

CM477_____ **1960. Giuseppe Garibaldi Issue**
4¢ **green** (126,252,000) .25 .20 ☐☐☐☐☐

CM478_____
8¢ **red, blue & ocher** (42,746,400) .25 .20 ☐☐☐☐☐

CM479_____ **1960. Walter F. George Issue**
4¢ **violet** (124,117,000) .25 .20 ☐☐☐☐☐

CM480_____ **1960. John Foster Dulles Issue**
4¢ **violet** (177,187,000) .25 .20 ☐☐☐☐☐

CM481_____ **1960. Andrew Carnegie Issue**
4¢ **claret** (119,840,000) .25 .20 ☐☐☐☐☐

CM482_____ **1960. Echo I Satellite Issue**
4¢ **violet** (125,290,000) .25 .20 ☐☐☐☐☐

CM483_____ **1961. Mahatma Gandhi Issue**
4¢ **red orange** (112,966,000) .25 .20 ☐☐☐☐☐

CM484_____
8¢ **red, blue & ocher** (41,644,200) .25 .20 ☐☐☐☐☐

CM485_____ **1961. Range Conservation Issue**
4¢ **blue, orange & indigo** (110,850,000) .25 .20 ☐☐☐☐☐

CM486_____ **1961. Horace Greeley Issue**
4¢ **violet** (98,616,000) .25 .20 ☐☐☐☐☐

CM487_____ **1961. Fort Sumter Issue**
4¢ **green** (101,125,000) .25 .20 ☐☐☐☐☐

CM488_____ **1962. Battle of Shiloh Issue**
4¢ **black on pink** (124,865,000) .25 .20 ☐☐☐☐☐

CM489_____ **1963. Battle of Gettysburg Issue**
5¢ **gray & blue** (79,905,000) .25 .20 ☐☐☐☐☐

CM490_____ **1964. Battle of the Wilderness Issue**
5¢ **brown, purple & black** (125,410,000) .25 .20 ☐☐☐☐☐

CM491_____ **1965. Appomattox Issue**
5¢ **blue & black** (112,845,000) .25 .20 ☐☐☐☐☐

CM492_____ **1961. Kansas Statehood Centennial Issue**
4¢ **brown, lake & green** on yellow paper (106,210,000) .25 .20 ☐☐☐☐☐

CM493_____ **1961. George William Norris Issue**
4¢ **blue green** (110,810,000) .25 .20 ☐☐☐☐☐

CM494_____ **1961. Naval Aviation Issue**
4¢ **blue** (116,995,000) .25 .20 ☐☐☐☐☐

CM495_____ **1961. Workman's Compensation Issue**
4¢ **ultramarine** on bluish paper (121,015,000) .25 .20 ☐☐☐☐☐

CM496_____ **1961. Frederic Remington Issue**
4¢ **blue, red & yellow** (111,600,000) .25 .20 ☐☐☐☐☐

CM497_____ **1961. 50th Anniversary of the Republic of China Issue**
4¢ **blue** (110,620,000) .25 .20 ☐☐☐☐☐

CM498_____ **1961. Naismith-Basketball Issue**
4¢ **brown** (109,110,000) .25 .20 ☐☐☐☐☐

CM499_____ **1961. Nursing Issue**
4¢ **blue, black, orange & flesh** (145,350,000) .25 .20 ☐☐☐☐☐

CM500_____ **1962. New Mexico Statehood Issue**
4¢ **light blue, bister & brown purple** (112,870,000) .25 .20 ☐☐☐☐☐

CM486

CM487

CM488

CM489

CM490

CM491
→

CM492

CM493

CM494

CM495

CM496

CM497

CM498

CM499

CM500

CM501

	MNHVF	UseVF

CM501_____ **1962. Arizona Statehood Issue**
4¢   scarlet, deep blue & green (121,820,000)   .25   .20 ❑❑❑❑❑

CM502_____ **1962. Project Mercury Issue**
4¢   deep blue & yellow (289,240,000)   .25   .20 ❑❑❑❑❑

CM503_____ **1962. Malaria Eradication Issue**
4¢   blue & bister (120,155,000)   .25   .20 ❑❑❑❑❑

CM504_____ **1962. Charles Evans Hughes Issue**
4¢   black on yellow paper (124,595,000)   .25   .20 ❑❑❑❑❑

CM505_____ **1962. Seattle World's Fair Issue**
4¢   red & deep blue (147,310,000)   .25   .20 ❑❑❑❑❑

CM506_____ **1962. Louisiana Statehood Commemorative Issue**
4¢   gray green, blue & vermilion (118,690,000)   .25   .20 ❑❑❑❑❑

CM507_____ **1962. Homestead Act Issue**
4¢   slate blue (122,730,000)   .25   .20 ❑❑❑❑❑

CM508_____ **1962. Girl Scouts of America Issue**
4¢   red (126,515,000)   .25   .20 ❑❑❑❑❑

CM509_____ **1962. Brien McMahon Issue**
4¢   violet (130,960,000)   .25   .20 ❑❑❑❑❑

CM510_____ **1962. National Apprenticeship Issue**
4¢   black, on buff (120,055,000)   .25   .20 ❑❑❑❑❑

CM511_____ **1962. Sam Rayburn Issue**
4¢   brown & blue (120,715,000)   .25   .20 ❑❑❑❑❑

CM512_____ **1962. Dag Hammarskjöld Issue**
4¢   black, brown & yellow (121,440,000)   .25   .20 ❑❑❑❑❑

CM513_____ **1962. Dag Hammarskjöld Special Issue**
4¢   black, brown & yellow (40,270,000)   .55   .25 ❑❑❑❑❑

CM514_____ **1962. Higher Education Issue**
4¢   blue, green & black (120,035,000)   .25   .20 ❑❑❑❑❑

CM515_____ **1962. Winslow Homer Issue**
4¢   multicolored (117,870,000)   .25   .20 ❑❑❑❑❑

CM516_____ **1963. Carolina Charter Issue**
5¢   dark carmine & brown (129,445,000)   .25   .20 ❑❑❑❑❑

CM517_____ **1963. Food for Peace Issue**
5¢   green, yellow & red (135,620,000)   .25   .20 ❑❑❑❑❑

CM518_____ **1963. West Virginia Statehood Issue**
5¢   green, red & black (137,540,000)   .25   .20 ❑❑❑❑❑

CM519_____ **1963. Emancipation Proclamation Issue**
5¢   bright blue, scarlet & indigo (132,435,000)   .25   .20 ❑❑❑❑❑

CM520_____ **1963. Alliance for Progress Issue**
5¢   bright blue & green (135,520,000)   .25   .20 ❑❑❑❑❑

CM521_____ **1963. Cordell Hull Issue**
5¢   blue green (131,420,000)   .25   .20 ❑❑❑❑❑

CM522_____ **1963. Eleanor Roosevelt Issue**
5¢   purple (133,170,000)   .25   .20 ❑❑❑❑❑

CM523_____ **1963. National Academy of Science Issue**
5¢   turquoise, blue & black (139,195,000)   .25   .20 ❑❑❑❑❑

CM524_____ **1963. City Mail Delivery Issue**
5¢   red, gray & blue, tagged (128,450,000)   .25   .20 ❑❑❑❑❑

CM525_____ **1963. International Red Cross Issue**
5¢   deep gray & red (116,665,000)   .25   .20 ❑❑❑❑❑

CM526_____ **1963. John James Audubon Issue**
5¢   multicolored (175,175,000)   .25   .20 ❑❑❑❑❑

CM527_____ **1964. Sam Houston Issue**
5¢   black (125,995,000)   .25   .20 ❑❑❑❑❑

CM502

CM503

CM504 →

CM505

CM506

CM507

↑ CM508

CM509

CM510

CM511 →

CM512

CM513

CM514

CM515

CM516

CM517

CM518

CM519

	MNHVF	UseVF

CM528_____   **1964. Charles M. Russell Issue**

5¢ **multicolored** (128,025,000)   .25   .20 ❑❑❑❑❑

CM529_____   **1964. New York World's Fair Issue**

5¢ **green** (145,700,000)   .25   .20 ❑❑❑❑❑

CM530_____   **1964. John Muir Issue**

5¢ **brown, green, brownish gray & olive green** (120,310,000)   .25   .20 ❑❑❑❑❑

CM531_____   **1964. John F. Kennedy Memorial Issue**

5¢ **gray blue** (500,000,000)   .25   .20 ❑❑❑❑❑

CM532_____   **1964. New Jersey Tercentenary Issue**

5¢ **ultramarine** (123,845,000)   .25   .20 ❑❑❑❑❑

CM533_____   **1964. Nevada Statehood Issue**

5¢ **multicolored** (122,825,000)   .25   .20 ❑❑❑❑❑

CM534_____   **1964. Register and Vote Issue**

5¢ **blue & red** (325,000,000)   .25   .20 ❑❑❑❑❑

CM535_____   **1964. William Shakespeare Issue**

5¢ **brown** on tan paper (123,245,000)   .25   .20 ❑❑❑❑❑

CM536_____   **1964. Doctors Mayo Issue**

5¢ **green** (123,355,000)   .25   .20 ❑❑❑❑❑

CM537_____   **1964. American Music Issue**

5¢ **red, gray & blue** on granite paper (126,370,000)   .25   .20 ❑❑❑❑❑

CM538_____   **1964. Homemakers Issue**

5¢ **multicolored** on buff (121,250,000)   .25   .20 ❑❑❑❑❑

CM539_____   **1964. Verrazano-Narrows Bridge Issue**

5¢ **green** (125,005,000)   .25   .20 ❑❑❑❑❑

CM540_____   **1964. Abstract Art Issue**

5¢ **blue, black & red** (125,800,000)   .25   .20 ❑❑❑❑❑

CM541_____   **1964. Amateur Radio Operators Issue**

5¢ **purple** (122,230,000)   .25   .20 ❑❑❑❑❑

CM542_____   **1965. Battle of New Orleans Issue**

5¢ **carmine, blue & slate** (115,695,000)   .25   .20 ❑❑❑❑❑

CM543_____   **1965. Sokol Centennial - Physical Fitness Issue**

5¢ **lake & deep slate** (115,095,000)   .25   .20 ❑❑❑❑❑

CM544_____   **1965. Crusade Against Cancer Issue**

5¢ **reddish violet, black & red** (116,560,000)   .25   .20 ❑❑❑❑❑

CM545_____   **1965. Winston Churchill Memorial Issue**

5¢ **black** (125,180,000)   .25   .20 ❑❑❑❑❑

CM546_____   **1965. Magna Carta Issue**

5¢ **black, yellow & reddish-violet** (120,135,000)   .25   .20 ❑❑❑❑❑

CM547_____   **1965. UN International Cooperation Year Issue**

5¢ **turquoise blue & slate** (115,405,000)   .25   .20 ❑❑❑❑❑

CM548_____   **1965. Salvation Army Issue**

5¢ **red, black & deep blue** (115,855,000)   .25   .20 ❑❑❑❑❑

CM549_____   **1965. Dante Alighieri Issue**

5¢ **carmine red** on light Venetian red paper (115,340,000)   .25   .20 ❑❑❑❑❑

CM550_____   **1965. Herbert Hoover Issue**

5¢ **red** (114,840,000)   .25   .20 ❑❑❑❑❑

CM551_____   **1965. Robert Fulton Issue**

5¢ **blue & black** (116,140,000)   .25   .20 ❑❑❑❑❑

CM552_____   **1965. European Settlement Issue**

5¢ **yellow, red & black** (116,900,000)   .25   .20 ❑❑❑❑❑

CM553_____   **1965. Traffic Safety Issue**

5¢ **green, black & red** (114,085,000)   .25   .20 ❑❑❑❑❑

CM554_____   **1965. John Singleton Copley Issue**

5¢ **black & tones of brown & olive** (114,880,000)   .25   .20 ❑❑❑❑❑

CM520

CM521 →

CM524 ←

CM522

CM523

CM525

CM526 →

CM527

CM528

CM529

CM530 ←

CM531

CM532

CM533

CM537

CM534

CM535

CM536

CM538

	MNHVF	UseVF

CM555_____ **1965. International Telecommunication Union Issue**
11¢ yellow, red & black (26,995,000)   .25   .20 ☐☐☐☐☐

CM556_____ **1965. Adlai Stevenson Issue**
5¢ light blue gray, black, red & blue (128,495,000)   .25   .20 ☐☐☐☐☐

CM557_____ **1966. Migratory Bird Treaty Issue**
5¢ red, blue & light blue (116,835,000)   .25   .20 ☐☐☐☐☐

CM558_____ **1966. Humane Treatment of Animals Issue**
5¢ reddish brown & black (117,470,000)   .25   .20 ☐☐☐☐☐

CM559_____ **1966. Indiana Statehood Issue**
5¢ blue, yellow & brown (123,770,000)   .25   .20 ☐☐☐☐☐

CM560_____ **1966. American Circus Issue**
5¢ red, blue, pink & black (131,270,000)   .25   .20 ☐☐☐☐☐

CM561_____ **1966. Sixth International Philatelic Exhibition Issue**
5¢ multicolored (122,285,000)   .25   .20 ☐☐☐☐☐

CM562_____ **1966. SIPEX Souvenir Sheet**
5¢ multicolored (14,680,000)   .30   .25 ☐☐☐☐☐

CM563_____ **1966. Bill of Rights Issue**
5¢ red & blue (114,160,000)   .25   .20 ☐☐☐☐☐

CM564_____ **1966. Polish Millennium Issue**
5¢ red (126,475,000)   .25   .20 ☐☐☐☐☐

CM565_____ **1966. National Park Service Issue**
5¢ multicolored (119,535,000)   .25   .20 ☐☐☐☐☐

CM566_____ **1966. Marine Corps Reserve Issue**
5¢ black, olive, red & blue (125,110,000)   .25   .20 ☐☐☐☐☐

CM567_____ **1966. General Federation of Women's Clubs Issue**
5¢ pink, blue & black (114,853,000)   .25   .20 ☐☐☐☐☐

CM568_____ **1966. Johnny Appleseed Issue**
5¢ black, red & green (124,290,000)   .25   .20 ☐☐☐☐☐

CM569_____ **1966. Beautification of America Issue**
5¢ black, green & pink (128,460,000)   .25   .20 ☐☐☐☐☐

CM570_____ **1966. Great River Road Issue**
5¢ salmon, blue, olive yellow & yellow green (127,585,000)   .25   .20 ☐☐☐☐☐

CM571_____ **1966. U.S. Savings Bond Issue**
5¢ red, blue & black (115,875,000)   .25   .20 ☐☐☐☐☐

CM572_____ **1966. Mary Cassatt Issue**
5¢ multicolored (114,015,000)   .25   .20 ☐☐☐☐☐

CM573_____ **1967. National Grange Issue**
5¢ brownish orange, green, orange & black (121,105,000)   .25   .20 ☐☐☐☐☐

CM574_____ **1967. Canada Centennial Issue**
5¢ blue, green, dark blue & olive green, tagged (132,045,000)   .25   .20 ☐☐☐☐☐

CM575_____ **1967. Erie Canal Sesquicentennial Issue**
5¢ dark blue, light blue, black, red, tagged (118,780,000)   .25   .20 ☐☐☐☐☐

CM576_____ **1967. Lions International Issue**
5¢ red, blue & black on granite paper, tagged (121,985,000)   .25   .20 ☐☐☐☐☐

CM577_____ **1967. Henry David Thoreau Issue**
5¢ red, black & green tagged (111,850,000)   .25   .20 ☐☐☐☐☐

CM578_____ **1967. Nebraska Statehood Issue**
5¢ yellow, green & brown tagged (117,225,000)   .25   .20 ☐☐☐☐☐

CM579_____ **1967. Voice of America Issue**
5¢ red, blue & black tagged (111,515,000)   .25   .20 ☐☐☐☐☐

CM580_____ **1967. Davy Crockett Issue**
5¢ green, black & yellow tagged (114,270,000)   .25   .20 ☐☐☐☐☐

CM581_____ **1967. Space Twins Issue**
5¢ dark blue, black & red tagged (120,865,000)   1.00   .35 ☐☐☐☐☐

CM540

CM542

CM539 CM541

CM543

CM544

CM545

CM546

CM547

CM548

CM549

CM550

CM551

CM552

CM553

CM554

CM556

CM555

CM557

CM558

CM559

CM560

CM562

CM563

CM561

CM564

CM565

CM566

CM567

CM568

CM569

CM570

CM571

CM572

CM573

CM574

CM575

CM576

CM577

CM578

CM579 ➡️

CM580

CM583 ➡️

CM581-82

Finland
Independence 1917-67

United States 5c

CM584

CM585

CM586

CM587 ➡️

CM588

CM589

LAW AND ORDER

CM590 ⬅️

REGISTER & VOTE

CM591 ⬅️

CM592

CM593

CM594

CM595

CM596

CM597

CM598

	MNHVF	UseVF

CM582_____

5¢ dark blue, red & blue, green tagged	1.00	.35 ☐☐☐☐☐

CM583_____   **1967. Urban Planning Issue**

5¢ dark blue, light blue & black tagged (110,675,000)	.25	.20 ☐☐☐☐☐

CM584_____   **1967. Finland Independence Issue**

5¢ blue tagged (110,670,000)	.25	.20 ☐☐☐☐☐

CM585_____   **1967. Thomas Eakins Issue**

5¢ gold & multicolored tagged (113,825,000)	.25	.20 ☐☐☐☐☐

CM586_____   **1967. Mississippi Statehood Issue**

5¢ green blue, blue green & brown tagged (113,330,000)	.25	.20 ☐☐☐☐☐

CM587_____   **1968. Illinois Statehood Issue**

6¢ multicolored tagged (141,350,000)	.25	.20 ☐☐☐☐☐

CM588_____   **1968. Hemisfair '68 Issue**

6¢ blue, pink, & white tagged (117,470,600)	.25	.20 ☐☐☐☐☐

CM589_____   **1968. Support Our Youth Issue**

6¢ red & blue tagged (147,120,000)	.25	.20 ☐☐☐☐☐

CM590_____   **1968. Law and Order Issue**

6¢ red, blue & black tagged (130,125,000)	.25	.20 ☐☐☐☐☐

CM591_____   **1968. Register and Vote Issue**

6¢ gold and black tagged (158,070,000)	.25	.20 ☐☐☐☐☐

CM592_____   **1968. Historic Flags Issue**

6¢ blue tagged (228,040,000)	.40	.30 ☐☐☐☐☐

CM593_____

6¢ red & blue tagged	.40	.30 ☐☐☐☐☐

CM594_____

6¢ green & blue tagged	.40	.30 ☐☐☐☐☐

CM595_____

6¢ red & blue tagged	.40	.30 ☐☐☐☐☐

CM596_____

6¢ gold & blue tagged	.40	.30 ☐☐☐☐☐

CM597_____

6¢ red & blue tagged	.40	.30 ☐☐☐☐☐

CM598_____

6¢ red, green & blue tagged	.40	.30 ☐☐☐☐☐

CM599_____

6¢ red & blue tagged	.40	.30 ☐☐☐☐☐

CM600_____

6¢ multicolored tagged	.40	.30 ☐☐☐☐☐

CM601_____

6¢ red, gold & blue tagged	.40	.30 ☐☐☐☐☐

CM602_____   **1968. Walt Disney Issue**

6¢ multicolored tagged (153,015,000)	.25	.20 ☐☐☐☐☐

CM603_____   **1968. Father Jacques Marquette Issue**

6¢ black, green & brown tagged (132,560,000)	.25	.20 ☐☐☐☐☐

CM604_____   **1968. Daniel Boone Issue**

6¢ red brown, brown, yellow & black tagged (130,385,000)	.25	.20 ☐☐☐☐☐

CM605_____   **1968. Arkansas River Navigation Issue**

6¢ blue, black & dark blue tagged (132,265,000)	.25	.20 ☐☐☐☐☐

CM606_____   **1968. Leif Erikson Issue**

6¢ brown (128,710,000)	.25	.20 ☐☐☐☐☐

CM607_____   **1968. Cherokee Strip Issue**

6¢ brown tagged (124,775,000)	.25	.20 ☐☐☐☐☐

CM608_____   **1968. John Trumbull Issue**

6¢ multicolored tagged (128,295,000)	.25	.20 ☐☐☐☐☐

CM599

CM600

CM601

CM602

CM603

CM604

CM605

CM606

CM607

CM608

CM609

CM610

CM615

CM611-614

CM616

CM617

	MNHVF	UseVF

CM609_____ **1968. Waterfowl Conservation Issue**
6¢ **multicolored** (142,245,000) .25 .20 ☐☐☐☐☐

CM610_____ **1968. Chief Joseph Issue**
6¢ **multicolored** tagged (125,100,000) .25 .20 ☐☐☐☐☐

CM611_____ **1969. Beautification of America Issue**
6¢ **multicolored** tagged (102,570,000) .30 .25 ☐☐☐☐☐

CM612_____
6¢ **multicolored** tagged .30 .25 ☐☐☐☐☐

CM613_____
6¢ **multicolored** tagged .30 .25 ☐☐☐☐☐

CM614_____
6¢ **multicolored** tagged .30 .25 ☐☐☐☐☐

CM615_____ **1969. American Legion Issue**
6¢ **red, black & blue** tagged (148,770,000) .25 .20 ☐☐☐☐☐

CM616_____ **1969. Grandma Moses Issue**
6¢ **multicolored** tagged (139,475,000) .25 .20 ☐☐☐☐☐

CM617_____ **1969. Apollo 8 Issue**
6¢ **gray, deep blue & blue** tagged (187,165,000) .25 .20 ☐☐☐☐☐
NOTE: Imperforate varieties, from printer's waste, exist.

CM618_____ **1969. W.C. Handy Issue**
6¢ **multicolored** tagged (125,555,000) .25 .20 ☐☐☐☐☐

CM619_____ **1969. Settlement of California Issue**
6¢ **multicolored** tagged (144,425,000) .25 .20 ☐☐☐☐☐

CM620_____ **1969. John Wesley Powell Issue**
6¢ **multicolored** tagged (133,100,000) .25 .20 ☐☐☐☐☐

CM621_____ **1969. Alabama Statehood Issue**
6¢ **multicolored** tagged (136,900,000) .25 .20 ☐☐☐☐☐

CM622_____ **1969. 11th International Botanical Congress Issue**
6¢ **multicolored** tagged (158,695,000) .30 .25 ☐☐☐☐☐

CM623_____
6¢ **multicolored** tagged .30 .25 ☐☐☐☐☐

CM624_____
6¢ **multicolored** tagged .30 .25 ☐☐☐☐☐

CM625_____
6¢ **multicolored** tagged .30 .25 ☐☐☐☐☐

CM626_____ **1969. Dartmouth College Case Issue**
6¢ **green** tagged (124,075,000) .25 .20 ☐☐☐☐☐

CM627_____ **1969. Professional Baseball Issue**
6¢ **yellow, red, black & green** tagged (129,925,000) 1.25 .20 ☐☐☐☐☐

CM628_____ **1969. Intercollegiate Football Issue**
6¢ **red & green** tagged (129,860,000) .45 .20 ☐☐☐☐☐
NOTE: The intaglio portion of CM628 was printed on a rotary press normally used for currency.

CM629_____ **1969. Dwight D. Eisenhower Issue**
6¢ **blue, black & reddish purple** tagged (138,976,000) .25 .20 ☐☐☐☐☐

CM630_____ **1969. Hope for the Crippled Issue**
6¢ **multicolored** tagged (124,565,000) .25 .20 ☐☐☐☐☐

CM631_____ **1969. William M. Harnett Issue**
6¢ **multicolored** tagged (124,729,000) .25 .20 ☐☐☐☐☐

CM632_____ **1970. Natural History Issue**
6¢ **multicolored** tagged (201,794,600) .25 .20 ☐☐☐☐☐

CM633_____
6¢ **multicolored** tagged .25 .20 ☐☐☐☐☐

CM634_____
6¢ **multicolored** tagged .25 .20 ☐☐☐☐☐

CM635_____
6¢ **multicolored** tagged .25 .20 ☐☐☐☐☐

CM618

CM619

CM620

CM621

CM622-625

CM626

CM627

CM628

CM629

CM630

CM631

CM636

CM637

CM632-635

CM638

CM639

	MNHVF	UseVF

CM636_____ **1970. Maine Statehood Issue**
6¢ **multicolored** tagged (171,850,000) .25 .20 ☐☐☐☐☐

CM637_____ **1970. Wildlife Conservation Issue**
6¢ **black** on tan (142,205,000) .25 .20 ☐☐☐☐☐

CM638_____ **1970. Edgar Lee Masters Issue**
6¢ **black** tagged (137,660,000) .25 .20 ☐☐☐☐☐

CM639_____ **1970. The 50th Anniversary of Woman Suffrage Issue**
6¢ **blue** tagged (135,125,000) .25 .20 ☐☐☐☐☐

CM640_____ **1970. South Carolina Issue**
6¢ **brown, black & red** tagged (135,895,000) .25 .20 ☐☐☐☐☐

CM641_____ **1970. Stone Mountain Issue**
6¢ **gray black** tagged (132,675,000) .25 .20 ☐☐☐☐☐

CM642_____ **1970. Fort Snelling Sesquicentennial Issue**
6¢ **multicolored** tagged (134,795,000) .25 .20 ☐☐☐☐☐

CM643_____ **1970. Anti-Pollution Issue**
6¢ **multicolored** tagged (161,600,000) .25 .20 ☐☐☐☐☐

CM644_____
6¢ **multicolored** tagged .25 .20 ☐☐☐☐☐

CM645_____
6¢ **multicolored** tagged .25 .20 ☐☐☐☐☐

CM646_____
6¢ **multicolored** tagged .25 .20 ☐☐☐☐☐

CM647_____ **1970. United Nations Issue**
6¢ **black, red & blue** tagged (127,610,000) .25 .20 ☐☐☐☐☐

CM648_____ **1970. Landing of the Pilgrims Issue**
6¢ **multicolored** tagged (129,785,000) .25 .20 ☐☐☐☐☐

CM649_____ **1970. U.S. Servicemen Issue**
6¢ **multicolored** tagged (134,380,000) .25 .20 ☐☐☐☐☐

CM650_____
6¢ **dark blue, black & red** tagged .25 .20 ☐☐☐☐☐

CM651_____ **1971. American Wool Issue**
6¢ **multicolored** tagged (135,305,000) .25 .20 ☐☐☐☐☐

CM652_____ **1971. Douglas MacArthur Issue**
6¢ **red, blue & black** tagged (134,840,000) .25 .20 ☐☐☐☐☐

CM653_____ **1971. Blood Donors Issue**
6¢ **red & blue** tagged (130,975,000) .25 .20 ☐☐☐☐☐

CM654_____ **1971. Missouri Statehood Issue**
8¢ **multicolored** tagged (161,235,000) .25 .20 ☐☐☐☐☐

CM655_____ **1971. Wildlife Conservation Issue**
8¢ **multicolored** tagged (175,680,000) .25 .20 ☐☐☐☐☐

CM656_____
8¢ **multicolored** tagged .25 .20 ☐☐☐☐☐

CM657_____
8¢ **multicolored** tagged .25 .20 ☐☐☐☐☐

CM658_____
8¢ **multicolored** tagged .25 .20 ☐☐☐☐☐

CM659_____ **1971. Antarctic Treaty Issue**
8¢ **red & dark blue** tagged (138,700,000) .25 .20 ☐☐☐☐☐

CM660_____ **1971. American Revolution Bicentennial Issue**
8¢ **gray, red, blue & black** tagged (138,165,000) .25 .20 ☐☐☐☐☐

CM661_____ **1971. Space Achievements Decade Issue**
8¢ **multicolored** tagged (176,295,000) .25 .20 ☐☐☐☐☐

CM662_____
8¢ **multicolored** tagged .25 .20 ☐☐☐☐☐

CM663_____ **1971. John Sloan Issue**
8¢ **multicolored** tagged (152,125,000) .25 .20 ☐☐☐☐☐

CM640

CM641

CM642

CM643-646

United Nations 25ᵗʰ Anniversary

CM647

CM648 →

CM649-650

CM651

DOUGLAS MacARTHUR

CM652

CM660

giving BLOOD saves lives

CM653

Missouri 1821-1971 United States 8c

CM654

CM659

CM655-658

CM663

Emily Dickinson

CM664

	MNHVF	UseVF

CM664_____ **1971. Emily Dickinson Issue**
8¢ **multicolored** tagged (142,845,000) .25 .20 ☐☐☐☐☐

CM665_____ **1971. San Juan Issue**
8¢ **multicolored** tagged (148,755,000) .25 .20 ☐☐☐☐☐

CM666_____ **1971. Prevent Drug Abuse Issue**
8¢ **blue, deep blue & black** tagged (139,080,000) .25 .20 ☐☐☐☐☐

CM667_____ **1971. CARE Issue**
8¢ **black, blue, violet & red lilac** tagged (130,755,000) .25 .20 ☐☐☐☐☐

CM668_____ **1971. Historic Preservation Issue**
8¢ **brown & dark beige** on buff, tagged (170,208,000) .25 .20 ☐☐☐☐☐

CM669_____
8¢ **brown & dark beige** on buff, tagged .25 .20 ☐☐☐☐☐

CM670_____
8¢ **brown & dark beige** on buff, tagged .25 .20 ☐☐☐☐☐

CM671_____
8¢ **brown & dark beige** on buff, tagged .25 .20 ☐☐☐☐☐

CM672_____ **1972. American Poets Issue**
8¢ **black, reddish brown & blue** tagged (137,355,000) .25 .20 ☐☐☐☐☐

CM673_____ **1972. Peace Corps Issue**
8¢ **dark blue, light blue & red** tagged (150,400,000) .25 .20 ☐☐☐☐☐

CM674_____ **1972. Yellowstone Park Issue**
8¢ **multicolored** tagged (164,096,000) .25 .20 ☐☐☐☐☐

CM675_____ **1972. Cape Hatteras Issue**
2¢ **multicolored** tagged (172,730,000) .25 .20 ☐☐☐☐☐

CM676_____
2¢ **multicolored** tagged .25 .20 ☐☐☐☐☐

CM677_____
2¢ **multicolored** tagged .25 .20 ☐☐☐☐☐

CM678_____
2¢ **multicolored** tagged .25 .20 ☐☐☐☐☐

CM679_____ **1972. Wolf Trap Farm Issue**
6¢ **multicolored** tagged (104,090,000) .25 .20 ☐☐☐☐☐

CM680_____ **1972. Mount McKinley Issue**
15¢ **multicolored** tagged (53,920,000) .25 .20 ☐☐☐☐☐

CM681_____ **1972. Family Planning Issue**
8¢ **multicolored** tagged (153,025,000) .25 .20 ☐☐☐☐☐

CM682_____ **1972. Colonial Craftsmen Issue**
8¢ **deep brown** on buff paper, tagged (201,890,000) .25 .20 ☐☐☐☐☐

CM683_____
8¢ **deep brown** on buff paper, tagged .25 .20 ☐☐☐☐☐

CM684_____
8¢ **deep brown** on buff paper, tagged .25 .20 ☐☐☐☐☐

CM685_____
8¢ **deep brown** on buff paper, tagged .25 .20 ☐☐☐☐☐

CM686_____ **1972. Olympic Games Issue**
6¢ **multicolored** tagged (67,335,000) .25 .20 ☐☐☐☐☐

CM687_____
8¢ **multicolored** tagged (96,240,000) .25 .20 ☐☐☐☐☐

CM688_____
15¢ **multicolored** tagged (46,340,000) .25 .20 ☐☐☐☐☐

CM661-662

CM665

Prevent drug abuse

CM666

CM667   CM668-671

CM672

Peace Corps

CM673

CM675-678

CM674

National Parks Centennial

CM679

CM680

Family Planning

CM681

CM682-685

	MNHVF	UseVF

CM689_____   **1972. Parent Teacher Association Issue**
8¢   **yellow & black** tagged (180,155,000)   .25   .20 ☐☐☐☐☐
CM690_____   **1972. Wildlife Conservation Issue**
8¢   **multicolored** tagged (198,364,800)   .25   .20 ☐☐☐☐☐
CM691_____
8¢   **multicolored** tagged   .25   .20 ☐☐☐☐☐
CM692_____
8¢   **multicolored** tagged   .25   .20 ☐☐☐☐☐
CM693_____
8¢   **multicolored** tagged   .25   .20 ☐☐☐☐☐
CM694_____   **1972. Mail Order Centennial Issue**
8¢   **multicolored** tagged (185,490,000)   .25   .20 ☐☐☐☐☐
NOTE: Tagging on this issue typically consists of a vertical bar, 10mm wide.
CM695_____   **1972. Osteopathic Medicine Issue**
8¢   **multicolored** tagged (162,335,000)   .25   .20 ☐☐☐☐☐
CM696_____   **1972. Tom Sawyer Issue**
8¢   **multicolored** tagged (162,789,950)   .25   .20 ☐☐☐☐☐
CM697_____   **1972. Pharmacy Issue**
8¢   **multicolored** tagged (165,895,000)   .25   .20 ☐☐☐☐☐
CM698_____   **1972. Stamp Collecting Issue**
8¢   **multicolored** tagged (166,508,000)   .25   .20 ☐☐☐☐☐
CM699_____   **1973. Love Issue**
8¢   **red, green, violet & blue** tagged (330,055,000)   .25   .20 ☐☐☐☐☐
CM700_____   **1973. Rise of the Spirit of Independence Issue**
8¢   **blue, greenish black & red** tagged (166,005,000)   .25   .20 ☐☐☐☐☐
CM701_____
8¢   **black, orange & ultramarine** tagged (163,050,000)   .25   .20 ☐☐☐☐☐
CM702_____
8¢   **blue, black, red & green** tagged (159,005,000)   .25   .20 ☐☐☐☐☐
CM703_____
8¢   **blue, black, yellow & red** tagged (147,295,000)   .25   .20 ☐☐☐☐☐
CM704_____   **1973. George Gershwin Issue**
8¢   **multicolored** (139,152,000)   .25   .20 ☐☐☐☐☐
CM705_____   **1973. Nicolaus Copernicus Issue**
8¢   **black & yellow** tagged (159,475,000)   .25   .20 ☐☐☐☐☐
CM706_____   **1973. Postal Service Employee Issue**
8¢   **multicolored** tagged (486,020,000)   .25   .20 ☐☐☐☐☐
CM707_____
8¢   **multicolored** tagged   .25   .20 ☐☐☐☐☐
CM708_____
8¢   **multicolored** tagged   .25   .20 ☐☐☐☐☐
CM709_____
8¢   **multicolored** tagged   .25   .20 ☐☐☐☐☐
CM710_____
8¢   **multicolored** tagged   .25   .20 ☐☐☐☐☐
CM711_____
8¢   **multicolored** tagged   .25   .20 ☐☐☐☐☐
CM712_____
8¢   **multicolored** tagged   .25   .20 ☐☐☐☐☐
CM713_____
8¢   **multicolored** tagged   .25   .20 ☐☐☐☐☐
CM714_____
8¢   **multicolored** tagged   .25   .20 ☐☐☐☐☐

CM686

CM687

CM688

CM689

CM690-693

CM695

CM694

CM696

CM697

CM698

CM699

CM700

CM701

CM703

CM702   CM705   CM704

	MNHVF	UseVF	

CM715_____

  8¢ **multicolored** tagged .25 .20 ☐☐☐☐☐

NOTE: Tagging consists of a 1/2 inch high horizontal band.

CM716_____ **1973. Harry S. Truman Issue**

  8¢ **red, black & blue** tagged (157,052,800) .25 .25 ☐☐☐☐☐

CM717_____ **1973. Boston Tea Party Issue**

  8¢ **multicolored** tagged (196,275,000) .25 .20 ☐☐☐☐☐

CM718_____

  8¢ **multicolored** tagged .25 .20 ☐☐☐☐☐

CM719_____

  8¢ **multicolored** tagged .25 .20 ☐☐☐☐☐

CM720_____

  8¢ **multicolored** tagged .25 .20 ☐☐☐☐☐

CM721_____ **1973. Progress in Electronics Issue**

  6¢ **multicolored** tagged (53,005,000) .25 .20 ☐☐☐☐☐

CM722_____

  8¢ **multicolored** tagged (159,775,000) .25 .20 ☐☐☐☐☐

CM723_____

  15¢ **multicolored** tagged (39,005,000) .25 .20 ☐☐☐☐☐

CM724_____ **1973. Robinson Jeffers Issue**

  8¢ **multicolored** tagged (128,048,000) .25 .20 ☐☐☐☐☐

CM725_____ **1973. Lyndon B. Johnson Issue**

  8¢ **multicolored** (152,624,000) .25 .20 ☐☐☐☐☐

CM726_____ **1973. Henry O. Tanner Issue**

  8¢ **multicolored** tagged (146,008,000) .25 .20 ☐☐☐☐☐

CM727_____ **1973. Willa Cather Issue**

  8¢ **multicolored** tagged (139,608,000) .25 .20 ☐☐☐☐☐

CM728_____ **1973. Angus Cattle Issue**

  8¢ **multicolored** tagged (145,430,000) .25 .20 ☐☐☐☐☐

CM729_____ **1974. Veterans of Foreign Wars Issue**

  10¢ **red & blue** tagged (145,430,000) .25 .20 ☐☐☐☐☐

CM730_____ **1974. Robert Frost Issue**

  10¢ **black** tagged (145,235,000) .25 .20 ☐☐☐☐☐

CM731_____ **1974. Expo 74 World's Fair Issue**

  10¢ **multicolored** tagged (135,052,000) .25 .20 ☐☐☐☐☐

CM732_____ **1974. Horse Racing Issue**

  10¢ **multicolored** tagged (156,750,000) .25 .20 ☐☐☐☐☐

CM733_____ **1974. Skylab Project Issue**

  10¢ **multicolored** tagged (164,670,000) .25 .20 ☐☐☐☐☐

CM734_____ **1974. Universal Postal Union Issue**

  10¢ **multicolored** tagged (190,154,680) .25 .20 ☐☐☐☐☐

CM735_____

  10¢ **multicolored** tagged .25 .20 ☐☐☐☐☐

CM736_____

  10¢ **multicolored** tagged .25 .20 ☐☐☐☐☐

CM737_____

  10¢ **multicolored** tagged .25 .20 ☐☐☐☐☐

CM738_____

  10¢ **multicolored** tagged .25 .20 ☐☐☐☐☐

CM739_____

  10¢ **multicolored** tagged .25 .20 ☐☐☐☐☐

CM740_____

  10¢ **multicolored** tagged .25 .20 ☐☐☐☐☐

CM741_____

  10¢ **multicolored** tagged .25 .20 ☐☐☐☐☐

CM706-715

Harry S. Truman

U.S. Postage 8 cents

CM717-720

CM716

CM721

CM722

CM723

CM724

CM725

CM726

CM727

CM728

CM729

CM730

	MNHVF	UseVF	

CM742_____   1974. Mineral Heritage Issue

10¢ **multicolored** tagged (167,212,800)   .25   .20 ☐☐☐☐☐

CM743_____

10¢ **multicolored** tagged   .25   .20 ☐☐☐☐☐

CM744_____

10¢ **multicolored** tagged   .25   .20 ☐☐☐☐☐

CM745_____

10¢ **multicolored** tagged   .25   .20 ☐☐☐☐☐

CM746_____   1974. Settlement of Kentucky Issue

10¢ **multicolored** tagged (156,265,000)   .25   .20 ☐☐☐☐☐

CM747_____   1974. First Continental Congress Issue

10¢ **dark blue & red** tagged (195,585,000)   .25   .20 ☐☐☐☐☐

CM748_____

10¢ **red & dark blue** tagged   .25   .20 ☐☐☐☐☐

CM749_____

10¢ **gray, dark blue & red** tagged   .25   .20 ☐☐☐☐☐

CM750_____

10¢ **gray, dark blue & red** tagged   .25   .20 ☐☐☐☐☐

CM751_____   1974. Chautauqua Tent Issue

10¢ **multicolored** tagged (151,335,000)   .25   .20 ☐☐☐☐☐

CM731

CM732

CM733

CM734-741

CM742-745

CM746

CM751

CM752

CM753

CM754

CM747-750

PIONEER ★ JUPITER

CM757

Retarded Children
Can Be Helped

CM755

CM756

CM758

Sybil Ludington Youthful Heroine

CM759

Salem Poor Gallant Soldier

CM760

Haym Salomon Financial Hero

CM761

Peter Francisco Fighter Extraordinary

CM762

	MNHVF	UseVF

CM752_____   **1974. Winter Wheat and Train Issue**
　　10¢ **multicolored** tagged (141,085,000) .25 .20 ☐☐☐☐☐
CM753_____   **1974. Energy Conservation Issue**
　　10¢ **multicolored** tagged (148,850,000) .25 .20 ☐☐☐☐☐
CM754_____   **1974. Legend of Sleepy Hollow Issue**
　　10¢ **dark blue, black, orange, & yellow** tagged (157,270,000) .25 .20 ☐☐☐☐☐
CM755_____   **1974. Help for Retarded Children Issue**
　　10¢ **light & dark brown** tagged (150,245,000) .25 .20 ☐☐☐☐☐
CM756_____   **1975. Benjamin West Issue**
　　10¢ **multicolored** tagged (156,995,000) .25 .20 ☐☐☐☐☐
CM757_____   **1975. Pioneer Space Issue**
　　10¢ **dark blue, yellow & red** tagged (173,685,000) .25 .20 ☐☐☐☐☐
NOTE: Imperforate varieties came from printer's waste.
CM758_____   **1975. Collective Bargaining Issue**
　　10¢ **multicolored** tagged (153,355,000) .25 .20 ☐☐☐☐☐
NOTE: Imperforate varieties came from printer's waste.
CM759_____   **1975. Contributors to the Cause Issue**
　　10¢ **multicolored** tagged (63,205,000) .25 .20 ☐☐☐☐☐
CM760_____
　　10¢ **multicolored** tagged (157,865,000) .25 .20 ☐☐☐☐☐
CM761_____
　　10¢ **multicolored** tagged (166,810,000) .25 .20 ☐☐☐☐☐
CM762_____
　　18¢ **multicolored** tagged (44,825,000) .25 .20 ☐☐☐☐☐
CM763_____   **1975. Mariner Space Issue**
　　10¢ **black, red, ultramarine & bister** tagged (158,600,000) .25 .20 ☐☐☐☐☐
CM764_____   **1975. Lexington and Concord Issue**
　　10¢ **multicolored** tagged (114,028,000) .25 .20 ☐☐☐☐☐
CM765_____   **1975. Paul Laurence Dunbar Issue**
　　10¢ **multicolored** tagged (146,365,000) .25 .20 ☐☐☐☐☐
CM766_____   **1975. D.W. Griffith Issue**
　　10¢ **multicolored** tagged (148,805,000) .25 .20 ☐☐☐☐☐
CM767_____   **1975. Bunker Hill Issue**
　　10¢ **multicolored** tagged (139,928,000) .25 .20 ☐☐☐☐☐
CM768_____   **1975. Military Services Bicentennial Issue**
　　10¢ **multicolored** tagged (179,855,000) .25 .20 ☐☐☐☐☐
CM769_____
　　10¢ **multicolored** tagged .25 .20 ☐☐☐☐☐
CM770_____
　　10¢ **multicolored** tagged .25 .20 ☐☐☐☐☐
CM771_____
　　10¢ **multicolored** tagged .25 .20 ☐☐☐☐☐
CM772_____   **1975. Apollo Soyuz Issue**
　　10¢ **multicolored** tagged (161,863,200) .25 .20 ☐☐☐☐☐
CM773_____
　　10¢ **multicolored** tagged .25 .20 ☐☐☐☐☐
CM774_____   **1975. World Peace Through Law Issue**
　　10¢ **green, gray blue & brown** tagged (146,615,000) .25 .20 ☐☐☐☐☐
CM775_____   **1975. International Women's Year Issue**
　　10¢ **blue, orange & dark blue** tagged (145,640,000) .25 .20 ☐☐☐☐☐
CM776_____   **1975. U.S. Postal Service Bicentennial Issue**
　　10¢ **multicolored** tagged (168,655,000) .25 .20 ☐☐☐☐☐
CM777_____
　　10¢ **multicolored** tagged .25 .20 ☐☐☐☐☐

CM763

Lexington & Concord 1775 by Sandham
US Bicentennial IOcents

CM764

Paul Laurence
Dunbar

American poet

CM765 ➤ 10 cents U.S. postage

CM766

CM767 ➤ Bunker Hill 1775 by Trumbull
US Bicentennial IOc

CM772

CONTINENTAL ARMY | CONTINENTAL NAVY
CONTINENTAL MARINES | AMERICAN MILITIA

CM768-771 ➤

CM773

World
Peace
through
LAW

USA
10c

CM774

USA
10c
INTERNATIONAL WOMEN'S YEAR

CM775

CM776-779

	MNHVF	UseVF	

CM778_____
  10¢ **multicolored** tagged .25 .20 ⬜⬜⬜⬜⬜
CM779_____
  10¢ **multicolored** tagged .25 .20 ⬜⬜⬜⬜⬜
CM780_____ **1975. Banking and Commerce Issue**
  10¢ **multicolored** tagged (146,196,000) .25 .20 ⬜⬜⬜⬜⬜
CM781_____
  10¢ **multicolored** tagged .25 .20 ⬜⬜⬜⬜⬜
CM782_____ **1976. Spirit of 76 Issue**
  13¢ **multicolored** tagged (219,455,000) .25 .20 ⬜⬜⬜⬜⬜
CM783_____
  13¢ **multicolored** tagged .25 .20 ⬜⬜⬜⬜⬜
CM784_____
  13¢ **multicolored** tagged .25 .20 ⬜⬜⬜⬜⬜
CM785_____ **1976. INTERPHIL Issue**
  13¢ **blue, red & ultramarine** tagged (157,825,000) .25 .20 ⬜⬜⬜⬜⬜
CM786_____ **1976. 50-State Flag Issue**
  13¢ **Delaware,** tagged (436,005,000) .55 .40 ⬜⬜⬜⬜⬜
CM787_____
  13¢ **Pennsylvania,** tagged .55 .40 ⬜⬜⬜⬜⬜
CM788_____
  13¢ **New Jersey,** tagged .55 .40 ⬜⬜⬜⬜⬜
CM789_____
  13¢ **Georgia,** tagged .55 .40 ⬜⬜⬜⬜⬜
CM790_____
  13¢ **Connecticut,** tagged .55 .40 ⬜⬜⬜⬜⬜
CM791_____
  13¢ **Massachusetts,** tagged .55 .40 ⬜⬜⬜⬜⬜
CM792_____
  13¢ **Maryland,** tagged .55 .40 ⬜⬜⬜⬜⬜
CM793_____
  13¢ **South Carolina,** tagged .55 .40 ⬜⬜⬜⬜⬜
CM794_____
  13¢ **New Hampshire,** tagged .55 .40 ⬜⬜⬜⬜⬜
CM795_____
  13¢ **Virginia,** tagged .55 .40 ⬜⬜⬜⬜⬜
CM796_____
  13¢ **New York,** tagged .55 .40 ⬜⬜⬜⬜⬜
CM797_____
  13¢ **North Carolina,** tagged .55 .40 ⬜⬜⬜⬜⬜
CM798_____
  13¢ **Rhode Island,** tagged .55 .40 ⬜⬜⬜⬜⬜
CM799_____
  13¢ **Vermont,** tagged .55 .40 ⬜⬜⬜⬜⬜
CM800_____
  13¢ **Kentucky,** tagged .55 .40 ⬜⬜⬜⬜⬜
CM801_____
  13¢ **Tennessee,** tagged .55 .40 ⬜⬜⬜⬜⬜
CM802_____
  13¢ **Ohio,** tagged .55 .40 ⬜⬜⬜⬜⬜
CM803_____
  13¢ **Louisiana,** tagged .55 .40 ⬜⬜⬜⬜⬜
CM804_____
  13¢ **Indiana,** tagged .55 .40 ⬜⬜⬜⬜⬜

CM780-781

CM782-784 ←

CM785

CM836

CM837

CM786-835

CM838

	MNHVF	UseVF
CM805_____		
13¢ **Mississippi,** tagged	.55	.40 ❑❑❑❑❑
CM806_____		
13¢ **Illinois,** tagged	.55	.40 ❑❑❑❑❑
CM807_____		
13¢ **Alabama,** tagged	.55	.40 ❑❑❑❑❑
CM808_____		
13¢ **Maine,** tagged	.55	.40 ❑❑❑❑❑
CM809_____		
13¢ **Missouri,** tagged	.55	.40 ❑❑❑❑❑
CM810_____		
13¢ **Arkansas,** tagged	.55	.40 ❑❑❑❑❑
CM811_____		
13¢ **Michigan,** tagged	.55	.40 ❑❑❑❑❑
CM812_____		
13¢ **Florida,** tagged	.55	.40 ❑❑❑❑❑
CM813_____		
13¢ **Texas,** tagged	.55	.40 ❑❑❑❑❑
CM814_____		
13¢ **Iowa,** tagged	.55	.40 ❑❑❑❑❑
CM815_____		
13¢ **Wisconsin,** tagged	.55	.40 ❑❑❑❑❑
CM816_____		
13¢ **California,** tagged	.55	.40 ❑❑❑❑❑
CM817_____		
13¢ **Minnesota,** tagged	.55	.40 ❑❑❑❑❑
CM818_____		
13¢ **Oregon,** tagged	.55	.40 ❑❑❑❑❑
CM819_____		
13¢ **Kansas,** tagged	.55	.40 ❑❑❑❑❑
CM820_____		
13¢ **West Virginia,** tagged	.55	.40 ❑❑❑❑❑
CM821_____		
13¢ **Nevada,** tagged	.55	.40 ❑❑❑❑❑
CM822_____		
13¢ **Nebraska,** tagged	.55	.40 ❑❑❑❑❑
CM823_____		
13¢ **Colorado,** tagged	.55	.40 ❑❑❑❑❑
CM824_____		
13¢ **North Dakota,** tagged	.55	.40 ❑❑❑❑❑
CM825_____		
13¢ **South Dakota,** tagged	.55	.40 ❑❑❑❑❑
CM826_____		
13¢ **Montana,** tagged	.55	.40 ❑❑❑❑❑
CM827_____		
13¢ **Washington,** tagged	.55	.40 ❑❑❑❑❑
CM828_____		
13¢ **Idaho,** tagged	.55	.40 ❑❑❑❑❑
CM829_____		
13¢ **Wyoming,** tagged	.55	.40 ❑❑❑❑❑
CM830_____		
13¢ **Utah,** tagged	.55	.40 ❑❑❑❑❑
CM831_____		
13¢ **Oklahoma,** tagged	.55	.40 ❑❑❑❑❑

CM839

CM840

CM841

CM842

CM843

CM844-847

CM848-851

CM852

CM853

	MNHVF	UseVF

CM832_____
13¢ **New Mexico,** tagged ... .55 .40 ▢▢▢▢▢
CM833_____
13¢ **Arizona,** tagged ... .55 .40 ▢▢▢▢▢
CM834_____
13¢ **Alaska,** tagged ... .55 .40 ▢▢▢▢▢
CM835_____
13¢ **Hawaii,** tagged ... .55 .40 ▢▢▢▢▢
CM836_____ **1976. Telephone Centennial Issue**
13¢ **black, purple & red,** on tan paper, tagged (159,915,000) ... .25 .20 ▢▢▢▢▢
CM837_____ **1976. Commercial Aviation Issue**
13¢ **multicolored** tagged (156,960,000) ... .25 .20 ▢▢▢▢▢
CM838_____ **1976. Chemistry Issue**
13¢ **multicolored** tagged (158,470,000) ... .25 .20 ▢▢▢▢▢
CM839_____ **1976. Bicentennial Souvenir Sheets**
65¢ **multicolored** tagged (1,990,500) ... 4.75 4.50 ▢▢▢▢▢
CM840_____
90¢ **multicolored** tagged (1,983,000) ... 6.00 5.75 ▢▢▢▢▢
CM841_____
$1.20 **multicolored** tagged (1,953,000) ... 8.25 8.00 ▢▢▢▢▢
CM842_____
$1.55 **multicolored** tagged (1,903,000) ... 10.75 10.50 ▢▢▢▢▢
CM843_____ **1976. Benjamin Franklin Issue**
13¢ **multicolored** tagged (164,890,000) ... .25 .20 ▢▢▢▢▢
CM844_____ **1976. Declaration of Independence Issue**
13¢ **multicolored** tagged (208,035,000) ... .25 .20 ▢▢▢▢▢
CM845_____
13¢ **multicolored** tagged ... .25 .20 ▢▢▢▢▢
CM846_____
13¢ **multicolored** tagged ... .25 .20 ▢▢▢▢▢
CM847_____
13¢ **multicolored** tagged ... .25 .20 ▢▢▢▢▢
CM848_____ **1976. Olympic Games Issue**
13¢ **multicolored** tagged (185,715,000) ... .25 .20 ▢▢▢▢▢
CM849_____
13¢ **multicolored** tagged ... .25 .20 ▢▢▢▢▢
CM850_____
13¢ **multicolored** tagged ... .25 .20 ▢▢▢▢▢
CM851_____
13¢ **multicolored** tagged ... .25 .20 ▢▢▢▢▢
CM852_____ **1976. Clara Maass Issue**
13¢ **multicolored** tagged (130,592,000) ... .25 .20 ▢▢▢▢▢
CM853_____ **1976. Adolph S. Ochs Issue**
13¢ **gray & black** tagged (158,332,800) ... .25 .20 ▢▢▢▢▢
CM854_____ **1977. Washington at Princeton Issue**
13¢ **multicolored** tagged (150,328,000) ... .25 .20 ▢▢▢▢▢
CM855_____ **1977. Sound Recording Issue**
13¢ **multicolored** tagged (176,830,000) ... .25 .20 ▢▢▢▢▢
CM856_____ **1977. Pueblo Indian Art Issue**
13¢ **multicolored** tagged (195,976,000) ... .25 .20 ▢▢▢▢▢
CM857_____
13¢ **multicolored** tagged ... .25 .20 ▢▢▢▢▢
CM858_____
13¢ **multicolored** tagged ... .25 .20 ▢▢▢▢▢

Washington at Princeton 1777 by Peale
US Bicentennial 13c

CM854

CM855

Zia: Museum of New Mexico
Pueblo Art USA 13c

San Ildefonso: Denver Art Museum
Pueblo Art USA 13c

Hopi: Heard Museum Phoenix
Pueblo Art USA 13c

Acoma: School of American Research
Pueblo Art USA 13c

CM856-859

USA·13c
50th Anniversary Solo Transatlantic Flight

CM860

COLORADO
13c usa
THE CENTENNIAL STATE

CM861

SA13c Papilio oregonius   USA13c Euphydryas phaet
Checkerspot
SA13c Colias eurydice   USA13c Anthocaris mide
Orange-Tip

CM862-865

Lafayette
US Bicentennial 13c

CM866

United States & Canada
Peace Bridge 1927-77
USA13c

CM871

the SEAMSTRESS for INDEPENDENCE USA 13c
the BLACKSMITH for INDEPENDENCE USA 13c
the WHEELWRIGHT for INDEPENDENCE USA 13c
the LEATHERWORKER for INDEPENDENCE USA 13c

CM867-870

Herkimer at Oriskany 1777 by Yohn
US Bicentennial 13 cents

CM872

First Civil Settlement·Alta California·1777

CM873

Drafting the Articles of Confederation
York Town, Pennsylvania 1777 13c USA

CM874

CM875

	MNHVF	UseVF

CM859_____
13¢ **multicolored** tagged   .25   .20 ☐☐☐☐☐
CM860_____   **1977. 50th Anniversary of Transatlantic Flight Issue**
13¢ **multicolored** tagged (208,820,000)   .25   .20 ☐☐☐☐☐
NOTE: Privately applied overprints on this stamp have no official status.
CM861_____   **1977. Colorado Statehood Issue**
13¢ **multicolored** tagged (190,005,000)   .25   .20 ☐☐☐☐☐
CM862_____   **1977. Butterfly Issue**
13¢ **multicolored** tagged (219,830,000)   .25   .20 ☐☐☐☐☐
CM863_____
13¢ **multicolored** tagged   .25   .20 ☐☐☐☐☐
CM864_____
13¢ **multicolored** tagged   .25   .20 ☐☐☐☐☐
CM865_____
13¢ **multicolored** tagged   .25   .20 ☐☐☐☐☐
CM866_____   **1977. Lafayette Issue**
13¢ **blue, black & red** (159,852,000)   .25   .20 ☐☐☐☐☐
CM867_____   **1977. Skilled Hands of Independence Issue**
13¢ **multicolored** tagged (188,310,000)   .25   .20 ☐☐☐☐☐
CM868_____
13¢ **multicolored** tagged   .25   .20 ☐☐☐☐☐
CM869_____
13¢ **multicolored** tagged   .25   .20 ☐☐☐☐☐
CM870_____
13¢ **multicolored**   .25   .20 ☐☐☐☐☐
CM871_____   **1977. Peace Bridge Issue**
13¢ **blue** tagged (163,625,000)   .25   .20 ☐☐☐☐☐
CM872_____   **1977. Herkimer at Oriskany Issue**
13¢ **multicolored** tagged (156,296,000)   .25   .20 ☐☐☐☐☐
CM873_____   **1977. Alta California Issue**
13¢ **multicolored** tagged (154,495,000)   .25   .20 ☐☐☐☐☐
CM874_____   **1977. Articles of Confederation Issue**
13¢ **red & dark brown** on cream paper, tagged (168,050,000)   .25   .20 ☐☐☐☐☐
CM875_____   **1977. Talking Pictures Issue**
13¢ **multicolored** tagged (156,810,000)   .25   .20 ☐☐☐☐☐
CM876_____   **1977. Surrender at Saratoga**
13¢ **multicolored** (153,736,000)   .25   .20 ☐☐☐☐☐
CM876A _____   **1977. Energy Issue**
13¢ **multicolored** tagged   .25   .20 ☐☐☐☐☐
CM876B _____
13¢ **multicolored** tagged   .25   .20 ☐☐☐☐☐
CM877_____   **1978. Carl Sandburg Issue**
13¢ **brown & black** tagged (156,560,000)   .25   .20 ☐☐☐☐☐
CM878_____   **1978. Captain Cook Issue**
13¢ **blue** tagged (202,155,000)   .25   .20 ☐☐☐☐☐
CM879_____
13¢ **green** tagged   .25   .20 ☐☐☐☐☐
CM880_____   **1978. Harriet Tubman Issue**
13¢ **multicolored** tagged (156,525,000)   .25   .20 ☐☐☐☐☐
CM881_____   **1978. American Quilts Issue**
13¢ **multicolored** tagged (165,182,000)   .25   .20 ☐☐☐☐☐
CM882_____
13¢ **multicolored** tagged   .25   .20 ☐☐☐☐☐

Surrender at Saratoga 1777 by Trumbull
US Bicentennial I3 cents

CM876

CM878-879

CM876A-876B

USA I3c

CM877

Harriet Tubman

Black Heritage USA 13c

CM880

CM881-884

CM890

CM885-888

French Alliance 1778

US Bicentennial I3c

CM889

CM891

Canadian International Philatelic Exhibition
Toronto

CM892

Photography USA 15c

CM893

	MNHVF	UseVF

CM883_____

13¢ **multicolored** tagged ... .25 ... .20 ☐☐☐☐☐

CM884_____

13¢ **multicolored** tagged ... .25 ... .20 ☐☐☐☐☐

CM885_____ **1978. American Dance Issue**

13¢ **multicolored** tagged (157,598,400) ... .25 ... .20 ☐☐☐☐☐

CM886_____

13¢ **multicolored** tagged ... .25 ... .20 ☐☐☐☐☐

CM887_____

13¢ **multicolored** tagged ... .25 ... .20 ☐☐☐☐☐

CM888_____

13¢ **multicolored** tagged ... .25 ... .20 ☐☐☐☐☐

CM889_____ **1978. French Alliance Issue**

13¢ **blue, black, & red** tagged (102,856,000) ... .25 ... .20 ☐☐☐☐☐

CM890_____ **1978. George Papanicolaou Issue**

13¢ **brown** tagged (152,270,000) ... .25 ... .20 ☐☐☐☐☐

CM891_____ **1978. Jimmie Rodgers Issue**

13¢ **multicolored** tagged (94,600,000) ... .25 ... .20 ☐☐☐☐☐

CM892_____ **1978. Canadian International Philatelic Exhibition**

$1.04 **multicolored** (10,400,000) ... 2.75 ... 2.00 ☐☐☐☐☐

CM893_____ **1978. Photography Issue**

15¢ **multicolored** tagged (161,228,000) ... .30 ... .20 ☐☐☐☐☐

CM894_____ **1978. George M. Cohan Issue**

15¢ **multicolored** tagged (151,570,000) ... .30 ... .20 ☐☐☐☐☐

CM895_____ **1978. Viking Missions Issue**

15¢ **multicolored** tagged (158,880,000) ... .30 ... .20 ☐☐☐☐☐

CM896_____ **1978. Wildlife Conservation Issue**

15¢ **Great Gray Owl,** tagged (186,550,000) ... .30 ... .20 ☐☐☐☐☐

CM897_____

15¢ **Saw Whet Owl,** tagged ... .30 ... .20 ☐☐☐☐☐

CM898_____

15¢ **Barred Owl,** tagged ... .30 ... .20 ☐☐☐☐☐

CM899_____

15¢ **Great Horned Owl,** tagged ... .30 ... .20 ☐☐☐☐☐

CM900_____ **1978. American Trees Issue**

15¢ **Giant Sequoia,** tagged (168,136,000) ... .30 ... .20 ☐☐☐☐☐

CM901_____

15¢ **Eastern White Pine,** tagged ... .30 ... .20 ☐☐☐☐☐

CM902_____

15¢ **White Oak,** tagged ... .30 ... .20 ☐☐☐☐☐

CM903_____

15¢ **Gray Birch,** tagged ... .30 ... .20 ☐☐☐☐☐

CM904_____ **1979. Robert F. Kennedy Issue**

15¢ **blue** tagged (159,297,000) ... .30 ... .20 ☐☐☐☐☐

CM905_____ **1979. Martin Luther King Jr. Issue**

15¢ **multicolored** tagged (166,435,000) ... .30 ... .20 ☐☐☐☐☐

CM906_____ **1979. International Year of the Child Issue**

15¢ **light & dark brown** tagged (162,535,000) ... .30 ... .20 ☐☐☐☐☐

CM907_____ **1979. John Steinbeck Issue**

15¢ **dark blue** tagged (155,000,000) ... .30 ... .20 ☐☐☐☐☐

CM908_____ **1979. Albert Einstein Issue**

15¢ **brown** tagged (157,310,000) ... .30 ... .20 ☐☐☐☐☐

CM909_____ **1979. Pennsylvania Toleware Issue**

15¢ **Coffee pot with straight spout** (174,096,000) ... .30 ... .20 ☐☐☐☐

CM894

CM895

CM896-899

CM900-903

CM904

CM905

CM906

CM907

CM908

CM909-912

CM913-916

CM917-920

	MNHVF	UseVF
CM910_____		
15¢ **Tea caddy**	.30	.20 ☐☐☐☐☐
CM911_____		
15¢ **Sugar bowl with lid**	.30	.20 ☐☐☐☐☐
CM912_____		
15¢ **Coffee pot with gooseneck spout**	.30	.20 ☐☐☐☐☐
CM913_____ **1979. American Architecture Issue**		
15¢ **University of Virginia Rotunda,** tagged (164,793,000)	.30	.20 ☐☐☐☐☐
CM914_____		
15¢ **Baltimore Cathedral,** tagged	.30	.20 ☐☐☐☐☐
CM915_____		
15¢ **Boston State House,** tagged	.30	.20 ☐☐☐☐☐
CM916_____		
15¢ **Philadelphia Exchange,** tagged	.30	.20 ☐☐☐☐☐
CM917_____ **1979. Endangered Flora Issue**		
15¢ **Persistent Trillium,** tagged (163,055,000)	.30	.20 ☐☐☐☐☐
CM918_____		
15¢ **Hawaiian Wild Broadbean,** tagged	.30	.20 ☐☐☐☐☐
CM919_____		
15¢ **Contra Costa Wallflower,** tagged	.30	.20 ☐☐☐☐☐
CM920_____		
15¢ **Antioch Dunes Evening Primrose,** tagged	.30	.20 ☐☐☐☐☐
CM921_____ **1979. Seeing Eye Dog Issue**		
15¢ **multicolored** tagged (161,860,000)	.30	.20 ☐☐☐☐☐
CM922_____ **1979. Special Olympics Issue**		
15¢ **multicolored** tagged (165,775,000)	.30	.20 ☐☐☐☐☐
CM923_____ **1979. Summer Games Issue**		
10¢ **multicolored** tagged (67,195,000)	.25	.25 ☐☐☐☐☐
CM924_____ **1979. John Paul Jones Issue**		
15¢ **multicolored** tagged (160,000,000, all perforation types)	.30	.20 ☐☐☐☐☐
NOTE: Imperforate errors are from printer's waste.		
CM924A _____		
15¢ **multicolored** tagged, perforated 11	.75	.25 ☐☐☐☐☐
CM924B _____		
15¢ **multicolored** tagged, perforated 12	2,800.00	1,000.00 ☐☐☐☐☐
CM925_____ **1979. Summer Games Issue**		
15¢ **Women runners,** tagged (186,905,000)	.25	.20 ☐☐☐☐☐
CM926_____		
15¢ **Women swimmers,** tagged	.25	.20 ☐☐☐☐☐
CM927_____		
15¢ **Pair of rowers,** tagged	.25	.20 ☐☐☐☐☐
CM928_____		
15¢ **Horse & Rider,** tagged	.25	.20 ☐☐☐☐☐
CM929_____ **1979. Will Rogers Issue**		
15¢ **multicolored** tagged (161,290,000)	.30	.20 ☐☐☐☐☐
CM930_____ **1979. Vietnam Veterans Issue**		
15¢ **multicolored** tagged (172,740,000)	.30	.20 ☐☐☐☐☐
CM931_____ **1980. W.C. Fields Issue**		
15¢ **multicolored** tagged (168,995,000)	.30	.20 ☐☐☐☐☐
CM932_____ **1980. Winter Games Issue**		
15¢ **Speed skater,** tagged (208,295,000) *(both perforation types)*	.30	.20 ☐☐☐☐☐
CM933_____		
15¢ **Ski jumper,** tagged	.30	.20 ☐☐☐☐☐

CM921

CM922

CM923

CM924

CM925-928

CM929

CM930

CM931

CM932-935
CM932A-935A

CM936

CM937-942

Frances Perkins
USA 15c

CM943

Emily Bissell
Crusader Against Tuberculosis
USA 15c

CM944

	MNHVF	UseVF

CM934_____

15¢ **Downhill skier,** tagged .30 .20 ☐☐☐☐☐

CM935_____

15¢ **Hockey goaltender,** tagged .30 .20 ☐☐☐☐☐

CM935A _____

15¢ **Speed Skater,** tagged .80 .75 ☐☐☐☐☐

CM935B _____

15¢ **Ski jumper,** tagged .80 .75 ☐☐☐☐☐

CM935C _____

15¢ **Downhill skier,** tagged .80 .75 ☐☐☐☐☐

CM935D _____

15¢ **Hockey goaltender,** tagged .80 .75 ☐☐☐☐☐

CM936_____   **1980. Benjamin Banneker Issue**

15¢ **multicolored** tagged (160,000,000) .30 .20 ☐☐☐☐☐

NOTE: Imperforates with misregistered colors are from printer's waste, have been fraudulently perforated to simulate CM936v. Genuine examples of this error have colors correctly registered. Expert certification recommended.

CM937_____   **1980. National Letter Writing Issue**

15¢ **"Letters Preserve Memories"** (232,134,000) .30 .20 ☐☐☐☐☐

CM938_____

15¢ **"Write Soon," (purple),** tagged .30 .20 ☐☐☐☐☐

CM939_____

15¢ **"Letters Lift Spirits,"** tagged .30 .20 ☐☐☐☐☐

CM940_____

15¢ **"Write Soon", (green),** tagged .30 .20 ☐☐☐☐☐

CM941_____

15¢ **"Letters Shape Opinions,"** tagged .30 .20 ☐☐☐☐☐

CM942_____

15¢ **"Write Soon," (red),** tagged .30 .20 ☐☐☐☐☐

CM943_____   **1980. Frances Perkins Issue**

15¢ **blue** tagged (163,510,000) .30 .20 ☐☐☐☐☐

CM944_____   **1980. Emily Bissell Issue**

15¢ **black & red** tagged (95,695,000) .30 .20 ☐☐☐☐☐

CM945_____   **1980. Helen Keller and Anne Sullivan Issue**

15¢ **multicolored** tagged (153,975,000) .30 .20 ☐☐☐☐☐

CM946_____   **1980. Veterans Administration Issue**

15¢ **red & dark blue** tagged (160,000,000) .30 .20 ☐☐☐☐☐

CM947_____   **1980. Bernardo de Galvez Issue**

15¢ **multicolored** tagged (103,850,000) .30 .20 ☐☐☐☐☐

CM948_____   **1980. Coral Reefs Issue**

15¢ **Brain Coral,** tagged (204,715,000) .30 .20 ☐☐☐☐☐

CM949_____

15¢ **Elkhorn Coral,** tagged .30 .20 ☐☐☐☐☐

CM950_____

15¢ **Chalice Coral,** tagged .30 .20 ☐☐☐☐☐

CM951_____

15¢ **Finger Coral,** tagged .30 .20 ☐☐☐☐☐

CM952_____   **1980. Organized Labor Issue**

15¢ **multicolored** tagged (166,545,000) .30 .20 ☐☐☐☐☐

CM953_____   **1980. Edith Wharton Issue**

15¢ **purple** tagged (163,310,000) .30 .20 ☐☐☐☐☐

CM954_____   **1980. Education in America Issue**

15¢ **multicolored** tagged (160,000,000) .30 .20 ☐☐☐☐☐

CM955_____   **1980. Pacific Northwest Masks Issue**

15¢ **Heiltsuk Bella Bella mask,** tagged (152,404,000) .30 .20 ☐☐☐☐☐

HELEN KELLER
ANNE SULLIVAN

CM945

CM946

CM947

CM948-951

Organized Labor
Proud and Free
USA 15c

CM952

CM953

Learning
never ends

CM954

CM955-958 ←

CM959-962

USA 15c
Everett Dirksen ← CM963

Black Heritage USA 15c ← CM964

CM965-968

	MNHVF	UseVF

CM956 _____
15¢ **Chikat Tlingit mask,** tagged — .30 — .20 ☐☐☐☐☐
CM957 _____
15¢ **Tlingit mask,** tagged — .30 — .20 ☐☐☐☐☐
CM958 _____
15¢ **Bella Coola mask,** tagged — .30 — .20 ☐☐☐☐☐
CM959 _____ **1980. American Architecture Issue**
15¢ **Smithsonian Institution,** tagged (152,720,000) — .30 — .20 ☐☐☐☐☐
CM960 _____
15¢ **Trinity Church,** tagged — .30 — .20 ☐☐☐☐☐
CM961 _____
15¢ **Pennsylvania Academy of the Fine Arts,** tagged — .30 — .20 ☐☐☐☐☐
CM962 _____
15¢ **Lyndhurst,** tagged — .30 — .20 ☐☐☐☐☐
CM963 _____ **1981. Everett Dirksen Issue**
15¢ **gray** tagged (160,155,000) — .30 — .20 ☐☐☐☐☐
CM964 _____ **1981. Whitney Moore Young Issue**
15¢ **multicolored** tagged (159,505,000) — .30 — .20 ☐☐☐☐☐
CM965 _____ **1981. Flower Issue**
18¢ **Rose,** tagged (210,633,000) — .30 — .20 ☐☐☐☐☐
CM966 _____
18¢ **Camellia,** tagged — .30 — .20 ☐☐☐☐☐
CM967 _____
18¢ **Dahlia,** tagged — .30 — .20 ☐☐☐☐☐
CM968 _____
18¢ **Lily,** tagged — .30 — .20 ☐☐☐☐☐
CM969 _____ **1981. American Red Cross Issue**
18¢ **multicolored** tagged (165,175,000) — .30 — .20 ☐☐☐☐☐
CM970 _____ **1981. Savings and Loan Issue**
18¢ **multicolored** tagged (107,240,000) — .30 — .20 ☐☐☐☐☐
CM971 _____ **1981. Space Achievement Issue**
18¢ **Astronaut on Moon,** tagged (337,819,000) — .30 — .20 ☐☐☐☐☐
CM972 _____
18¢ **Pioneer II & Saturn,** tagged — .30 — .20 ☐☐☐☐☐
CM973 _____
18¢ **Skylab & Sun,** tagged — .30 — .20 ☐☐☐☐☐
CM974 _____
18¢ **Hubble Space Telescope,** tagged — .30 — .20 ☐☐☐☐☐
CM975 _____
18¢ **Space Shuttle in orbit,** tagged — .30 — .20 ☐☐☐☐☐
CM976 _____
18¢ **Space Shuttle with arm deployed,** tagged — .30 — .20 ☐☐☐☐☐
CM977 _____
18¢ **Space Shuttle at launch,** tagged — .30 — .20 ☐☐☐☐☐
CM978 _____
18¢ **Space Shuttle at landing,** tagged — .30 — .20 ☐☐☐☐☐
CM979 _____ **1981. Professional Management Issue**
18¢ **blue & black** tagged (99,420,000) — .30 — .20 ☐☐☐☐☐
CM980 _____ **1981. Save Wildlife Habitats Issue**
18¢ **Blue heron,** tagged (178,930,000) — .30 — .20 ☐☐☐☐☐
CM981 _____
18¢ **Badger,** tagged — .30 — .20 ☐☐☐☐☐
CM982 _____
18¢ **Grizzly bear,** tagged — .30 — .20 ☐☐☐☐☐

CM969

CM970

CM971-978

CM979

CM984

CM980-983

CM986

CM985

CM991
→

CM987-990

CM992
→

	MNHVF	UseVF

CM983_____

18¢ **Ruffed grouse,** tagged | .30 | .20 ☐☐☐☐☐

CM984_____ **1981. Disabled Persons Issue**

18¢ **multicolored** tagged (100,265,000) | .30 | .20 ☐☐☐☐☐

CM985_____ **1981. Edna St. Vincent Millay Issue**

18¢ **multicolored** tagged (99,615,000) | .30 | .25 ☐☐☐☐☐

CM986_____ **1981. Beat Alcoholism Issue**

18¢ **blue & black** tagged (97,535,000) | .65 | .20 ☐☐☐☐☐

CM987_____ **1981. American Architecture Issue**

18¢ **N.Y. University Library,** tagged (167,308,000) | .30 | .20 ☐☐☐☐☐

CM988_____

18¢ **Biltmore House,** tagged | .30 | .20 ☐☐☐☐☐

CM989_____

18¢ **Palace of Arts,** tagged | .30 | .20 ☐☐☐☐☐

CM990_____

18¢ **National Farmers Bank Building,** tagged | .30 | .20 ☐☐☐☐☐

CM991_____ **1981. Bobby Jones Issue**

18¢ **green** tagged (99,170,000) | .30 | .20 ☐☐☐☐☐

CM992_____ **1981. (Mildred) Babe Zaharias Issue**

18¢ **light violet** tagged (101,625,000) | .30 | .20 ☐☐☐☐☐

CM993_____ **1981. Frederic Remington Issue**

18¢ **multicolored** tagged (101,155,000) | .30 | .20 ☐☐☐☐☐

CM994_____ **1981. James Hoban Issue**

18¢ **multicolored** tagged (101,200,000) | .30 | .20 ☐☐☐☐☐

CM995_____

20¢ **multicolored** tagged (167,360,000) | .30 | .20 ☐☐☐☐☐

CM996_____ **1981. Battle of Yorktown and the Virginia Capes Issue**

18¢ **multicolored** tagged (162,420,000) | .30 | .20 ☐☐☐☐☐

CM997_____

18¢ **multicolored** tagged | .30 | .20 ☐☐☐☐☐

CM998_____ **1981. John Hanson Issue**

20¢ **multicolored** tagged (167,130,000) | .30 | .20 ☐☐☐☐☐

CM999_____ **1981. Desert Plants Issue**

20¢ **Barrel cactus,** tagged (191,560,000) | .35 | .20 ☐☐☐☐☐

CM1000_____

20¢ **Agave,** tagged | .35 | .20 ☐☐☐☐☐

CM1001_____

20¢ **Beavertail cactus,** tagged | .35 | .20 ☐☐☐☐☐

CM1002_____

20¢ **Saguaro,** tagged | .35 | .20 ☐☐☐☐☐

CM1003_____ **1982. Franklin D. Roosevelt Issue**

20¢ **blue** tagged (163,939,200) | .35 | .20 ☐☐☐☐☐

CM1004_____ **1982. Love Issue**

20¢ **multicolored** tagged | .35 | .20 ☐☐☐☐☐

CM1004A _____

20¢ **multicolored** tagged, perforated 11 x 10 1/2 | 1.00 | .25 ☐☐☐☐☐

CM1005_____ **1982. George Washington Issue**

20¢ **multicolored** tagged (180,700,000) | .35 | .20 ☐☐☐☐☐

CM1006_____ **1982. State Birds and Flowers**

20¢ **Alabama, multicolored,** tagged (666,950,000) | 1.00 | .50 ☐☐☐☐☐

CM1007_____

20¢ **Alaska, multicolored,** tagged | 1.00 | .50 ☐☐☐☐☐

CM1008_____

20¢ **Arizona, multicolored,** tagged | 1.00 | .50 ☐☐☐☐☐

CM1009_____
  20¢ **Arkansas, multicolored,** tagged   1.00   .50 ☐☐☐☐☐
CM1010_____
  20¢ **California, multicolored,** tagged   1.00   .50 ☐☐☐☐☐
CM1011_____
  20¢ **Colorado, multicolored,** tagged   1.00   .50 ☐☐☐☐☐
CM1012_____
  20¢ **Connecticut, multicolored,** tagged   1.00   .50 ☐☐☐☐☐
CM1013_____
  20¢ **Delaware, multicolored,** tagged   1.00   .50 ☐☐☐☐☐

CM993

CM994

CM995

CM996-997

CM998

CM999-1002

CM1003

CM1004

CM1005

	MNHVF	UseVF

CM1014_____
20¢ **Florida, multicolored,** tagged .... 1.00 .50 ☐☐☐☐☐
CM1015_____
20¢ **Georgia, multicolored,** tagged .... 1.00 .50 ☐☐☐☐☐
CM1016_____
20¢ **Hawaii, multicolored,** tagged .... 1.00 .50 ☐☐☐☐☐
CM1017_____
20¢ **Idaho, multicolored,** tagged .... 1.00 .50 ☐☐☐☐☐
CM1018_____
20¢ **Illinois, multicolored,** tagged .... 1.00 .50 ☐☐☐☐☐
CM1019_____
20¢ **Indiana, multicolored,** tagged .... 1.00 .50 ☐☐☐☐☐
CM1020_____
20¢ **Iowa, multicolored,** tagged .... 1.00 .50 ☐☐☐☐☐
CM1021_____
20¢ **Kansas, multicolored,** tagged .... 1.00 .50 ☐☐☐☐☐
CM1022_____
20¢ **Kentucky, multicolored,** tagged .... 1.00 .50 ☐☐☐☐☐
CM1023_____
20¢ **Louisiana, multicolored,** tagged .... 1.00 .50 ☐☐☐☐☐
CM1024_____
20¢ **Maine, multicolored,** tagged .... 1.00 .50 ☐☐☐☐☐
CM1025_____
20¢ **Maryland, multicolored,** tagged .... 1.00 .50 ☐☐☐☐☐
CM1026_____
20¢ **Massachusetts, multicolored,** tagged .... 1.00 .50 ☐☐☐☐☐
CM1027_____
20¢ **Michigan, multicolored,** tagged .... 1.00 .50 ☐☐☐☐☐
CM1028_____
20¢ **Minnesota, multicolored,** tagged .... 1.00 .50 ☐☐☐☐☐
CM1029_____
20¢ **Mississippi, multicolored,** tagged .... 1.00 .50 ☐☐☐☐☐
CM1030_____
20¢ **Missouri, multicolored,** tagged .... 1.00 .50 ☐☐☐☐☐
CM1031_____
20¢ **Montana, multicolored,** tagged .... 1.00 .50 ☐☐☐☐☐
CM1032_____
20¢ **Nebraska, multicolored,** tagged .... 1.00 .50 ☐☐☐☐☐
CM1033_____
20¢ **Nevada, multicolored,** tagged .... 1.00 .50 ☐☐☐☐☐
CM1034_____
20¢ **New Hampshire, multicolored,** tagged .... 1.00 .50 ☐☐☐☐☐
CM1035_____
20¢ **New Jersey, multicolored,** tagged .... 1.00 .50 ☐☐☐☐☐
CM1036_____
20¢ **New Mexico, multicolored,** tagged .... 1.00 .50 ☐☐☐☐☐
CM1037_____
20¢ **New York, multicolored,** tagged .... 1.00 .50 ☐☐☐☐☐
CM1038_____
20¢ **North Carolina, multicolored,** tagged .... 1.00 .50 ☐☐☐☐☐
CM1039_____
20¢ **North Dakota, multicolored,** tagged .... 1.00 .50 ☐☐☐☐☐
CM1040_____
20¢ **Ohio, multicolored,** tagged .... 1.00 .50 ☐☐☐☐☐

CM1006v-1055v

CM1056

CM1058-1061

CM1057

CM1062

CM1063

	MNHVF	UseVF

CM1041_____

20¢ **Oklahoma, multicolored,** tagged — 1.00 — .50 ☐☐☐☐☐

CM1042_____

20¢ **Oregon, multicolored,** tagged — 1.00 — .50 ☐☐☐☐☐

CM1043_____

20¢ **Pennsylvania, multicolored,** tagged — 1.00 — .50 ☐☐☐☐☐

CM1044_____

20¢ **Rhode Island, multicolored,** tagged — 1.00 — .50 ☐☐☐☐☐

CM1045_____

20¢ **South Carolina, multicolored,** tagged — 1.00 — .50 ☐☐☐☐☐

CM1046_____

20¢ **South Dakota, multicolored,** tagged — 1.00 — .50 ☐☐☐☐☐

CM1047_____

20¢ **Tennessee, multicolored,** tagged — 1.00 — .50 ☐☐☐☐☐

CM1048_____

20¢ **Texas multicolored,** tagged — 1.00 — .50 ☐☐☐☐☐

CM1049_____

20¢ **Utah, multicolored,** tagged — 1.00 — .50 ☐☐☐☐☐

CM1050_____

20¢ **Vermont, multicolored,** tagged — 1.00 — .50 ☐☐☐☐☐

CM1051_____

20¢ **Virginia, multicolored,** tagged — 1.00 — .50 ☐☐☐☐☐

CM1052_____

20¢ **Washington, multicolored,** tagged — 1.00 — .50 ☐☐☐☐☐

CM1053_____

20¢ **West Virginia, multicolored,** tagged — 1.00 — .50 ☐☐☐☐☐

CM1054_____

20¢ **Wisconsin, multicolored,** tagged — 1.00 — .50 ☐☐☐☐☐

CM1055_____

20¢ **Wyoming, multicolored,** tagged — 1.00 — .50 ☐☐☐☐☐

NOTE: *Because most plate block collectors consider that a plate block contains at least one copy of each stamp in the issue, a plate block of the State Birds and Flowers Issue is considered to be a full pane of 50 stamps.*

CM1056_____   **1982. Netherlands Issue**

20¢ **orange, red, blue & dark gray** tagged (109,245,000) — .35 — .20 ☐☐☐☐☐

CM1057_____   **1982. Library of Congress Issue**

20¢ **black & red** tagged (112,535,000) — .35 — .20 ☐☐☐☐☐

CM1058_____   **1982. Knoxville World's Fair Issue**

20¢ **Solar energy,** tagged (124,640,000) — .35 — .20 ☐☐☐☐☐

CM1059_____

20¢ **Synthetic fuels,** tagged — .35 — .20 ☐☐☐☐☐

CM1060_____

20¢ **Breeder reactor,** tagged — .35 — .20 ☐☐☐☐☐

CM1061_____

20¢ **Fossil fuels,** tagged — .35 — .20 ☐☐☐☐☐

CM1062_____   **1982. Horatio Alger Issue**

20¢ **red & black** on tan paper tagged (107,605,000) — .35 — .20 ☐☐☐☐☐

CM1063_____   **1982. Aging Together Issue**

20¢ **brown** tagged (173,160,000) — .35 — .20 ☐☐☐☐☐

CM1064_____   **1982. Barrymore Family Issue**

20¢ **multicolored** tagged (107,285,000) — .35 — .20 ☐☐☐☐☐

CM1065_____   **1982. Mary Walker Issue**

20¢ **multicolored** tagged (109,040,000) — .35 — .20 ☐☐☐☐☐

CM1066_____   **1982. International Peace Garden Issue**

20¢ **multicolored** tagged (183,270,000) — .35 — .20 ☐☐☐☐☐

	MNHVF	UseVF

CM1067_____ **1982. America's Libraries Issue**
 20¢ **red & black** tagged (169,495,000)   .35   .20 ☐☐☐☐☐
CM1068_____ **1982. Jackie Robinson Issue**
 20¢ **multicolored** tagged (164,235,000)   2.50   .20 ☐☐☐☐☐
CM1069_____ **1982. Touro Synagogue Issue**
 20¢ **multicolored** tagged (110,130,000)   .35   .20 ☐☐☐☐☐
CM1070_____ **1982. Wolf Trap Farm Issue**
 20¢ **multicolored** tagged (110,995,000)   .35   .20 ☐☐☐☐☐
CM1071_____ **1982. American Architecture Issue**
 20¢ **Falling Water,** tagged (165,340,000)   .35   .20 ☐☐☐☐☐
CM1072_____
 20¢ **Illinois Institute of Technology,** tagged   .35   .20 ☐☐☐☐☐
CM1073_____
 20¢ **Gropius House,** tagged   .35   .20 ☐☐☐☐☐
CM1074_____
 20¢ **Washington International Airport,** tagged   .35   .20 ☐☐☐☐☐

CM1064

CM1065

CM1066

CM1067

CM1068

CM1069

CM1071-1074

CM1070

CM1075

CM1076

CM1077

	MNHVF	UseVF	

CM1075_____   **1982. Francis of Assisi Issue**
20¢ **multicolored** tagged (174,180,000) .35 .20 ☐☐☐☐☐

CM1076_____   **1982. Ponce de Leon Issue**
20¢ **multicolored** tagged (110,261,000) .35 .20 ☐☐☐☐☐

CM1077_____   **1983. Science and Industry Issue**
20¢ **multicolored** tagged (118,555,000) .35 .20 ☐☐☐☐☐

CM1078_____   **1983. Sweden Issue**
20¢ **multicolored** tagged (118,225,000) .30 .20 ☐☐☐☐☐

CM1079_____   **1983. Ballooning Issue**
20¢ *Intrepid,* tagged (226,128,000) .35 .20 ☐☐☐☐☐

CM1080_____
20¢ **Hot air ballooning,** tagged .35 .20 ☐☐☐☐☐

CM1081_____
20¢ **Hot air ballooning,** tagged .35 .20 ☐☐☐☐☐

CM1082_____
20¢ *Explorer II,* tagged .35 .20 ☐☐☐☐☐

CM1083_____   **1983. Civilian Conservation Corps Issue**
20¢ **multicolored** tagged (114,290,000) .35 .20 ☐☐☐☐☐

CM1084_____   **1983. Joseph Priestly Issue**
20¢ **multicolored** tagged (165,000,000) .35 .20 ☐☐☐☐☐

CM1085_____   **1983. Volunteer Issue**
20¢ **red & black** tagged (120,430,000) .35 .20 ☐☐☐☐☐

CM1086_____   **1983. German Concord Issue**
20¢ **brown** tagged (117,025,000) .35 .20 ☐☐☐☐☐

CM1087_____   **1983. Physical Fitness Issue**
20¢ **multicolored** tagged (111,775,000) .35 .20 ☐☐☐☐☐

CM1088_____   **1983. Brooklyn Bridge Issue**
20¢ **blue** tagged (181,700,000) .35 .20 ☐☐☐☐☐

CM1089_____   **1983. Tennessee Valley Authority Issue**
20¢ **multicolored** tagged (114,250,000) .35 .20 ☐☐☐☐☐

CM1090_____   **1983. Medal of Honor Issue**
20¢ **multicolored** tagged (108,820,000) .35 .20 ☐☐☐☐☐

CM1091_____   **1983. Scott Joplin Issue**
20¢ **multicolored** tagged (115,200,000) .35 .20 ☐☐☐☐☐

CM1092_____   **1983. Babe Ruth Issue**
20¢ **blue** tagged (184,950,000) .35 .20 ☐☐☐☐☐

CM1093_____   **1983. Nathaniel Hawthorne Issue**
20¢ **multicolored** tagged (110,925,000) .35 .20 ☐☐☐☐☐

CM1094_____   **1983. 1984 Olympic Issue**
13¢ **Discus,** tagged (395,424,000) .25 .20 ☐☐☐☐☐

CM1095_____
13¢ **High jump,** tagged .25 .20 ☐☐☐☐☐

CM1096_____
13¢ **Archery,** tagged .25 .20 ☐☐☐☐☐

CM1097_____
13¢ **Boxing,** tagged .25 .20 ☐☐☐☐☐

CM1098_____   **1983. Treaty of Paris Issue**
20¢ **multicolored** tagged (104,340,000) .35 .20 ☐☐☐☐☐

CM1099_____   **1983. Civil Service Issue**
20¢ **beige, blue & red** tagged (114,725,000) .35 .20 ☐☐☐☐☐

CM1100_____   **1983. Metropolitan Opera Issue**
20¢ **dark carmine & yellow orange** tagged (112,525,000) .35 .20 ☐☐☐☐☐

CM1101_____   **1983. American Inventors Issue**
20¢ **Charles Steinmetz,** tagged (193,055,000) .35 .20 ☐☐☐☐☐

CM1078

CM1079-1082

CM1083

CM1085

CM1086

CM1084

CM1087

CM1088

CM1090

CM1091

CM1089

CM1092

CM1093

CM1094-1097

	MNHVF	UseVF	

CM1102_____
20¢ **Edwin Armstrong,** tagged .... .35 .20 ☐☐☐☐☐
CM1103_____
20¢ **Nikola Tesla,** tagged .... .35 .20 ☐☐☐☐☐
CM1104_____
20¢ **Philo T. Farnsworth,** tagged .... .35 .20 ☐☐☐☐☐
CM1105_____   **1983. Streetcar Issue**
20¢ **NYC's First Horsecar,** tagged .... .35 .20 ☐☐☐☐☐
CM1106_____
20¢ **Montgomery electric,** tagged .... .35 .20 ☐☐☐☐☐
CM1107_____
20¢ **"Bobtail" Horsecar,** tagged .... .35 .20 ☐☐☐☐☐
CM1108_____
20¢ **St. Charles Streetcar,** tagged .... .35 .20 ☐☐☐☐☐
CM1109_____   **1983. Martin Luther Issue**
20¢ **multicolored** tagged (165,000,000) .... .35 .20 ☐☐☐☐☐
CM1110_____   **1984. Alaska Statehood Issue**
20¢ **multicolored** tagged (120,000,000) .... .35 .20 ☐☐☐☐☐
CM1111_____   **1984. Winter Olympics Issue**
20¢ **Ice dancing,** tagged (319,675,000) .... .35 .20 ☐☐☐☐☐
CM1112_____
20¢ **Alpine skiing,** tagged .... .35 .20 ☐☐☐☐☐
CM1113_____
20¢ **Cross-country skiing,** tagged .... .35 .20 ☐☐☐☐☐
CM1114_____
20¢ **Ice hockey,** tagged .... .35 .20 ☐☐☐☐☐
CM1115_____   **1984. Federal Deposit Insurance Corporation Issue**
20¢ **multicolored** tagged (103,975,000) .... .35 .20 ☐☐☐☐☐
CM1116_____   **1984. Love Issue**
20¢ **multicolored** tagged (554,675,000) .... .35 .20 ☐☐☐☐☐
CM1117_____   **1984. Carter G. Woodson Issue**
20¢ **multicolored** tagged (120,000,000) .... .35 .20 ☐☐☐☐☐
CM1118_____   **1984. Soil and Water Conservation Issue**
20¢ **multicolored** tagged (106,975,000) .... .35 .20 ☐☐☐☐☐
CM1119_____   **1984. Credit Union Act of 1934 Issue**
20¢ **multicolored** tagged (107,325,000) .... .35 .20 ☐☐☐☐☐
CM1120_____   **1984. Orchids Issue**
20¢ **Wild Pink Orchid,** tagged (306,912,000) .... .35 .20 ☐☐☐☐☐
CM1121_____
20¢ **Yellow Lady's-Slipper,** tagged .... .35 .20 ☐☐☐☐☐
CM1122_____
20¢ **Spreading Pogonia,** tagged .... .35 .20 ☐☐☐☐☐
CM1123_____
20¢ **Pacific Calypso Orchid,** tagged .... .35 .20 ☐☐☐☐☐
CM1124_____   **1984. Hawaii Statehood Issue**
20¢ **multicolored** tagged (120,000,000) .... .35 .20 ☐☐☐☐☐
CM1125_____   **1984. National Archives Issue**
20¢ **multicolored** tagged (108,000,000) .... .35 .20 ☐☐☐☐☐
CM1126_____   **1984. Summer Olympics Issue**
20¢ **Men's diving,** tagged (313,350,000) .... .35 .20 ☐☐☐☐☐
CM1127_____
20¢ **Women's long jump,** tagged .... .35 .20 ☐☐☐☐☐
CM1128_____
20¢ **Wrestling,** tagged .... .35 .20 ☐☐☐☐☐

Treaty of Paris 1783
US Bicentennial 2O cents

CM1098

CM1099

CIVIL SERVICE 1883 1983 USA 20c

CM1100

Charles Steinmetz — ELECTRICAL THEORIES — 20c
Edwin Armstrong — FREQUENCY MODULATION — 20c
Nikola Tesla — INDUCTION MOTOR — 20c
Philo T. Farnsworth — FIRST TELEVISION CAMERA — 20c

CM1101-1104

Martin Luther
1483-1983 USA 2Oc

CM1109

USA 20c
1959-1984 Alaska Statehood

CM1110

First American streetcar, New York City, 1832
Early electric streetcar, Montgomery, Ala., 1886
"Bobtail" horsecar, Sulphur Rock, Ark., 1926
St. Charles streetcar, New Orleans, La., 1923

CM1105-1108

CM1111-1114

FEDERAL DEPOSIT INSURANCE CORPORATION
50TH ANNIVERSARY
USA 20c

CM1115

LOVE LOVE LOVE LOVE LOVE USA 20c

CM1116

Carter G. Woodson
Black Heritage USA 20c

CM1117

	MNHVF	UseVF

CM1129_____
20¢ **Women's kayacking,** tagged .35 .20 ☐☐☐☐☐

CM1130_____ **1984. Louisiana World Exposition Issue**
20¢ **multicolored** tagged (130,320,000) .35 .20 ☐☐☐☐☐

CM1131_____ **1984. Health Research Issue**
20¢ **multicolored** tagged (120,000,000) .35 .20 ☐☐☐☐☐

CM1132_____ **1984. Douglas Fairbanks Issue**
20¢ **multicolored** tagged (117,050,000) .35 .20 ☐☐☐☐☐

CM1133_____ **1984. Jim Thorpe Issue**
20¢ **dark brown** tagged (115,725,000) .75 .20 ☐☐☐☐☐

CM1134_____ **1984. John McCormack Issue**
20¢ **multicolored** tagged (116,600,000) .35 .20 ☐☐☐☐☐

CM1118

CM1119

Wild pink *Arethusa bulbosa*

Yellow lady's-slipper *Cypripedium calceolus*

Spreading pogonia *Cleistes divaricata*

Pacific calypso *Calypso bulbosa*

CM1120-1123

CM1124

CM1125

CM1130

Performing Arts USA 20c

CM1132

CM1131

CM1126-1129

CM1133

CM1134

CM1135

CM1136

CM1137

CM1138

CM1142-1145

Horace Moses
Founder, Junior Achievement
USA 20c

CM1139

CM1140

CM1141

CM1146

CM1147

CM1148

A Nation of
Readers   CM1149
USA 20c   ←

CM1150

	MNHVF	UseVF

CM1135_____   **1984. St. Lawrence Seaway Issue**
20¢ **multicolored** tagged (120,000,000) — .35 — .20 ☐☐☐☐☐

CM1136_____   **1984. Wetlands Preservation Issue**
20¢ **blue** tagged (123,575,000) — .35 — .20 ☐☐☐☐☐

CM1137_____   **1984. Roanoke Voyages Issue**
20¢ **multicolored** tagged (120,000,000) — .35 — .20 ☐☐☐☐☐

CM1138_____   **1984. Herman Melville Issue**
20¢ **blue green** tagged (117,125,000) — .35 — .20 ☐☐☐☐☐

CM1139_____   **1984. Horace Moses Issue**
20¢ **orange & dark brown** tagged (117,225,000) — .35 — .20 ☐☐☐☐☐

CM1140_____   **1984. Smokey the Bear Issue**
20¢ **multicolored** tagged (95,525,000) — .35 — .20 ☐☐☐☐☐

CM1141_____   **1984. Roberto Clemente Issue**
20¢ **multicolored** tagged (119,125,000) — 2.75 — .20 ☐☐☐☐☐

CM1142_____   **1984. American Dogs Issue**
20¢ **Beagle & Terrier,** tagged (216,260,000) — .35 — .20 ☐☐☐☐☐

CM1143_____
20¢ **Retriever & Cocker Spaniel,** tagged — .35 — .20 ☐☐☐☐☐

CM1144_____
20¢ **Malamute & Collie,** tagged — .35 — .20 ☐☐☐☐☐

CM1145_____
20¢ **Coonhound & Foxhound,** tagged — .35 — .20 ☐☐☐☐☐

CM1146_____   **1984. Crime Prevention Issue**
20¢ **multicolored** tagged (120,000,000) — .35 — .20 ☐☐☐☐☐

CM1147_____   **1984. Family Unity Issue**
20¢ **multicolored** tagged (117,625,000) — .35 — .20 ☐☐☐☐☐

CM1148_____   **1984. Eleanor Roosevelt Issue**
20¢ **blue** tagged (112,896,000) — .35 — .20 ☐☐☐☐☐

CM1149_____   **1984. Nation of Readers Issue**
20¢ **brown & dark red** tagged, (116,500,000) — .35 — .20 ☐☐☐☐☐

CM1150_____   **1984. Hispanic Americans Issue**
20¢ **multicolored** tagged (108,140,000) — .35 — .20 ☐☐☐☐☐

CM1151_____   **1984. Vietnam Veterans Memorial Issue**
20¢ **multicolored** tagged (105,300,000) — .35 — .20 ☐☐☐☐☐

CM1152_____   **1985. Jerome Kern Issue**
22¢ **multicolored** tagged (124,500,000) — .35 — .20 ☐☐☐☐☐

CM1153_____   **1985. Mary McLeod Bethune Issue**
22¢ **multicolored** tagged (120,000,000) — .35 — .20 ☐☐☐☐☐

CM1154_____   **1985. Duck Decoys Issue**
22¢ **Broadbill decoy,** tagged (300,000,000) — .40 — .20 ☐☐☐☐☐

CM1155_____
22¢ **Mallard decoy,** tagged — .40 — .20 ☐☐☐☐☐

CM1156_____
22¢ **Canvasback decoy,** tagged — .40 — .20 ☐☐☐☐☐

CM1157_____
22¢ **Redhead decoy,** tagged — .40 — .20 ☐☐☐☐☐

CM1158_____   **1985. Special Olympics Issue**
22¢ **multicolored** tagged (120,580,000) — .35 — .20 ☐☐☐☐☐

CM1159_____   **1985. Love Issue**
22¢ **multicolored** tagged (729,700,000) — .35 — .20 ☐☐☐☐☐

CM1160_____   **1985. Rural Electrification Administration Issue**
22¢ **multicolored** tagged (124,750,000) — .35 — .20 ☐☐☐☐☐

CM1161_____   **1985. Ameripex 86 Issue**
22¢ **multicolored** tagged (203,496,000) — .35 — .20 ☐☐☐☐☐

Vietnam Veterans Memorial USA 20c

CM1151

Broadbill Decoy
Folk Art USA 22

Mallard Decoy
Folk Art USA 22

Canvasback Decoy
Folk Art USA 22

Redhead Decoy
Folk Art USA 22

CM1154-1157

JEROME KERN

Performing Arts USA

CM1152

Mary McLeod Bethune

Black Heritage USA 22

CM1153

LOVE
USA 22

CM1159

22 USA
Rural Electrification Administration 1935 1985

CM1160

22 USA
Winter Special Olympics

CM1158

A-bigail Adams

USA 22

CM1162

CM1163

USA 22
F.A. Bartholdi, Statue of Liberty Sculptor

CM1164

AMERIPEX 86
International Stamp Show, Chicago
May 22 to June 1, 1986

US POSTAGE
USA 22

CM1161

Veterans Korea
USA 22

USA 22
Quarter horse

USA 22
Morgan

USA 22
Saddlebred

USA 22
Appaloosa

CM1167-1170

Social Security Act 1935-1985 USA 22

CM1165

Veterans World War I
USA 22

CM1166

	MNHVF	UseVF

CM1162_____   1985. Abigail Adams Issue
22¢ multicolored tagged (126,325,000) | .35 | .20 ☐☐☐☐☐

CM1163_____   1985. Frederic Auguste Bartholdi Issue
22¢ multicolored tagged (130,000,000) | .35 | .20 ☐☐☐☐☐

CM1164_____   1985. Korean War Veterans Issue
22¢ gray green & rose red tagged (119,975,000) | .35 | .20 ☐☐☐☐☐

CM1165_____   1985. Social Security Act Issue
22¢ dark blue & light blue tagged (120,000,000) | .35 | .20 ☐☐☐☐☐

CM1166_____   1985. World War I Veterans Issue
22¢ green & red tagged (119,975,000) | .35 | .20 ☐☐☐☐☐

CM1167_____   1985. American Horses Issue
22¢ Quarter horse, tagged (147,940,000) | 2.75 | .20 ☐☐☐☐☐

CM1168_____
22¢ Morgan, tagged | 2.75 | .20 ☐☐☐☐☐

CM1169_____
22¢ Saddlebred, tagged | 2.75 | .20 ☐☐☐☐☐

CM1170_____
22¢ Appaloosa, tagged | 2.75 | .20 ☐☐☐☐☐

CM1171_____   1985. Public Education Issue
22¢ multicolored tagged (120,000,000) | .35 | .20 ☐☐☐☐☐

CM1172_____   1985. International Youth Year Issue
22¢ YMCA youth camping, tagged (130,000,000) | 1.00 | .20 ☐☐☐☐☐

CM1173_____
22¢ Boy Scouts, tagged | 1.00 | .20 ☐☐☐☐☐

CM1174_____
22¢ Big Brothers/Sisters, tagged | 1.00 | .20 ☐☐☐☐☐

CM1175_____
22¢ Camp Fire, tagged | 1.00 | .20 ☐☐☐☐☐

CM1176_____   1985. Help End Hunger Issue
22¢ multicolored tagged (129,000,000) | .35 | .20 ☐☐☐☐☐

CM1177_____   1986. Arkansas Statehood Issue
22¢ multicolored tagged | .35 | .20 ☐☐☐☐☐

CM1178_____   1986. Stamp Collecting Booklet Issue
22¢ Covers & handstamp, tagged (67,996,800) | .40 | .20 ☐☐☐☐☐

CM1179_____
22¢ Youth w/albums, tagged | .40 | .20 ☐☐☐☐☐

CM1180_____
22¢ Magnifier & stamp, tagged | .40 | .20 ☐☐☐☐☐

CM1181_____
22¢ AMERIPEX '86 souvenir sheet, tagged | .40 | .20 ☐☐☐☐☐
The complete booklet contains 2 panes.

CM1182_____   1986. Love Stamp Issue
22¢ multicolored tagged (947,450,000) | .35 | .20 ☐☐☐☐☐

CM1183_____   1986. Sojourner Truth Issue
22¢ multicolored tagged (130,000,000) | .35 | .20 ☐☐☐☐☐

CM1184_____   1986. Republic of Texas Issue
22¢ dark blue, dark red & dark gray tagged (136,500,000) | .35 | .20 ☐☐☐☐☐

CM1185_____   1986. Fish Booklet Issue
22¢ Muskellunge, tagged (219,990,000) | 1.75 | .20 ☐☐☐☐☐

CM1186_____
22¢ Atlantic cod, tagged | 1.75 | .20 ☐☐☐☐☐

CM1187_____
22¢ Largemouth bass, tagged | 1.75 | .20 ☐☐☐☐☐

Public Education

CM1171

Boy Scouts   USA | YMCA Youth Camping   USA

Camp Fire   USA | Big Brothers/Big Sisters   USA

CM1172-1175

Help End Hunger USA 22

CM1176

STAMP COLLECTING | STAMP COLLECTING | STAMP COLLECTING | STAMP COLLECTING

USA 22 | USA 22 | USA 22 | USA 22

CM1178-1181

Arkansas
Statehood
1836-1986
Old State House
Little Rock

USA 22

CM1177

CM1185-1189

Muskellunge

Atlantic Cod

LOVE
USA 22

CM1182

Sojourner Truth 22

Black Heritage USA

CM1183

USA 22

San Jacinto 1836
Republic of Texas

CM1184

Largemouth Bass 22 USA

Bluefin Tuna

USA 22

Catfish

USA 22

Public Hospitals USA 22

CM1190

Duke
Ellington
22 USA

CM1191

	MNHVF	UseVF

CM1188_____
22¢ **Bluefin tuna,** tagged — 1.75 — .20 ☐☐☐☐☐
CM1189_____
22¢ **Catfish,** tagged — 1.75 — .20 ☐☐☐☐☐
NOTE: The complete booklet contains 2 panes.
CM1190_____ **1986. Public Hospitals Issue**
22¢ **multicolored** tagged (130,000,000) — .35 — .20 ☐☐☐☐☐
CM1191_____ **1986. Duke Ellington Issue**
22¢ **multicolored** tagged (130,000,000) — .35 — .20 ☐☐☐☐☐
CM1192_____ **1986. Presidents Souvenir Sheets**
$1.98 **Souvenir sheet of 9** (5,825,050) — 5.25 — 4.50 ☐☐☐☐☐
CM1193_____ **1986. Presidents Souvenir Sheets**
$1.98 **Souvenir sheet of 9** (5,825,050) — 5.25 — 4.50 ☐☐☐☐☐
CM1194_____ **1986. Presidents Souvenir Sheets**
$1.98 **Souvenir sheet of 9** (5,825,050) — 5.25 — 4.50 ☐☐☐☐☐
CM1195_____ **1986. Presidents Souvenir Sheets**
$1.98 **Souvenir sheet of 9** (5,825,050) — 5.25 — 4.50 ☐☐☐☐☐
CM1196_____ **1986. Arctic Explorers Issue**
22¢ **E.K. Kane,** (130,000,000) — 1.10 — .20 ☐☐☐☐☐
CM1197_____
22¢ **A.W. Greely** — 1.10 — .20 ☐☐☐☐☐
CM1198_____
22¢ **V. Stefansson** — 1.10 — .20 ☐☐☐☐☐
CM1199_____
22¢ **R.E. Peary & M. Henson** — 1.10 — .20 ☐☐☐☐☐
CM1200_____ **1986. Statue of Liberty Issue**
22¢ **red & blue** (220,725,000) — .35 — .20 ☐☐☐☐☐
CM1201_____ **1986. Navajo Art Issue**
22¢ **multicolored** (240,525,000) — .40 — .20 ☐☐☐☐☐
CM1202_____
22¢ **multicolored** — .40 — .20 ☐☐☐☐☐
CM1203_____
22¢ **multicolored** — .40 — .20 ☐☐☐☐☐
CM1204_____
22¢ **multicolored** — .40 — .20 ☐☐☐☐☐
CM1205_____ **1986. T.S. Eliot Issue**
22¢ **copper red** (131,700,000) — .35 — .20 ☐☐☐☐☐
CM1206_____ **1986. Woodcarved Figurines Issue**
22¢ **Highlander figure,** tagged (240,000,000) — .40 — .20 ☐☐☐☐☐
CM1207_____
22¢ **Ship figurehead,** tagged — .40 — .20 ☐☐☐☐☐
CM1208_____
22¢ **Nautical figure,** tagged — .40 — .20 ☐☐☐☐☐
CM1209_____
22¢ **Cigar Store figure,** tagged — .40 — .20 ☐☐☐☐☐
CM1210_____ **1987. Michigan Statehood Issue**
22¢ **multicolored** tagged (167,430,000) — .35 — .20 ☐☐☐☐☐
CM1211_____ **1987. Pan-American Games Issue**
22¢ **multicolored** tagged (166,555,000) — .35 — .20 ☐☐☐☐☐
CM1212_____ **1987. Love Stamp Issue**
22¢ **multicolored** tagged (811,560,000) — .35 — .20 ☐☐☐☐☐
CM1213_____ **1987. Jean-Baptiste du Sable Issue**
22¢ **multicolored** tagged (142,905,000) — .35 — .20 ☐☐☐☐☐

Presents of
the United States: I

AMERIPEX 86
International
Stamp Show
Chicago, Illinois
May 22-June 1, 1986

CM1192 ←

Presidents of
the United States: II

AMERIPEX 86
International
Stamp Show
Chicago, Illinois
May 22-June 1, 1986

CM1193 →

Presidents of
the United States: III

AMERIPEX 86
International
Stamp Show
Chicago, Illinois
May 22-June 1, 1986

CM1194 ←

Presidents of
the United States: IV

AMERIPEX 86
International
Stamp Show
Chicago, Illinois
May 22-June 1, 1986

CM1195 →

	MNHVF	UseVF

CM1214_____   **1987. Enrico Caruso Issue**
22¢ **multicolored** tagged (130,000,000)   .35   .20 ☐☐☐☐☐
CM1215_____   **1987. Girl Scouts Issue**
22¢ **multicolored** tagged (149,980,000)   .35   .20 ☐☐☐☐☐
CM1216_____   **1987. Special Occasions Issue**
22¢ **Congratulations,** tagged (610,425,000)   1.75   .40 ☐☐☐☐☐
CM1217_____
22¢ **Get Well,** tagged   1.75   .40 ☐☐☐☐☐
CM1218_____
22¢ **Thank You,** tagged   1.75   .40 ☐☐☐☐☐
CM1219_____
22¢ **Love You, Dad,** tagged   1.75   .40 ☐☐☐☐☐
CM1220_____
22¢ **Best Wishes,** tagged   1.75   .40 ☐☐☐☐☐
CM1221_____
22¢ **Happy Birthday,** tagged   1.75   .40 ☐☐☐☐☐
CM1222_____
22¢ **Love You, Mother,** tagged   1.75   .40 ☐☐☐☐☐
CM1223_____
22¢ **Keep in Touch,** tagged   1.75   .40 ☐☐☐☐☐
NOTE: Nos. CM1224 and CM1225 are not assigned.
CM1226_____   **1987. United Way Issue**
22¢ **multicolored** tagged (156,995,000)   .35   .20 ☐☐☐☐☐
CM1227_____   **1987. American Wildlife Issue**
22¢ **Barn Swallow,** tagged   1.50   .55 ☐☐☐☐☐
CM1228_____
22¢ **Monarch Butterfly,** tagged   1.50   .55 ☐☐☐☐☐
CM1229_____
22¢ **Bighorn Sheep,** tagged   1.50   .55 ☐☐☐☐☐
CM1230_____
22¢ **Broad-tailed Hummingbird,** tagged   1.50   .55 ☐☐☐☐☐
CM1231_____
22¢ **Cottontail,** tagged   1.50   .55 ☐☐☐☐☐
CM1232_____
22¢ **Osprey,** tagged   1.50   .55 ☐☐☐☐☐
CM1233_____
22¢ **Mountain Lion,** tagged   1.50   .55 ☐☐☐☐☐
CM1234_____
22¢ **Luna Moth,** tagged   1.50   .55 ☐☐☐☐☐
CM1235_____
22¢ **Mule Deer,** tagged   1.50   .55 ☐☐☐☐☐
CM1236_____
22¢ **Gray Squirrel,** tagged   1.50   .55 ☐☐☐☐☐
CM1237_____
22¢ **Armadillo,** tagged   1.50   .55 ☐☐☐☐☐
CM1238_____
22¢ **Eastern Chipmunk,** tagged   1.50   .55 ☐☐☐☐☐
CM1239_____
22¢ **Moose,** tagged   1.50   .55 ☐☐☐☐☐
CM1240_____
22¢ **Black Bear,** tagged   1.50   .55 ☐☐☐☐☐
CM1241_____
22¢ **Tiger Swallowtail,**   1.50   .55 ☐☐☐☐☐
CM1242_____
22¢ **Bobwhite,** tagged   1.50   .55 ☐☐☐☐☐

CM1196-1199

CM1200

CM1201-1204

CM1205

CM1206-1209

CM1210

CM1211

CM1212

CM1213

CM1216-1223

CM1214

CM1215

	MNHVF	UseVF
CM1243_____		
22¢ **Ringtail,** tagged	1.50	.55 ☐☐☐☐☐
CM1244_____		
22¢ **Red-winged Blackbird,** tagged	1.50	.55 ☐☐☐☐☐
CM1245_____		
22¢ **American Lobster,** tagged	1.50	.55 ☐☐☐☐☐
CM1246_____		
22¢ **Black-tailed Jack Rabbit, Rabbit,** tagged	1.50	.55 ☐☐☐☐☐
CM1247_____		
22¢ **Scarlet Tanager,** tagged	1.50	.55 ☐☐☐☐☐
CM1248_____		
22¢ **Woodchuck,** tagged	1.50	.55 ☐☐☐☐☐
CM1249_____		
22¢ **Roseate Spoonbill,** tagged	1.50	.55 ☐☐☐☐☐
CM1250_____		
22¢ **Bald Eagle,** tagged	1.50	.55 ☐☐☐☐☐
CM1251_____		
22¢ **Alaskan Brown Bear,** tagged	1.50	.55 ☐☐☐☐☐
CM1252_____		
22¢ **Iiwi,** tagged	1.50	.55 ☐☐☐☐☐
CM1253_____		
22¢ **Badger,** tagged	1.50	.55 ☐☐☐☐☐
CM1254_____		
22¢ **Pronghorn,** tagged	1.50	.55 ☐☐☐☐☐
CM1255_____		
22¢ **River Otter,** tagged	1.50	.55 ☐☐☐☐☐
CM1256_____		
22¢ **Ladybug,** tagged	1.50	.55 ☐☐☐☐☐
CM1257_____		
22¢ **Beaver,** tagged	1.50	.55 ☐☐☐☐☐
CM1258_____		
22¢ **White-tailed Deer,** tagged	1.50	.55 ☐☐☐☐☐
CM1259_____		
22¢ **Blue Jay,** tagged	1.50	.55 ☐☐☐☐☐
CM1260_____		
22¢ **Pika,** tagged	1.50	.55 ☐☐☐☐☐
CM1261_____		
22¢ **Bison,** tagged	1.50	.55 ☐☐☐☐☐
CM1262_____		
22¢ **Snowy Egret,** tagged	1.50	.55 ☐☐☐☐☐
CM1263_____		
22¢ **Gray Wolf,** tagged	1.50	.55 ☐☐☐☐☐
CM1264_____		
22¢ **Mountain Goat,** tagged	1.50	.55 ☐☐☐☐☐
CM1265_____		
22¢ **Deer Mouse,** tagged	1.50	.55 ☐☐☐☐☐
CM1266_____		
22¢ **Black-tailed Prairie Dog,** tagged	1.50	.55 ☐☐☐☐☐
CM1267_____		
22¢ **Box Turtle,** tagged	1.50	.55 ☐☐☐☐☐
CM1268_____		
22¢ **Wolverine,** tagged	1.50	.55 ☐☐☐☐☐
CM1269_____		
22¢ **American Elk,** tagged	1.50	.55 ☐☐☐☐☐

	MNHVF	UseVF

CM1270_____
22¢ **California Sea Lion,** tagged | 1.50 | .55 ☐☐☐☐☐
CM1271_____
22¢ **Mockingbird,** tagged | 1.50 | .55 ☐☐☐☐☐
CM1272_____
22¢ **Raccoon,** tagged | 1.50 | .55 ☐☐☐☐☐
CM1273_____
22¢ **Bobcat,** tagged | 1.50 | .55 ☐☐☐☐☐
CM1274_____
22¢ **Black-footed Ferret,** tagged | 1.50 | .55 ☐☐☐☐☐
CM1275_____
22¢ **Canada Goose,** tagged | 1.50 | .55 ☐☐☐☐☐
CM1276_____
22¢ **Red Fox,** tagged | 1.50 | .55 ☐☐☐☐☐
CM1277_____ **1987. Delaware Statehood Issue**
22¢ **multicolored** tagged (166,725,000) | .35 | .20 ☐☐☐☐☐
CM1278_____ **1987. Friendship with Morocco Issue**
22¢ **red & black** tagged (157,475,000) | .35 | .20 ☐☐☐☐☐
CM1279_____ **1987. William Faulkner Issue**
22¢ **green** tagged (156,225,000) | .35 | .20 ☐☐☐☐☐
NOTE: Imperforate singles are untagged and from printer's waste.
CM1280_____ **1987. Lacemaking Issue**
22¢ **Squash blossoms,** tagged (163,980,000) | .40 | .20 ☐☐☐☐☐
CM1281_____
22¢ **Floral design,** tagged | .40 | .20 ☐☐☐☐☐
CM1282_____
22¢ **Floral lace design,** tagged | .40 | .20 ☐☐☐☐☐
CM1283_____
22¢ **Dogwood blossoms,** tagged | .40 | .20 ☐☐☐☐☐
CM1284_____ **1987. Pennsylvania Statehood Issue**
22¢ **multicolored** tagged (186,575,000) | .35 | .20 ☐☐☐☐☐
CM1285_____ **1987. Constitution Bicentennial Issue**
22¢ **The Bicentennial...,** tagged (584,340,000) | .75 | .25 ☐☐☐☐☐
CM1286_____
22¢ **We the people...,** tagged | .75 | .25 ☐☐☐☐☐
CM1287_____
22¢ **Establish justice...,** tagged | .75 | .25 ☐☐☐☐☐
CM1288_____
22¢ **And secure... liberty...,** tagged | .75 | .25 ☐☐☐☐☐
CM1289_____
22¢ **Do ordain...,** tagged | .75 | .25 ☐☐☐☐☐
CM1290_____ **1987. New Jersey Statehood Issue**
22¢ **multicolored** tagged (184,325,000) | .35 | .20 ☐☐☐☐☐
CM1291_____ **1987. Constitution Bicentennial Issue**
22¢ **multicolored** tagged (168,995,000) | .35 | .20 ☐☐☐☐☐
CM1292_____ **1987. Certified Public Accountants Issue**
22¢ **multicolored** tagged (163,120,000) | .35 | .20 ☐☐☐☐☐
CM1293_____ **1987. Steam Locomotive Issue**
22¢ *Stourbridge Lion,* tagged | .75 | .25 ☐☐☐☐☐
CM1294_____
22¢ *Best Friend of Charleston,* tagged | .75 | .25 ☐☐☐☐☐
CM1295_____
22¢ *John Bull,* tagged | .75 | .25 ☐☐☐☐☐

	MNHVF	UseVF	

CM1296_____
22¢ *Brother Jonathan,* tagged .75 .25 ☐☐☐☐☐
CM1297_____
22¢ *Gowan & Marx,* tagged .75 .25 ☐☐☐☐☐
CM1298_____ **1988. Georgia Statehood Issue**
22¢ **multicolored** tagged (165,845,000) .35 .20 ☐☐☐☐☐
CM1299_____ **1988. Connecticut Statehood Issue**
22¢ **multicolored** tagged (155,170,000) .35 .20 ☐☐☐☐☐
CM1300_____ **1988. Winter Olympics Issue**
22¢ **multicolored** tagged (158,870,000) .35 .20 ☐☐☐☐☐
CM1301_____ **1988. Australia Bicentennial Issue**
22¢ **multicolored** tagged (145,560,000) .35 .20 ☐☐☐☐☐
CM1302_____ **1988. James Weldon Johnson Issue**
22¢ **multicolored** tagged (97,300,000) .35 .20 ☐☐☐☐☐
CM1303_____ **1988. Cats Issue**
22¢ **Siamese, Exotic Shorthair,** tagged (158,556,000) 1.00 .20 ☐☐☐☐☐
CM1304_____
22¢ **Abyssinian, Himalayan,** tagged 1.00 .20 ☐☐☐☐☐
CM1305_____
22¢ **Maine Coon Cat, Burmese,** tagged 1.00 .20 ☐☐☐☐☐
CM1306_____
22¢ **American Shorthair, Persian,** tagged 1.00 .20 ☐☐☐☐☐
CM1307_____ **1988. Massachusetts Statehood Issue**
22¢ **dark blue & dark red** tagged (102,100,000) .35 .20 ☐☐☐☐☐
CM1308_____ **1988. Maryland Statehood Issue**
22¢ **multicolored** tagged (103,325,000) .35 .20 ☐☐☐☐☐
CM1309_____ **1988. Knute Rockne Issue**
22¢ **multicolored** tagged (97,300,000) .35 .20 ☐☐☐☐☐
CM1310_____ **1988. South Carolina Statehood Issue**
25¢ **multicolored** tagged (162,045,000) .40 .20 ☐☐☐☐☐
CM1311_____ **1988. Francis Ouimet Issue**
25¢ **multicolored** tagged (153,045,000) .40 .20 ☐☐☐☐☐
CM1312_____ **1988. New Hampshire Statehood Issue**
25¢ **multicolored** tagged (153,295,000) .40 .20 ☐☐☐☐☐
CM1313_____ **1988. Virginia Statehood Issue**
25¢ **multicolored** tagged (153,295,000) .40 .20 ☐☐☐☐☐
CM1314_____ **1988. Love Issue**
25¢ **multicolored** tagged (841,240,000) .40 .20 ☐☐☐☐☐
CM1315_____ **1988. New York Statehood Issue**
25¢ **multicolored** tagged (183,290,000) .40 .20 ☐☐☐☐☐
CM1316_____ **1988. Love Issue**
45¢ **multicolored** tagged (169,765,000) 1.35 .20 ☐☐☐☐☐
CM1317_____ **1988. Summer Olympic Games Issue**
25¢ **multicolored** tagged (157,215,000) .40 .20 ☐☐☐☐☐
CM1318_____ **1988. Classic Cars Issue**
25¢ **Locomobile,** tagged (635,238,000) 2.00 .50 ☐☐☐☐☐
CM1319_____
25¢ **Pierce-Arrow,** tagged 2.00 .50 ☐☐☐☐☐
CM1320_____
25¢ **Cord,** tagged 2.00 .50 ☐☐☐☐☐
CM1321_____
25¢ **Packard,** tagged 2.00 .50 ☐☐☐☐☐
CM1322_____
25¢ **Duesenberg,** tagged 2.00 .50 ☐☐☐☐☐

CM1227-1276

CM1226

Dec 7,1787   USA

CM1277

Friendship with Morocco 1787-1987

CM1278

CM1279

CM1280-1283

Dec 12,1787 Pennsylvania

CM1284

CM1285-1289

	MNHVF	UseVF

CM1323_____   **1988. Antarctic Explorers Issue**
  25¢ **Nathaniel Palmer,** tagged (162,142,500)   1.00   .20 ☐☐☐☐☐
CM1324_____
  25¢ **Lt. Charles Wilkes,** tagged   1.00   .20 ☐☐☐☐☐
CM1325_____
  25¢ **Richard E. Byrd,** tagged   1.00   .20 ☐☐☐☐☐
CM1326_____
  25¢ **Lincoln Ellsworth,** tagged   1.00   .20 ☐☐☐☐☐
CM1327_____   **1988. Carousel Animal Issue**
  25¢ **Deer,** tagged (305,015,000)   1.00   .20 ☐☐☐☐☐
CM1328_____
  25¢ **Horse,** tagged   1.00   .20 ☐☐☐☐☐
CM1329_____
  25¢ **Camel,** tagged   1.00   .20 ☐☐☐☐☐
CM1330_____
  25¢ **Goat,** tagged   1.00   .20 ☐☐☐☐☐
CM1331_____   **1988. Special Occasions Issue**
  25¢ **multicolored** tagged (480,000,000)   1.00   .20 ☐☐☐☐☐
CM1332_____
  25¢ **multicolored** tagged   1.00   .20 ☐☐☐☐☐
CM1333_____
  25¢ **multicolored** tagged   1.00   .20 ☐☐☐☐☐
CM1334_____
  25¢ **multicolored** tagged   1.00   .20 ☐☐☐☐☐
CM1335_____   **1989. Montana Statehood Issue**
  25¢ **multicolored** tagged   .40   .20 ☐☐☐☐☐
CM1336_____   **1989. A. Philip Randolph Issue**
  25¢ **multicolored** tagged (151,675,000)   .40   .20 ☐☐☐☐☐
CM1337_____   **1989. North Dakota Statehood Issue**
  25¢ **multicolored** tagged (163,000,000)   .40   .20 ☐☐☐☐☐
CM1338_____   **1989. Washington Statehood Issue**
  25¢ **multicolored** tagged (264,625,000)   .40   .20 ☐☐☐☐☐
CM1339_____   **1989. Steamboats Issue**
  25¢ *Experiment,* tagged (204,984,000)   .75   .20 ☐☐☐☐☐
CM1340_____
  25¢ *Phoenix,* tagged   .75   .20 ☐☐☐☐☐
CM1341_____
  25¢ *New Orleans,* tagged   .75   .20 ☐☐☐☐☐
CM1342_____
  25¢ *Washington,* tagged   .75   .20 ☐☐☐☐☐
CM1343_____
  25¢ *Walk in the Water,* tagged   .75   .20 ☐☐☐☐☐
CM1344_____   **1989. World Stamp Expo A'89 Issue**
  25¢ **red, gray & black** (103,835,000)   .40   .20 ☐☐☐☐☐
CM1345_____   **1989. Arturo Toscanini Issue**
  25¢ **multicolored** tagged (152,250,000)   .40   .20 ☐☐☐☐☐
CM1346_____   **1989. House of Representatives Issue**
  25¢ **multicolored** tagged (138,760,000)   .40   .20 ☐☐☐☐☐
CM1347_____   **1989. Senate Issue**
  25¢ **multicolored** tagged (137,985,000)   .40   .20 ☐☐☐☐☐
CM1348_____   **1989. Executive Branch Issue**
  25¢ **multicolored** tagged (138,580,000)   .40   .20 ☐☐☐☐☐
CM1349_____   **1989. South Dakota Statehood Issue**
  25¢ **multicolored** tagged (164,680,000)   .40   .20 ☐☐☐☐☐

Dec 18, 1787   USA
New Jersey 22

CM1290

CM1291

CM1292

Stourbridge Lion 1829   USA 22

Best Friend of Charleston 1830   USA 22

John Bull 1831   USA 22

Brother Jonathan 1832   USA 22

Gowan & Marx 1839   USA 22

CM1293-1297

January 2, 1788
Georgia

CM1298

January 9, 1788
Connecticut

CM1299

22 USA

CM1300

Happy Bicentennial Australia!

1788
1988   USA 22

CM1301

James Weldon Johnson
22

Lift ev-'ry voice and sing
Black Heritage USA

CM1302

22 USA

Feb 6, 1788
Massachusetts ◄

CM1307

April 28, 1788   USA
Maryland   22

CM1308

USA 22
Siamese Cat, Exotic Shorthair Cat

USA 22
Abyssinian Cat, Himalayan Cat

USA 22
Maine Coon Cat, Burmese Cat

USA 22
American Shorthair Cat, Persian Cat

CM1303-1306

22 USA

KNUTE ROCKNE

CM1309

25 USA

May 23, 1788
South Carolina

CM1310

	MNHVF	UseVF

CM1350_____   **1989. Lou Gehrig Issue**
25¢ **multicolored** tagged (138,760,000) — 1.10 — .20 ☐☐☐☐☐

CM1351_____   **1989. Ernest Hemingway Issue**
25¢ **multicolored** tagged (191,755,000) — .40 — .20 ☐☐☐☐☐

CM1352_____   **1989. Moon Landing Anniversary Issue**
$2.40 **multicolored** tagged — 6.00 — 2.25 ☐☐☐☐☐

CM1353_____   **1989. North Carolina Statehood Issue**
25¢ **multicolored** tagged (179,800,000) — .40 — .20 ☐☐☐☐☐

CM1354_____   **1989. Letter Carriers Issue**
25¢ **multicolored** tagged (188,400,000) — .40 — .20 ☐☐☐☐☐

CM1355_____   **1989. Bill of Rights Issue**
25¢ **multicolored** tagged (191,860,000) — .40 — .20 ☐☐☐☐☐

CM1356_____   **1989. Dinosaurs Issue**
25¢ **Tyrannosaurus,** tagged — 1.25 — .20 ☐☐☐☐☐

CM1357_____
25¢ **Pteranodon,** tagged — 1.25 — .20 ☐☐☐☐☐

CM1358_____
25¢ **Stegosaurus,** tagged — 1.25 — .20 ☐☐☐☐☐

CM1359_____
25¢ **Apatosaurus,** tagged — 1.25 — .20 ☐☐☐☐☐

CM1360_____   **1989. America Issue**
25¢ **multicolored** tagged (137,410,000) — .40 — .20 ☐☐☐☐☐

CM1361_____   **1989. World Stamp Expo '89 Souvenir Sheet**
$3.60 **Souvenir sheet of 4** (2,017,225) — 20.00 — 13.50 ☐☐☐☐☐

CM1362_____   **1989. Classic Mail Transportation Issue**
25¢ **Stagecoach,** tagged (163,824,000) — .75 — .20 ☐☐☐☐☐

CM1363_____
25¢ **Steamboat,** tagged — .75 — .20 ☐☐☐☐☐

CM1364_____
25¢ **Biplane,** tagged — .75 — .20 ☐☐☐☐☐

CM1365_____
25¢ **Early automobile,** tagged — .75 — .20 ☐☐☐☐☐

CM1366_____   **1989. Classic Mail Transportation Souvenir Sheet Issue**
$1 **multicolored Souvenir sheet,** tagged — 5.00 — 4.00 ☐☐☐☐☐

CM1367_____   **1990. Idaho Statehood Issue**
25¢ **multicolored** tagged — .40 — .20 ☐☐☐☐☐

CM1368_____   **1990. Love Issue**
25¢ **multicolored** tagged perforated 12 x 13 — .40 — .20 ☐☐☐☐☐

CM1369_____
25¢ **multicolored** tagged perforated 11 1/2 on 2 or 3 sides — .40 — .20 ☐☐☐☐☐

CM1370_____   **1990. Ida B. Wells Issue**
25¢ **multicolored** tagged — .40 — .20 ☐☐☐☐☐

CM1371_____   **1990. Supreme Court Issue**
25¢ **multicolored** tagged — .40 — .20 ☐☐☐☐☐

CM1372_____   **1990. Wyoming Statehood Issue**
25¢ **multicolored** tagged — .40 — .20 ☐☐☐☐☐

CM1373_____   **1990. Classic Films Issue**
25¢ *Wizard of Oz,* tagged — 2.00 — .20 ☐☐☐☐☐

CM1374_____
25¢ *Gone with The Wind,* tagged — 2.00 — .20 ☐☐☐☐☐

CM1375_____
25¢ *Beau Geste,* tagged — 2.00 — .20 ☐☐☐☐☐

CM1376_____
25¢ *Stagecoach,* tagged — 2.00 — .20 ☐☐☐☐☐

CM1311

CM1312

CM1313

CM1314

CM1315

CM1316

CM1317

1928 Locomobile

1929 Pierce-Arrow

1931 Cord

1932 Packard

1935 Duesenberg

CM1318-1322

CM1323-1326

CM1327-1330

CM1331

CM1332

CM1334

CM1333

	MNHVF	UseVF

CM1377_____   1990. Marianne Moore Issue
25¢ **multicolored** tagged .40 .20 ☐☐☐☐☐

CM1378_____   1990. American Lighthouses Issue
25¢ **Admiralty Head,** tagged .40 .20 ☐☐☐☐☐

CM1379_____
25¢ **Cape Hatteras,** tagged .40 .20 ☐☐☐☐☐

CM1380_____
25¢ **West Quoddy Head,** tagged .40 .20 ☐☐☐☐☐

CM1381_____
25¢ **American Shoals,** tagged .40 .20 ☐☐☐☐☐

CM1382_____
25¢ **Sandy Hook,** tagged .40 .20 ☐☐☐☐☐

CM1383_____   1990. Rhode Island Statehood Issue
25¢ **multicolored** tagged .40 .20 ☐☐☐☐☐

CM1384_____   1990. Olympic Athletes Issue
25¢ **Jesse Owens,** tagged .40 .20 ☐☐☐☐☐

CM1385_____
25¢ **Ray Ewry,** tagged .40 .20 ☐☐☐☐☐

CM1386_____
25¢ **Hazel Wightman,** tagged .40 .20 ☐☐☐☐☐

CM1387_____
25¢ **Eddie Eagan,** tagged .40 .20 ☐☐☐☐☐

CM1388_____
25¢ **Helene Madison,** tagged .40 .20 ☐☐☐☐☐

CM1389_____   1990. American Indian Headdresses Issue
25¢ **Assiniboine,** tagged .40 .20 ☐☐☐☐☐

CM1390_____
25¢ **Cheyenne,** tagged .40 .20 ☐☐☐☐☐

CM1391_____
25¢ **Commanche,** tagged .40 .20 ☐☐☐☐☐

CM1392_____
25¢ **Flathead,** tagged .40 .20 ☐☐☐☐☐

CM1393_____
25¢ **Shoshone,** tagged .40 .20 ☐☐☐☐☐

CM1394_____   1990. Micronesia and Marshall Islands Issue
25¢ **Micronesia,** tagged .40 .20 ☐☐☐☐☐

CM1395_____
25¢ **Marshall Islands,** tagged .40 .20 ☐☐☐☐☐

CM1396_____   1990. Sea Mammals Issue
25¢ **Killer Whale,** tagged (278,264,000) .75 .20 ☐☐☐☐☐

CM1397_____
25¢ **Northern Sea Lion,** tagged .75 .20 ☐☐☐☐☐

CM1398_____
25¢ **Sea Otter,** tagged .75 .20 ☐☐☐☐☐

CM1399_____
25¢ **Dolphin,** tagged .75 .20 ☐☐☐☐☐

CM1400_____   1990. America Issue
25¢ **multicolored** tagged (143,995,000) .40 .20 ☐☐☐☐☐

CM1401_____   1990. Dwight D. Eisenhower Issue
25¢ **multicolored** tagged (142,692,000) .45 .20 ☐☐☐☐☐

CM1402_____   1991. Switzerland 700th Anniversary Issue
50¢ **multicolored** tagged (103,648,000) .75 .35 ☐☐☐☐☐

CM1403_____   1991. Vermont Statehood Issue
29¢ **multicolored** tagged (179,990,000) .45 .20 ☐☐☐☐☐

CM1335

CM1336

CM1337

CM1338

CM1344

CM1345

CM1339-1343

CM1346

CM1347

CM1348

 CM1349

CM1350

CM1351

CM1352

CM1353

	MNHVF	UseVF

CM1404_____   **1991. U.S. Savings Bond Issue**

29¢ **multicolored** tagged (150,560,000)   .45   .20 ☐☐☐☐☐

CM1405_____   **1991. Love Issue**

29¢ **multicolored** tagged, perforated 12 1/2 x 13   .45   .20 ☐☐☐☐☐

CM1405A _____

29¢ **multicolored** tagged, perforated 11   .45   .20 ☐☐☐☐☐

CM1406_____

29¢ **multicolored** tagged, perforated 11 on two or three sides   .45   .20 ☐☐☐☐☐

CM1407_____

52¢ **multicolored** tagged   .75   .35 ☐☐☐☐☐

CM1408_____   **1991. William Saroyan Issue**

29¢ **multicolored** tagged (161,498,000)   .45   .20 ☐☐☐☐☐

CM1409_____   **1991. Fishing Flies Issue**

29¢ **Royal Wulff,** tagged (744,918,000)   .45   .20 ☐☐☐☐☐

CM1410_____

29¢ **Jack Scott,** tagged   .45   .20 ☐☐☐☐☐

CM1354

CM1355

CM1356-1359

CM1360

WORLD STAMP EXPO'89ₛₘ

The classic 1869 U.S. Abraham Lincoln stamp is reborn in these four larger versions commemorating World Stamp Expo'89, held in Washington, D.C. during the 20th Universal Postal Congress of the UPU. These stamps show the issued colors and three of the trial proof color combinations.

©USPS 1989

CM1361

CM1362, 1366a (upper left)
CM1363, 1366b (upper right)
CM1364, 1366c (lower left)
CM1365, 1366d (lower right)

20th Universal Postal Congress

A review of historical methods of delivering the mail in the United States is the theme of these four stamps issued in commemoration of the convening of the 20th Universal Postal Congress in Washington, D.C. from November 13 through December 14, 1989. The United States, as host nation to the Congress for the first time in ninety-two years, welcomed more than 1,000 delegates from most of the member nations of the Universal Postal Union to the major international event.
©USPS 1989

CM1366

CM1367

CM1368-1369

CM1372

Wyoming

CM1370

CM1371

CM1373-1376

CM1377

CM1378-1382

CM1383

CM1384-1388

CM1389-1393

	MNHVF	UseVF

CM1411_____
29¢ **Apte Tarpon,** tagged — .45 — .20 ☐☐☐☐☐
CM1412_____
29¢ **Lefty's Deceiver,** tagged — .45 — .20 ☐☐☐☐☐
CM1413_____
29¢ **Muddler Minnow,** tagged — .45 — .20 ☐☐☐☐☐
CM1414_____ **1991. Cole Porter Issue**
29¢ **multicolored** tagged (149,848,000) — .45 — .20 ☐☐☐☐☐
CM1415_____ **1991. Desert Shield-Desert Storm Issue**
29¢ **multicolored** tagged (200,003,000) — .45 — .20 ☐☐☐☐☐
CM1416_____ **1991. Desert Shield-Desert Storm Booklet Issue**
29¢ **multicolored** tagged (200,000,000) — .45 — .20 ☐☐☐☐☐
CM1417_____ **1991. Olympic Track and Field Issue**
29¢ **Pole vault,** tagged (170,025,000) — .45 — .20 ☐☐☐☐☐
CM1418_____
29¢ **Discus,** tagged — .45 — .20 ☐☐☐☐☐
CM1419_____
29¢ **Women's sprint,** tagged — .45 — .20 ☐☐☐☐☐
CM1420_____
29¢ **Javelin,** tagged — .45 — .20 ☐☐☐☐☐
CM1421_____
29¢ **Women's hurdles,** tagged — .45 — .20 ☐☐☐☐☐
CM1422_____ **1991. Numismatics Issue**
29¢ **multicolored** tagged (150,310,000) — .45 — .20 ☐☐☐☐☐
CM1423_____ **1991. Basketball Centennial Issue**
29¢ **multicolored** tagged (149,810,000) — .45 — .20 ☐☐☐☐☐
CM1424_____ **1991. American Comedians Issue**
29¢ **Laurel & Hardy,** tagged (699,978,000) — .45 — .20 ☐☐☐☐☐
CM1425_____
29¢ **Bergen & McCarthy,** tagged — .45 — .20 ☐☐☐☐☐
CM1426_____
29¢ **Jack Benny,** tagged — .45 — .20 ☐☐☐☐☐
CM1427_____
29¢ **Fanny Brice,** tagged — .45 — .20 ☐☐☐☐☐
CM1428_____
29¢ **Abbott & Costello,** tagged — .45 — .20 ☐☐☐☐☐
CM1429_____ **1991. 1941: A World At War Issue**
$2.90 **Commemorative pane of 10** — 9.00 — 5.00 ☐☐☐☐☐
CM1430_____ **1991. District of Columbia Bicentennial Issue**
29¢ **multicolored** tagged (699,978,000) — .45 — .20 ☐☐☐☐☐
CM1431_____ **1991. Jan E. Matzeliger Issue**
29¢ **multicolored** tagged (148,973,000) — .45 — .20 ☐☐☐☐☐
CM1432_____ **1991. Space Exploration Issue**
29¢ **Mercury,** tagged (333,948,000) — .45 — .20 ☐☐☐☐☐
CM1433_____
29¢ **Venus,** tagged — .45 — .20 ☐☐☐☐☐
CM1434_____
29¢ **Earth,** tagged — .45 — .20 ☐☐☐☐☐
CM1435_____
29¢ **Moon,** tagged — .45 — .20 ☐☐☐☐☐
CM1436_____
29¢ **Mars,** tagged — .45 — .20 ☐☐☐☐☐
CM1437_____
29¢ **Jupiter,** tagged — .45 — .20 ☐☐☐☐☐

CM1394-1395

CM1396-1399

CM1400

CM1401

CM1402

CM1403

CM1404

CM1405-1406

CM1407

CM1409-1413

NUMISMATICS

CM1422

CM1408

CM1414

CM1415-1416

CM1423

CM1417-1421

	MNHVF	UseVF
CM1438_____		
29¢ **Saturn,** tagged	.45	.20 ☐☐☐☐☐
CM1439_____		
29¢ **Uranus,** tagged	.45	.20 ☐☐☐☐☐
CM1440_____		
29¢ **Neptune,** tagged	.45	.20 ☐☐☐☐☐
CM1441_____		
29¢ **Pluto,** tagged	.45	.20 ☐☐☐☐☐
CM1442_____ **1992. Winter Olympics Issue**		
29¢ **multicolored** tagged	.45	.20 ☐☐☐☐☐
CM1443_____		
29¢ **multicolored** tagged	.45	.20 ☐☐☐☐☐
CM1444_____		
29¢ **multicolored** tagged	.45	.20 ☐☐☐☐☐
CM1445_____		
29¢ **multicolored** tagged	.45	.20 ☐☐☐☐☐
CM1446_____		
29¢ **multicolored** tagged	.45	.20 ☐☐☐☐☐
CM1447_____ **1992. World Columbian Stamp Expo '92 Issue**		
29¢ **multicolored** tagged	.45	.20 ☐☐☐☐☐
CM1448_____ **1992. W.E.B. Du Bois Issue**		
29¢ **multicolored** tagged	.45	.20 ☐☐☐☐☐
CM1449_____ **1992. Love Issue**		
29¢ **multicolored** tagged	.45	.20 ☐☐☐☐☐
CM1450_____ **1992. Olympic Baseball Issue**		
29¢ **multicolored** tagged	1.00	.20 ☐☐☐☐☐
CM1451_____ **1992. Voyage of Columbus Issue**		
29¢ **Seeking Support,** tagged	1.00	.20 ☐☐☐☐☐
CM1452_____		
29¢ **Atlantic Crossing,** tagged	1.00	.20 ☐☐☐☐☐
CM1453_____		
29¢ **Approaching Land,** tagged	1.00	.20 ☐☐☐☐☐
CM1454_____		
29¢ **Coming Ashore,** tagged	1.00	.20 ☐☐☐☐☐
CM1455_____ **1992. New York Stock Exchange Issue**		
29¢ **multicolored** tagged	.45	.20 ☐☐☐☐☐
CM1456_____ **1992. Columbian Souvenir Sheets**		
85¢ **Sheet of three**	3.00	☐☐☐☐☐
NOTE: Imperforate souvenir sheets are very probably the result of printer's waste.		
CM1457_____ **1992. Columbian Souvenir Sheets**		
$1.05 **Sheet of three**	2.50	☐☐☐☐☐
CM1458_____ **1992. Columbian Souvenir Sheets**		
$2.25 **Sheet of three**	5.00	☐☐☐☐☐
CM1459_____ **1992. Columbian Souvenir Sheets**		
$3.14 **Sheet of three**	8.50	☐☐☐☐☐
CM1460_____ **1992. Columbian Souvenir Sheets**		
$4.07 **Sheet of three**	9.00	☐☐☐☐☐
CM1461_____ **1992. Columbian Souvenir Sheets**		
$5 **Sheet of one, black** like CM15	12.00	8.50 ☐☐☐☐☐
CM1462_____ **1992. Space Achievements Issue**		
29¢ **Space Shuttle,** tagged	1.00	.20 ☐☐☐☐☐
CM1463_____		
29¢ **Space station,** tagged	1.00	.20 ☐☐☐☐☐

CM1424-1428

District of Columbia Bicentennial

CM1430 →

Pennsylvania Avenue, circa 1903

Burma Road, 717-mile lifeline to China · America's first peacetime draft, 1940 · U.S. supports allies with Lend-Lease Act · Atlantic Charter sets war aims of allies · America becomes "arsenal of democracy"

1941: A World at War

Destroyer Reuben James sunk October 31 · Civil Defense mobilizes Americans at home · First Liberty ship delivered December 30 · Japanese bomb Pearl Harbor, December 7 · U.S. declares war on Japan, December 8

CM1429

Jan E. Matzeliger

Black Heritage USA

CM1431

CM1442

CM1443

MERCURY MARINER 10 · VENUS MARINER 2 · EARTH LANDSAT · MOON LUNAR ORBITER
JUPITER PIONEER 11 · SATURN VOYAGER 2 · URANUS VOYAGER 2 · NEPTUNE VOYAGER 2

CM1432-1441

	MNHVF	UseVF	

CM1464_____
29¢ **Apollo & Vostok craft,** tagged — 1.00 — .20 ☐☐☐☐☐

CM1465_____
29¢ **Soyuz, Mercury & Gemini craft,** tagged — 1.00 — .20 ☐☐☐☐☐

CM1466_____   **1992. Alaska Highway Issue**
29¢ **multicolored** tagged — .45 — .20 ☐☐☐☐☐

CM1467_____   **1992. Kentucky Statehood Issue**
29¢ **multicolored** tagged — .45 — .20 ☐☐☐☐☐

CM1468_____   **1992. Summer Olympic Games Issue**
29¢ **Soccer,** tagged — .45 — .20 ☐☐☐☐☐

CM1469_____
29¢ **Gymnastics,** tagged — .45 — .20 ☐☐☐☐☐

CM1470_____
29¢ **Volleyball,** tagged — .45 — .20 ☐☐☐☐☐

CM1471_____
29¢ **Boxing,** tagged — .45 — .20 ☐☐☐☐☐

CM1472_____
29¢ **Swimming,** tagged — .45 — .20 ☐☐☐☐☐

CM1473_____   **1992. Hummingbirds Issue**
29¢ **Ruby-throated,** tagged — .45 — .20 ☐☐☐☐☐

CM1474_____
29¢ **Broad-billed,** tagged — .45 — .20 ☐☐☐☐☐

CM1475_____
29¢ **Costa's,** tagged — .45 — .20 ☐☐☐☐☐

CM1476_____
29¢ **Rufous,** tagged — .45 — .20 ☐☐☐☐☐

CM1477_____
29¢ **Calliope,** tagged — .45 — .20 ☐☐☐☐☐

CM1478_____   **1992. Wildflowers Issue**
29¢ **Indian Paintbrush,** tagged — .95 — .60 ☐☐☐☐☐

CM1479_____
29¢ **Fragrant Water Lily,** tagged — .95 — .60 ☐☐☐☐☐

CM1480_____
29¢ **Meadow Beauty,** tagged — .95 — .60 ☐☐☐☐☐

CM1444

CM1445

CM1446

CM1447

CM1448

CM1449

CM1450

CM1455

CM1451-1454 ←

CM1456 →

CM1457 ←

CM1458

CM1459

CM1460

CM1461

	MNHVF	UseVF

CM1481_____
29¢ **Jack-in-the-Pulpit,** tagged .95 .60 ☐☐☐☐☐
CM1482_____
29¢ **California Poppy,** tagged .95 .60 ☐☐☐☐☐
CM1483_____
29¢ **Large-Flowered Trillium,** tagged .95 .60 ☐☐☐☐☐
CM1484_____
29¢ **Tickseed,** tagged .95 .60 ☐☐☐☐☐
CM1485_____
29¢ **Shooting Star,** tagged .95 .60 ☐☐☐☐☐
CM1486_____
29¢ **Stream Violet,** tagged .95 .60 ☐☐☐☐☐
CM1487_____
29¢ **Bluets,** tagged .95 .60 ☐☐☐☐☐
CM1488_____
29¢ **Herb Robert,** tagged .95 .60 ☐☐☐☐☐
CM1489_____
29¢ **Marsh Marigold,** tagged .95 .60 ☐☐☐☐☐
CM1490_____
29¢ **Sweet White Violet,** tagged .95 .60 ☐☐☐☐☐
CM1491_____
29¢ **Claret Cup Cactus,** tagged .95 .60 ☐☐☐☐☐
CM1492_____
29¢ **White Mountain Avens,** tagged .95 .60 ☐☐☐☐☐
CM1493_____
29¢ **Sessile Bellwort,** tagged .95 .60 ☐☐☐☐☐
CM1494_____
29¢ **Blue Flag,** tagged .95 .60 ☐☐☐☐☐
CM1495_____
29¢ **Harlequin Lupine,** tagged .95 .60 ☐☐☐☐☐
CM1496_____
29¢ **Twinflower,** tagged .95 .60 ☐☐☐☐☐
CM1497_____
29¢ **Common Sunflower,** tagged .95 .60 ☐☐☐☐☐
CM1498_____
29¢ **Sego Lily,** tagged .95 .60 ☐☐☐☐☐
CM1499_____
29¢ **Virginia Bluebells,** tagged .95 .60 ☐☐☐☐☐
CM1500_____
29¢ **Ohi'a Lehua,** tagged .95 .60 ☐☐☐☐☐
CM1501_____
29¢ **Rosebud Orchid,** tagged .95 .60 ☐☐☐☐☐
CM1502_____
29¢ **Showy Evening Primrose,** tagged .95 .60 ☐☐☐☐☐
CM1503_____
29¢ **Fringed Gentian,** tagged .95 .60 ☐☐☐☐☐
CM1504_____
29¢ **Yellow Lady's-Slipper,** tagged .95 .60 ☐☐☐☐☐
CM1505_____
29¢ **Passionflower,** tagged .95 .60 ☐☐☐☐☐
CM1506_____
29¢ **Bunchberry,** tagged .95 .60 ☐☐☐☐☐
CM1507_____
29¢ **Pasqueflower,** tagged .95 .60 ☐☐☐☐☐

CM1462-1465

CM1466 ←

CM1467

CM1468-1472

CM1473-1477

CM1478-1527

	MNHVF	UseVF

CM1508_____
29¢ **Round-Lobed Hepatica,** tagged .95 .60 ❏❏❏❏❏
CM1509_____
29¢ **Wild Columbine,** tagged .95 .60 ❏❏❏❏❏
CM1510_____
29¢ **Fireweed,** tagged .95 .60 ❏❏❏❏❏
CM1511_____
29¢ **Indian Pond Lily,** tagged .95 .60 ❏❏❏❏❏
CM1512_____
29¢ **Turk's Cap Lily,** tagged .95 .60 ❏❏❏❏❏
CM1513_____
29¢ **Dutchman's Breeches,** tagged .95 .60 ❏❏❏❏❏
CM1514_____
29¢ **Trumpet Honeysuckle,** tagged .95 .60 ❏❏❏❏❏
CM1515_____
29¢ **Jacob's Ladder,** tagged .95 .60 ❏❏❏❏❏
CM1516_____
29¢ **Plains Prickly Pear,** tagged .95 .60 ❏❏❏❏❏
CM1517_____
29¢ **Moss Campion,** tagged .95 .60 ❏❏❏❏❏
CM1518_____
29¢ **Bearberry,** tagged .95 .60 ❏❏❏❏❏
CM1519_____
29¢ **Mexican Hat,** tagged .95 .60 ❏❏❏❏❏
CM1520_____
29¢ **Harebell,** tagged .95 .60 ❏❏❏❏❏
CM1521_____
29¢ **Desert Five Spot,** tagged .95 .60 ❏❏❏❏❏
CM1522_____
29¢ **Smooth Solomon's Seal,** tagged .95 .60 ❏❏❏❏❏
CM1523_____
29¢ **Red Maids,** tagged .95 .60 ❏❏❏❏❏
CM1524_____
29¢ **Yellow Skunk Cabbage,** tagged .95 .60 ❏❏❏❏❏
CM1525_____
29¢ **Rue Anemone,** tagged .95 .60 ❏❏❏❏❏
CM1526_____
29¢ **Standing Cypress,** tagged .95 .60 ❏❏❏❏❏
CM1527_____
29¢ **Wild Flax,** tagged .95 .60 ❏❏❏❏❏
CM1528_____ **1992. 1942: Into The Battle Issue**
$2.90 **Sheet of 10** 9.00 5.00 ❏❏❏❏❏
CM1529_____ **1992. Dorothy Parker Issue**
29¢ **multicolored** tagged .45 .20 ❏❏❏❏❏
CM1530_____ **1992. Theodore von Kármán Issue**
29¢ **multicolored** tagged .45 .20 ❏❏❏❏❏
CM1531_____ **1992. Minerals Issue**
29¢ **Azurite,** tagged .45 .20 ❏❏❏❏❏
CM1532_____
29¢ **Copper,** tagged .45 .20 ❏❏❏❏❏
CM1533_____
29¢ **Variscite,** tagged .45 .20 ❏❏❏❏❏
CM1534_____
29¢ **Wulfenite,** tagged .45 .20 ❏❏❏❏❏

	MNHVF	UseVF

CM1535_____   **1992. Juan Rodríguez Cabrillo Issue**
29¢ **multicolored** tagged   .45   .20 ❑❑❑❑❑
CM1536_____   **1992. Wild Animals Issue**
29¢ **Giraffe,** tagged   .45   .20 ❑❑❑❑❑
CM1537_____
29¢ **Giant Panda,** tagged   .45   .20 ❑❑❑❑❑
CM1538_____
29¢ **Flamingo,** tagged   .45   .20 ❑❑❑❑❑
CM1539_____
29¢ **King Penquins,** tagged   .45   .20 ❑❑❑❑❑
CM1540_____
29¢ **White Bengal Tiger,** tagged   .45   .20 ❑❑❑❑❑
CM1541_____   **1992. New Year Issue**
29¢ **multicolored** tagged   .45   .20 ❑❑❑❑❑
CM1542_____   **1993. Elvis Presley Issue**
29¢ **multicolored** tagged   .45   .20 ❑❑❑❑❑
CM1543_____   **1993. Space Fantasy Issue**
29¢ **Saturn Rings,** tagged   .45   .20 ❑❑❑❑❑
CM1544_____
29¢ **Two oval crafts,** tagged   .45   .20 ❑❑❑❑❑
CM1545_____
29¢ **Spacemen & Jet Pack,** tagged   .45   .20 ❑❑❑❑❑
CM1546_____
29¢ **Craft & lights,** tagged   .45   .20 ❑❑❑❑❑
CM1547_____
29¢ **Three crafts,** tagged   .45   .20 ❑❑❑❑❑
CM1548_____   **1993. Percy Lavon Julian Issue**
29¢ **multicolored** tagged   .45   .20 ❑❑❑❑❑
CM1549_____   **1993. Oregon Trail Issue**
29¢ **multicolored** tagged   .45   .20 ❑❑❑❑❑
CM1550_____   **1993. World University Games Issue**
29¢ **multicolored** tagged   .45   .20 ❑❑❑❑❑
CM1551_____   **1993. Grace Kelly Issue**
29¢ **blue** tagged   .45   .20 ❑❑❑❑❑
CM1552_____   **1993. Oklahoma! Issue**
29¢ **multicolored** tagged   .45   .20 ❑❑❑❑❑
CM1553_____   **1993. Circus Issue**
29¢ **Trapeze Artist,** tagged   .45   .20 ❑❑❑❑❑
CM1554_____
29¢ **Elephant,** tagged   .45   .20 ❑❑❑❑❑
CM1555_____
29¢ **Clown,** tagged   .45   .20 ❑❑❑❑❑
CM1556_____
29¢ **Ringmaster,** tagged   .45   .20 ❑❑❑❑❑
CM1557_____   **1993. Cherokee Strip Land Run Centennial Issue**
29¢ **multicolored** tagged   .45   .20 ❑❑❑❑❑
CM1558_____   **1993. Dean Acheson Issue**
29¢ **multicolored** tagged   .45   .20 ❑❑❑❑❑
CM1559_____   **1993. Sporting Horses Issue**
29¢ **Steeplechase,** tagged   .45   .20 ❑❑❑❑❑
CM1560_____
29¢ **Thoroughbred racing,** tagged   .45   .20 ❑❑❑❑❑
CM1561_____
29¢ **Harness racing,** tagged   .45   .20 ❑❑❑❑❑
CM1562_____
29¢ **Polo,** tagged   .45   .20 ❑❑❑❑❑

		MNHVF	UseVF

CM1563_____   1993. Garden Flowers Issue

29¢ **Hyacinth,** tagged — .45 — .20 ☐☐☐☐☐

CM1564_____

29¢ **Daffodil,** tagged — .45 — .20 ☐☐☐☐☐

CM1565_____

29¢ **Tulip,** tagged — .45 — .20 ☐☐☐☐☐

CM1566_____

29¢ **Iris,** tagged — .45 — .20 ☐☐☐☐☐

CM1567_____

29¢ **Lilac,** tagged — .45 — .20 ☐☐☐☐☐

CM1568_____   1993. 1943: Turning The Tide Issue

$2.90 **Commemorative pane of 10** — 8.75 — 7.00 ☐☐☐☐☐

CM1569_____   1993. Hank Williams Issue

29¢ **multicolored** tagged — .45 — .20 ☐☐☐☐☐

CM1570_____   1993. Rock 'n Roll - Rhythm & Blues Issue

29¢ **Elvis Presley,** tagged — .45 — .20 ☐☐☐☐☐

CM1571_____

29¢ **Buddy Holly,** tagged — .45 — .20 ☐☐☐☐☐

CM1572_____

29¢ **Richie Valens,** tagged — .45 — .20 ☐☐☐☐☐

CM1573_____

29¢ **Bill Haley,** tagged — .45 — .20 ☐☐☐☐☐

CM1574_____

29¢ **Dinah Washington,** tagged — .45 — .20 ☐☐☐☐☐

CM1575_____

29¢ **Otis Redding,** tagged — .45 — .20 ☐☐☐☐☐

CM1576_____

29¢ **Clyde McPhatter,** tagged — .45 — .20 ☐☐☐☐☐

CM1528

CM1529

CM1530

CM1531-1534

CM1535

Giraffe

Giant Panda

Flamingo

King Penguins

White Bengal Tiger

CM1536-1540

CM1541

CM1542

CM1543-1547

CM1548

CM1549

CM1550

CM1551

CM1552

	MNHVF	UseVF

CM1577_____
29¢ **multicolored** tagged .45 .20 ☐☐☐☐☐
CM1578_____
29¢ **multicolored** tagged .45 .20 ☐☐☐☐☐
CM1579_____
29¢ **multicolored** tagged .45 .20 ☐☐☐☐☐
CM1580_____
29¢ **multicolored** tagged .45 .20 ☐☐☐☐☐
CM1581_____
29¢ **multicolored** tagged .45 .20 ☐☐☐☐☐
CM1582_____
29¢ **multicolored** tagged .45 .20 ☐☐☐☐☐
CM1583_____
29¢ **multicolored** tagged .45 .20 ☐☐☐☐☐

NOTE: The vertically oriented pane of eight consists of the following stamps, from top to bottom: CM1577, CM1578, CM1579, CM1580, CM1581, CM1582, CM1583, CM1577. The vertically oriented pane of four consists of the following stamps, from top to bottom: CM1581, CM1582, CM1583, CM1584. A complete booklet consists of two panes of eight and one pane of four.

CM1584_____   **1993. Joe Louis Issue**
29¢ **multicolored** tagged .45 .20 ☐☐☐☐☐
CM1585_____   **1993. Broadway Musicals Issue**
29¢ *Show Boat,* tagged .45 .20 ☐☐☐☐☐
CM1586_____
29¢ *Porgy & Bess,* tagged .45 .20 ☐☐☐☐☐
CM1587_____
29¢ *Oklahoma!,* tagged .45 .20 ☐☐☐☐☐
CM1588_____
29¢ *My Fair Lady,* tagged .45 .20 ☐☐☐☐☐
CM1589_____   **1993. National Postal Museum Issue**
29¢ **Benjamin Franklin,** tagged .45 .20 ☐☐☐☐☐
CM1590_____
29¢ **Civil War soldier writing letter** .45 .20 ☐☐☐☐☐
CM1591_____
29¢ **Charles Lindbergh,** tagged .45 .20 ☐☐☐☐☐
CM1592_____
29¢ **Letters & date stamp,** tagged .45 .20 ☐☐☐☐☐
CM1593_____   **1993. Recognizing Deafness/American Sign Language Issue**
29¢ **Mother and child,** tagged .45 .20 ☐☐☐☐☐
CM1594_____
29¢ **Sign "I love you"** .45 .20 ☐☐☐☐☐
CM1595_____   **1993. Country Music Issue**
29¢ **Hank Williams,** tagged .45 .20 ☐☐☐☐☐
CM1596_____
29¢ **The Carter Family,** tagged .45 .20 ☐☐☐☐☐
CM1597_____
29¢ **Patsy Cline,** tagged .45 .20 ☐☐☐☐☐
CM1598_____
29¢ **Bob Wills,** tagged .45 .20 ☐☐☐☐☐

NOTE: Gravure by American Bank Note Co., perforated 11 on one or two sides, from booklet panes.

CM1599_____
29¢ **Hank Williams,** tagged .45 .20 ☐☐☐☐☐
CM1600_____
29¢ **The Carter Family,** tagged .45 .20 ☐☐☐☐☐
CM1601_____
29¢ **Patsy Cline,** tagged .45 .20 ☐☐☐☐☐

CM1557

CM1558

CM1553-1556

CM1559-1562

CM1563-1567

CM1569

CM1568

	MNHVF	UseVF	

CM1602_____
29¢ **Bob Wills,** tagged ... .45 ... .20 ☐☐☐☐☐

CM1603_____ **1993. Youth Classics Issue**
29¢ *Rebecca,* tagged ... .45 ... .20 ☐☐☐☐☐

CM1604_____
29¢ *Little House,* tagged ... .60 ... .20 ☐☐☐☐☐

CM1605_____
29¢ *Huck Finn,* tagged ... .60 ... .20 ☐☐☐☐☐

CM1606_____
29¢ *Little Women,* tagged ... .45 ... .20 ☐☐☐☐☐

CM1607_____ **1993. Commonwealth of the Northern Mariana Islands Issue**
29¢ **multicolored** tagged ... .45 ... .20 ☐☐☐☐☐

CM1608_____ **1993. Columbus Landing in Puerto Rico Issue**
29¢ **multicolored** tagged ... .45 ... .20 ☐☐☐☐☐

CM1609_____ **1993. AIDS Awareness Issue**
29¢ **red & black** tagged ... .45 ... .20 ☐☐☐☐☐

CM1610_____ **1994. Winter Olympics Issue**
29¢ **Downhill skiing,** tagged ... .45 ... .20 ☐☐☐☐☐

CM1611_____
29¢ **Luge,** tagged ... .45 ... .20 ☐☐☐☐☐

CM1612_____
29¢ **Figure skating,** tagged ... .45 ... .20 ☐☐☐☐☐

CM1613_____
29¢ **Cross-country skiing,** tagged ... .45 ... .20 ☐☐☐☐☐

CM1614_____
29¢ **Hockey,** tagged ... .45 ... .20 ☐☐☐☐☐

CM1615_____ **1994. Edward R. Murrow Issue**
29¢ **brown** tagged ... .45 ... .20 ☐☐☐☐☐

CM1616_____ **1994. Love Issue**
29¢ **multicolored** tagged ... .45 ... .20 ☐☐☐☐☐

CM1617_____ **1994. Dr. Allison Davis Issue**
29¢ **red brown & brown** tagged ... .45 ... .20 ☐☐☐☐☐

CM1618_____ **1994. New Year Issue**
29¢ **multicolored** tagged ... .45 ... .20 ☐☐☐☐☐

CM1619_____ **1994. Love Issues**
29¢ **multicolored** tagged ... .45 ... .20 ☐☐☐☐☐

CM1620_____
52¢ **multicolored** tagged ... 1.50 ... .35 ☐☐☐☐☐

CM1621_____ **1994. Buffalo Soldiers Issue**
29¢ **multicolored** tagged ... .45 ... .20 ☐☐☐☐☐

CM1622_____ **1994. Silent Screen Stars Issue**
29¢ **Rudolph Valentino,** tagged ... .45 ... .20 ☐☐☐☐☐

CM1623_____
29¢ **Clara Bow,** tagged ... .45 ... .20 ☐☐☐☐☐

CM1624_____
29¢ **Charlie Chaplin,** tagged ... .45 ... .20 ☐☐☐☐☐

CM1625_____
29¢ **Lon Chaney,** tagged ... .45 ... .20 ☐☐☐☐☐

CM1626_____
29¢ **John Gilbert,** tagged ... .45 ... .20 ☐☐☐☐☐

CM1627_____
29¢ **Zasu Pitts,** tagged ... .45 ... .20 ☐☐☐☐☐

CM1628_____
29¢ **Harold Lloyd,** tagged ... .45 ... .20 ☐☐☐☐☐

CM1584

CM1570, CM1577
(first stamp)
CM1571, CM1582
(second stamp)
CM1572, CM1580
(third stamp)
CM1573, CM1578
(fourth stamp)
CM1574, CM1583
(fifth stamp)
CM1575, CM1581
(sixth stamp)
CM1576, CM1579
(seventh stamp)

CM1585-1588

CM1595, CM 1599
(first stamp)
CM1596, CM1600
(second stamp)
CM1597, CM1601
(third stamp)
CM1598, CM1602
(fourth stamp)

CM1589-1592

CM1603-1606

CM1593-1594

	MNHVF	UseVF

CM1629_____
29¢ **Keystone Cops,** tagged .45 .20 ☐☐☐☐☐
CM1630_____
29¢ **Theda Bara,** tagged .45 .20 ☐☐☐☐☐
CM1631_____
29¢ **Buster Keaton,** tagged .45 .20 ☐☐☐☐☐
CM1632_____ **1994. Garden Flowers Issue**
29¢ **multicolored,** tagged .45 .20 ☐☐☐☐☐
CM1633_____
29¢ **multicolored** tagged .45 .20 ☐☐☐☐☐
CM1634_____
29¢ **multicolored** tagged .45 .20 ☐☐☐☐☐
CM1635_____
29¢ **multicolored** tagged .45 .20 ☐☐☐☐☐
CM1636_____
29¢ **multicolored** tagged .45 .20 ☐☐☐☐☐
CM1637_____ **1994. World Cup Soccer Championship Issue**
29¢ **multicolored** phosphored paper .75 .20 ☐☐☐☐☐
CM1638_____
40¢ **multicolored** phosphored paper 1.00 .35 ☐☐☐☐☐
CM1639_____
50¢ **multicolored** phosphored paper 1.50 .50 ☐☐☐☐☐
CM1640_____
$1.19 **Souvenir Sheet** 3.75 3.00 ☐☐☐☐☐
CM1641_____ **1994. 1944: Road to Victory Issue**
$2.90 **Commemorative pane of 10,** tagged 8.75 7.00 ☐☐☐☐☐
CM1642_____ **1994. Love Issue**
29¢ **multicolored** tagged .50 .20 ☐☐☐☐☐
CM1643_____ **1994. Norman Rockwell Issue**
29¢ **multicolored** tagged .50 .20 ☐☐☐☐☐
CM1644_____
$2 **multicolored** tagged 6.00 5.00 ☐☐☐☐☐
CM1645_____ **1994. Moon Landing Anniversary Issue**
29¢ **multicolored** tagged .50 .25 ☐☐☐☐☐
CM1646_____ **1994. Locomotives Issue**
29¢ **Hudson's General,** tagged .75 .50 ☐☐☐☐☐
CM1647_____
29¢ **McQueen's Jupiter,** tagged .75 .50 ☐☐☐☐☐
CM1648_____
29¢ **Eddy's No. 242,** tagged .75 .50 ☐☐☐☐☐
CM1649_____
29¢ **Ely's No. 10,** tagged .75 .50 ☐☐☐☐☐
CM1650_____
29¢ **Buchannan's No. 999,** tagged .75 .50 ☐☐☐☐☐
CM1651_____ **1994. George Meany Issue**
29¢ **blue** tagged .50 .20 ☐☐☐☐☐
CM1652_____ **1994. Popular Singers Issue**
29¢ **Al Jolson,** tagged .75 .50 ☐☐☐☐☐
CM1653_____
29¢ **Bing Crosby,** tagged .75 .50 ☐☐☐☐☐
CM1654_____
29¢ **Ethel Waters,** tagged .75 .50 ☐☐☐☐☐
CM1655_____
29¢ **Nat "King" Cole,** tagged .47 .50 ☐☐☐☐☐

	MNHVF	UseVF

CM1656_____
  29¢ **Ethel Merman,** tagged   .75   .50 ☐☐☐☐☐
CM1657_____ **1994. James Thurber Issue**
  29¢ **multicolored** tagged   .50   .20 ☐☐☐☐☐

CM1607

CM1608

CM1609

CM1615

CM1610-1614

CM1616

CM1617

CM1618

CM1619

CM1620

CM1621

CM1622-1631

	MNHVF	UseVF	

CM1658_____ **1994. Blues and Jazz Singers Issue**

29¢ **Bessie Smith,** tagged — .50 — .25 ☐☐☐☐☐

CM1659_____

29¢ **Muddy Waters,** tagged — .50 — .25 ☐☐☐☐☐

CM1660_____

29¢ **Billie Holiday,** tagged — .50 — .25 ☐☐☐☐☐

CM1661_____

29¢ **Robert Johnson,** tagged — .50 — .25 ☐☐☐☐☐

CM1662_____

29¢ **Jimmy Rushing,** tagged — .50 — .25 ☐☐☐☐☐

CM1663_____

29¢ **"Ma" Rainy,** tagged — .50 — .25 ☐☐☐☐☐

CM1664_____

29¢ **Mildred Bailey,** tagged — .50 — .25 ☐☐☐☐☐

CM1665_____

29¢ **Howlin' Wolf,** tagged — .50 — .25 ☐☐☐☐☐

CM1666_____ **1994. Wonders of the Seas Issue**

29¢ **Porcupine fish,** tagged — .75 — .25 ☐☐☐☐☐

CM1667_____

29¢ **Dolphin,** tagged — .75 — .25 ☐☐☐☐☐

CM1668_____

29¢ **Nautilus & ship's wheel,** tagged — .75 — .25 ☐☐☐☐☐

CM1632-1636

CM1642 →

CM1643 →

From our doughboys in WWI to our astronauts striding across the moon, Norman Rockwell's artwork has captured America's traditional values along with the characteristic optimism of its people. Rockwell loved people, and people loved him. He was an enormously skilled technician and, according to several new reassessments, a true artist. He had a genius for capturing the emotional content of the commonplace. © USPS 1993

1894
1994

CM1644a-1644d

CM1645 →

First Moon Landing, 1969

CM1640

CM1641

	MNHVF	UseVF	
CM1669_____			
29¢ **Fish & coral,** tagged	.75	.25	☐☐☐☐☐
CM1670_____ **1994. Cranes Issue**			
29¢ **Black-necked crane,** tagged	.45	.20	☐☐☐☐☐
CM1671_____			
29¢ **Whooping crane,** tagged	.45	.20	☐☐☐☐☐
CM1671A _____ **1993-1994. Legends of the West Issue**			
$5.80 **Legends of the West commemorative pane,** tagged, *(earliest known use Dec. 14, 1993)*			
	195.00		☐☐☐☐☐
CM1672_____ **1994. Revised Legends of the West Issue**			
29¢ **Home on the Range,** tagged	.45	.20	☐☐☐☐☐

CM1646-1650

CM1651

CM1657

CM1652-1656

CM1658-1665 ➡

	MNHVF	UseVF

CM1673_____
  29¢ **Buffalo Bill,** tagged   .45   .20 □□□□□
CM1674_____
  29¢ **Jim Bridger,** tagged   .45   .20 □□□□□
CM1675_____
  29¢ **Annie Oakley,** tagged   .45   .20 □□□□□
CM1676_____
  29¢ **Native American Culture,** tagged   .45   .20 □□□□□

CM1666-1669

CM1670-1671

CM1671A ◄

	MNHVF	UseVF

CM1677_____
29¢ **Chief Joseph,** tagged — .45 — .20 ☐☐☐☐☐
CM1678_____
29¢ **Bill Pickett,** tagged — .45 — .20 ☐☐☐☐☐
CM1679_____
29¢ **Bat Masterson,** tagged — .45 — .20 ☐☐☐☐☐
CM1680_____
29¢ **John Fremont,** tagged — .45 — .20 ☐☐☐☐☐
CM1681_____
29¢ **Wyatt Earp,** tagged — .45 — .20 ☐☐☐☐☐
CM1682_____
29¢ **Nellie Cashman,** tagged — .45 — .20 ☐☐☐☐☐
CM1683_____
29¢ **Charles Goodnight,** tagged — .45 — .20 ☐☐☐☐☐
CM1684_____
29¢ **Geronimo,** tagged — .45 — .20 ☐☐☐☐☐
CM1685_____
29¢ **Kit Carson,** tagged — .45 — .20 ☐☐☐☐☐
CM1686_____
29¢ **Wild Bill Hickok,** tagged — .45 — .20 ☐☐☐☐☐
CM1687_____
29¢ **Western Wildlife,** tagged — .45 — .20 ☐☐☐☐☐
CM1688_____
29¢ **Jim Beckwourth,** tagged — .45 — .20 ☐☐☐☐☐
CM1689_____
29¢ **Bill Tilghman,** tagged — .45 — .20 ☐☐☐☐☐
CM1690_____
29¢ **Sacagawea,** tagged — .45 — .20 ☐☐☐☐☐
CM1691_____
29¢ **Overland Mail,** tagged — .45 — .20 ☐☐☐☐☐

NOTE: Because this issue also was made available to collectors in full six-pane printing sheets, gutter pairs and blocks and cross-gutter multiples also exist.

CM1692_____ **1994. Bureau of Engraving and Printing Centennial Souvenir Issue**
$8 **multicolored** tagged, *(Nov. 3, 1994)* — 20.00 — 14.50 ☐☐☐☐☐

NOTE: Listings for minor double transfers refer to any of approximately 10 different ones that are known.

CM1693_____ **1994. New Year Issue**
29¢ **multicolored** tagged — .50 — .20 ☐☐☐☐☐

CM1694_____ **1995. Love Cherub Issue**
32¢ **multicolored** phosphored paper — .50 — .20 ☐☐☐☐☐

NOTE: Self-adhesive booklet, offset and intaglio by Banknote Corp. of America, imperforate (die cut).

CM1695_____
32¢ **multicolored** phosphored paper — .50 — .20 ☐☐☐☐☐

CM1696_____ **1995. Florida Sesquicentennial Issue**
32¢ **multicolored** phosphored paper — .50 — .20 ☐☐☐☐☐

CM1697_____ **1995. Earth Day Issue**
32¢ **Clean Earth,** phosphored paper — .50 — .20 ☐☐☐☐☐

CM1698_____
32¢ **Solar Power,** phosphored paper — .50 — .20 ☐☐☐☐☐

CM1699_____
32¢ **Tree Planting,** phosphored paper — .50 — .20 ☐☐☐☐☐

CM1700_____
32¢ **Clean Beaches,** phosphored paper — .50 — .20 ☐☐☐☐☐

CM1701_____ **1995. Richard M. Nixon Issue**
32¢ **multicolored** phosphored paper — .50 — .20 ☐☐☐☐☐

CM1691y

CM1693

CM1694

CM1695

CM1692

CM1697-1700

CM1696

CM1701

CM1702

	MNHVF	UseVF

CM1702_____   **1995. Bessie Coleman Issue**

32¢ **red & black** phosphored paper .50 .20 ☐☐☐☐☐

CM1703_____   **1995. Love Cherub Issue**

32¢ **multicolored** phosphored paper .50 .20 ☐☐☐☐☐

CM1704_____   **1995. Love Cherub Booklet Issue**

32¢ **multicolored** phosphored paper .50 .20 ☐☐☐☐☐

CM1705_____

55¢ **multicolored** phosphored paper 1.00 .35 ☐☐☐☐☐

CM1706_____   **1995. Love Cherub Self-Adhesive Booklet Issue**

55¢ **multicolored** phosphored paper 1.00 .35 ☐☐☐☐☐

CM1707_____   **1995. Recreational Sports Issue**

32¢ **Bowling,** phosphored paper .50 .20 ☐☐☐☐☐

CM1708_____

32¢ **Tennis,** phosphored paper .50 .20 ☐☐☐☐☐

CM1709_____

32¢ **Golf,** phosphored paper .50 .20 ☐☐☐☐☐

CM1710_____

32¢ **Volleyball,** phosphored paper .50 .20 ☐☐☐☐☐

CM1711_____

32¢ **Baseball,** phosphored paper .50 .20 ☐☐☐☐☐

CM1712_____   **1995. POW & MIA Issue**

32¢ **multicolored** phosphored paper .50 .20 ☐☐☐☐☐

CM1713_____   **1995. Marilyn Monroe Issue**

32¢ **multicolored** block tagged .75 .20 ☐☐☐☐☐

NOTE: Because this issue also was made available to collectors in full six-pane printing sheets, gutter pairs and blocks and cross-gutter multiples also exist.

CM1714_____   **1995. Texas Sesquicentennial Issue**

32¢ **multicolored** phosphored paper .50 .20 ☐☐☐☐☐

CM1715_____   **1995. Lighthouses Issue**

32¢ **Split Rock,** phosphored paper .50 .20 ☐☐☐☐☐

CM1716_____

32¢ **St. Joseph,** phosphored paper .50 .20 ☐☐☐☐☐

CM1717_____

32¢ **Spectacle Reef,** phosphored paper .50 .20 ☐☐☐☐☐

CM1718_____

32¢ **Marblehead,** phosphored paper .50 .20 ☐☐☐☐☐

CM1719_____

32¢ **Thirty Mile Point,** phosphored paper .50 .20 ☐☐☐☐☐

CM1720_____   **1995. United Nations Issue**

32¢ **blue** phosphored paper .50 .20 ☐☐☐☐☐

CM1721_____   **1995. Civil War Issue**

32¢ *Monitor and Virginia* .75 .50 ☐☐☐☐☐

CM1722_____

32¢ **Robert E. Lee** .75 .50 ☐☐☐☐☐

CM1723_____

32¢ **Clara Barton** .75 .50 ☐☐☐☐☐

CM1724_____

32¢ **Ulysses S. Grant** .75 .50 ☐☐☐☐☐

CM1725_____

32¢ **Battle of Shiloh** .75 .50 ☐☐☐☐☐

CM1726_____

32¢ **Jefferson Davis** .75 .50 ☐☐☐☐☐

CM1727_____

32¢ **David Farragut** .75 .50 ☐☐☐☐☐

CM1703

CM1704

CM1705

CM1706

CM1712

CM1714

CM1707-1711

CM1715-1719

CM1713

CM1720

CM1721-1740

	MNHVF	UseVF	

CM1728_____
32¢ **Frederick Douglass** .75 .50 ☐☐☐☐☐
CM1729_____
32¢ **Raphael Semmes** .75 .50 ☐☐☐☐☐
CM1730_____
32¢ **Abraham Lincoln** .75 .50 ☐☐☐☐☐
CM1731_____
32¢ **Harriet Tubman** .75 .50 ☐☐☐☐☐
CM1732_____
32¢ **Stand Watie** .75 .50 ☐☐☐☐☐
CM1733_____
32¢ **Joseph E. Johnston** .75 .50 ☐☐☐☐☐
CM1734_____
32¢ **Winfield Hancock** .75 .50 ☐☐☐☐☐
CM1735_____
32¢ **Mary Chesnut** .75 .50 ☐☐☐☐☐
CM1736_____
32¢ **Battle of Chancellorsville** .75 .50 ☐☐☐☐☐
CM1737_____
32¢ **William T. Sherman** .75 .50 ☐☐☐☐☐
CM1738_____
32¢ **Phoebe Pember** .75 .50 ☐☐☐☐☐
CM1739_____
32¢ **"Stonewall" Jackson** .75 .50 ☐☐☐☐☐
CM1740_____
32¢ **Battle of Gettysburg** .75 .50 ☐☐☐☐☐

NOTE: Because this issue also was made available to collectors in full six-pane printing sheets, gutter pairs and blocks and cross-gutter multiples also exist.

CM1741_____   **1995. Carousel Horses Issue**
32¢ **Golden horse,** phosphored paper .50 .20 ☐☐☐☐☐
CM1742_____
32¢ **Black horse,** phosphored paper .50 .20 ☐☐☐☐☐
CM1743_____
32¢ **Armored horse,** phosphored paper .50 .20 ☐☐☐☐☐
CM1744_____
32¢ **Brown horse,** phosphored paper .50 .20 ☐☐☐☐☐

CM1741-1744
←

CM1745

CM1746

	MNHVF	UseVF

CM1745_____   **1995. Woman Suffrage Issue**
32¢ **multicolored,** phosphored paper   .50   .20 ☐☐☐☐☐
CM1746_____   **1995. Louis Armstrong Issue**
32¢ **multicolored,** phosphored paper   .50   .20 ☐☐☐☐☐
NOTE: For a similar design with "32" in black, see CM1749.
CM1747_____   **1995. 1945: Victory at Last Issue**
$3.20 **Commemorative pane of 10,** overall tagged   9.00   8.00 ☐☐☐☐☐
CM1748_____   **1995. Jazz Musicians Issue**
32¢ **Coleman Hawkins,** phosphored paper   .50   .20 ☐☐☐☐☐
CM1749_____
32¢ **Louis Armstrong,** phosphored paper   .50   .20 ☐☐☐☐☐
CM1750_____
32¢ **James P. Johnson,** phosphored paper   .50   .20 ☐☐☐☐☐
CM1751_____
32¢ **"Jelly Roll" Morton,** phosphored paper   .50   .20 ☐☐☐☐☐
CM1752_____
32¢ **Charles Parker,** phosphored paper   .50   .20 ☐☐☐☐☐
CM1753_____
32¢ **Eubie Blake,** phosphored paper   .50   .20 ☐☐☐☐☐
CM1754_____
32¢ **Charlie Mingus,** phosphored paper   .50   .20 ☐☐☐☐☐
CM1755_____
32¢ **Thelonious Monk,** phosphored paper   .50   .20 ☐☐☐☐☐
CM1756_____
32¢ **John Coltrane,** phosphored paper   .50   .20 ☐☐☐☐☐
CM1757_____
32¢ **Erroll Garner,** phosphored paper   .50   .20 ☐☐☐☐☐
CM1758_____   **1995. Garden Flowers Issue**
32¢ **Aster,** overall tagged   .50   .20 ☐☐☐☐☐
CM1759_____
32¢ **Chrysanthemum,** overall tagged   .50   .20 ☐☐☐☐☐

CM1747

	MNHVF	UseVF	

CM1760_____

32¢ **Dahlia,** overall tagged .50 .20 ☐☐☐☐☐

CM1761_____

32¢ **Hydrangea,** overall tagged .50 .20 ☐☐☐☐☐

CM1762_____

32¢ **Rudbeckia,** overall tagged .50 .20 ☐☐☐☐☐

CM1763_____ **1995. Republic of Palau Issue**

32¢ **multicolored** phosphored paper .50 .20 ☐☐☐☐☐

CM1764_____ **1995. Comic Strip Classics Issue**

32¢ **The Yellow Kid** .75 .50 ☐☐☐☐☐

CM1765_____

32¢ **Katzenjammer Kids** .75 .50 ☐☐☐☐☐

CM1766_____

32¢ **Little Nemo in Slumberland** .75 .50 ☐☐☐☐☐

CM1767_____

32¢ **Bringing Up Father** .75 .50 ☐☐☐☐☐

CM1768_____

32¢ **Krazy Kat** .75 .50 ☐☐☐☐☐

CM1769_____

32¢ **Rube Goldberg's Inventions** .75 .50 ☐☐☐☐☐

CM1770_____

32¢ **Toonerville Folks** .75 .50 ☐☐☐☐☐

CM1748-1757

CM1758-1762

CM1763

CM1764-1783

CM1784

CM1785

CM1786

	MNHVF	UseVF
CM1771_____		
32¢ **Gasoline Alley**	.75	.50 ☐☐☐☐☐
CM1772_____		
32¢ **Barney Google**	.75	.50 ☐☐☐☐☐
CM1773_____		
32¢ **Little Orphan Annie**	.75	.50 ☐☐☐☐☐
CM1774_____		
32¢ **Popeye**	.75	.50 ☐☐☐☐☐
CM1775_____		
32¢ **Blondie**	.75	.50 ☐☐☐☐☐
CM1776_____		
32¢ **Dick Tracy**	.75	.50 ☐☐☐☐☐
CM1777_____		
32¢ **Alley Oop**	.75	.50 ☐☐☐☐☐
CM1778_____		
32¢ **Nancy**	.75	.50 ☐☐☐☐☐
CM1779_____		
32¢ **Flash Gordon**	.75	.50 ☐☐☐☐☐
CM1780_____		
32¢ **Li'l Abner**	.75	.50 ☐☐☐☐☐
CM1781_____		
32¢ **Terry & the Pirates**	.75	.50 ☐☐☐☐☐
CM1782_____		
32¢ **Prince Valiant**	.75	.50 ☐☐☐☐☐
CM1783_____		
32¢ **Brenda Starr**	.75	.50 ☐☐☐☐☐

NOTE: *Because this issue also was made available to collectors in full six-pane printing sheets, gutter pairs and blocks and cross-gutter multiples also exist.*

	MNHVF	UseVF
CM1784_____ **1995. U.S. Naval Academy Issue**		
32¢ **multicolored** phosphored paper	.50	.20 ☐☐☐☐☐
CM1785_____ **1995. Tennessee Williams Issue**		
32¢ **multicolored** phosphored paper	.50	.20 ☐☐☐☐☐
CM1786_____ **1995. James K. Polk Issue**		
32¢ **reddish brown** phosphored paper	.50	.20 ☐☐☐☐☐
CM1787_____ **1995. Antique Automobiles Issue**		
32¢ **Duryea,** phosphored paper	.75	.50 ☐☐☐☐☐
CM1788_____		
32¢ **Haynes,** phosphored paper	.75	.50 ☐☐☐☐☐
CM1789_____		
32¢ **Columbia,** phosphored paper	.75	.50 ☐☐☐☐☐
CM1790_____		
32¢ **Winton,** phosphored paper	.75	.50 ☐☐☐☐☐
CM1791_____		
32¢ **White,** phosphored paper	.75	.50 ☐☐☐☐☐
CM1792_____ **1996. Utah Centennial Issue**		
32¢ **multicolored** tagged (120,000,000)	.50	.20 ☐☐☐☐☐
CM1793_____ **1996. Garden Flowers Issue**		
32¢ **Crocus,** phosphored paper (160,000,000)	.50	.20 ☐☐☐☐☐
CM1794_____		
32¢ **Winter Aconite,** phosphored paper	.50	.20 ☐☐☐☐☐
CM1795_____		
32¢ **Pansy,** phosphored paper	.50	.20 ☐☐☐☐☐
CM1796_____		
32¢ **Snowdrop,** phosphored paper	.50	.20 ☐☐☐☐☐

	MNHVF	UseVF

CM1797_____

32¢ **Anemone,** phosphored paper | .50 | .20 ☐☐☐☐☐

CM1798_____   **1996. Love Cherub Issue**

32¢ **multicolored** tagged (2,550,000,000) | .50 | .20 ☐☐☐☐☐

CM1799_____   **1996. Ernest E. Just Issue**

32¢ **black & gray** tagged (92,100,000) | .50 | .20 ☐☐☐☐☐

CM1800_____   **1996. Smithsonian Institution Sesquicentennial Issue**

32¢ **multicolored** tagged (115,600,000) | .50 | .20 ☐☐☐☐☐

CM1801_____   **1996. New Years Issue**

32¢ **multicolored** tagged (93,150,000) | .50 | .20 ☐☐☐☐☐

CM1802_____   **1996. Pioneers of Communications Issue**

32¢ **Eadweard Muybridge,** phosphored paper (23,292,500) | .50 | .20 ☐☐☐☐☐

CM1803_____

32¢ **Ottmar Mergenthaler,** phosphored paper | .50 | .20 ☐☐☐☐☐

CM1804_____

32¢ **Frederic E. Ives,** phosphored paper | .50 | .20 ☐☐☐☐☐

CM1805_____

32¢ **William Dickson,** phosphored paper | .50 | .20 ☐☐☐☐☐

CM1806_____   **1996. Fulbright Scholarships Issue**

32¢ **multicolored** tagged (111,000,000) | .50 | .20 ☐☐☐☐☐

CM1807_____   **1996. Marathon Issue**

32¢ **multicolored** tagged (209,450,000) | .50 | .20 ☐☐☐☐☐

CM1798

CM1792 ← → CM1799

CM1787-1791

CM1793-1797

CM1800

CM1801

	MNHVF	UseVF

CM1808_____   **1996. Atlanta 1996 Centennial Olympic Games Issue**
  32¢ **Javelin**   .75   .50 ☐☐☐☐☐
CM1809_____
  32¢ **Whitewater canoeing**   .75   .50 ☐☐☐☐☐
CM1810_____
  32¢ **Women's running**   .75   .50 ☐☐☐☐☐
CM1811_____
  32¢ **Women's platform diving**   .75   .50 ☐☐☐☐☐
CM1812_____
  32¢ **Men's cycling**   .75   .50 ☐☐☐☐☐
CM1813_____
  32¢ **Freestyle wrestling**   .75   .50 ☐☐☐☐☐
CM1814_____
  32¢ **Women's gymnastics**   .75   .50 ☐☐☐☐☐
CM1815_____
  32¢ **Women's sailboarding**   .75   .50 ☐☐☐☐☐
CM1816_____
  32¢ **Men's shot put**   .75   .50 ☐☐☐☐☐
CM1817_____
  32¢ **Women's soccer**   .75   .50 ☐☐☐☐☐
CM1818_____
  32¢ **Beach volleyball**   .75   .50 ☐☐☐☐☐
CM1819_____
  32¢ **Men's rowing**   .75   .50 ☐☐☐☐☐
CM1820_____
  32¢ **Men's sprinting events**   .75   .50 ☐☐☐☐☐
CM1821_____
  32¢ **Women's swimming**   .75   .50 ☐☐☐☐☐
CM1822_____
  32¢ **Women's softball**   .75   .50 ☐☐☐☐☐
CM1823_____
  32¢ **Men's hurdles**   .75   .50 ☐☐☐☐☐
CM1824_____
  32¢ **Men's swimming (backstroke)**   .75   .50 ☐☐☐☐☐
CM1825_____
  32¢ **Men's gymnastics (pommel horse)**   .75   .50 ☐☐☐☐☐
CM1826_____
  32¢ **Equestrian events**   .75   .50 ☐☐☐☐☐
CM1827_____
  32¢ **Men's basketball**   .75   .50 ☐☐☐☐☐

NOTE: Because this issue also was made available to collectors in full six-pane printing sheets, gutter pairs and blocks and cross-gutter multiples also exist.

CM1828_____   **1996. Georgia O'Keeffe Issue**
  32¢ **multicolored** tagged (156,300,000)   .50   .20 ☐☐☐☐☐
CM1829_____   **1996. Tennessee Bicentennial Issue**
  32¢ **multicolored** tagged (100,000,000)   .50   .20 ☐☐☐☐☐
CM1830_____   **1996. Tennessee Bicentennial Booklet Issue**
  32¢ **multicolored** tagged (60,120,000)   .75   .20 ☐☐☐☐☐
CM1831_____   **1996. American Indian Dances Issue**
  32¢ **Fancy Dance,** tagged (27,850,000)   .75   .50 ☐☐☐☐☐
CM1832_____
  32¢ **Butterfly Dance,** tagged   .75   .50 ☐☐☐☐☐
CM1833_____
  32¢ **Traditional Dance,** tagged   .75   .50 ☐☐☐☐☐

CM1802-1805

CM1806

CM1807

CM1808-1827

	MNHVF	UseVF

CM1834_____
  32¢ **Raven Dance,** tagged   .75   .50 ☐☐☐☐☐
CM1835_____
  32¢ **Hoop Dance,** tagged   .75   .50 ☐☐☐☐☐
CM1836_____ **1996. Prehistoric Animals Issue**
  32¢ **Eohippus,** tagged (22,218,000)   .75   .50 ☐☐☐☐☐
CM1837_____
  32¢ **Woolly Mammoth,** tagged   .75   .50 ☐☐☐☐☐
CM1838_____
  32¢ **Mastodon,** tagged   .75   .50 ☐☐☐☐☐
CM1839_____
  32¢ **Saber-tooth Cat,** tagged   .75   .50 ☐☐☐☐☐
CM1840_____ **1996. Breast Cancer Awareness Issue**
  32¢ **multicolored** tagged (95,600,000)   .50   .20 ☐☐☐☐☐
CM1841_____ **1996. James Dean Issue**
  32¢ **multicolored** tagged (300,000,000)   .50   .20 ☐☐☐☐☐
NOTE: Because this issue also was made available to collectors in full six-pane printing sheets, gutter pairs and blocks and cross-gutter multiples also exist.
CM1842_____ **1996. Folk Heroes Issue**
  32¢ **Mighty Casey,** tagged (23,681,250)   .50   .20 ☐☐☐☐☐
CM1843_____
  32¢ **Paul Bunyan,** tagged   .50   .20 ☐☐☐☐☐
CM1844_____
  32¢ **John Henry,** tagged   .50   .20 ☐☐☐☐☐
CM1845_____
  32¢ **Pecos Bill,** tagged   .50   .20 ☐☐☐☐☐
CM1846_____ **1996. Olympic Games Centennial Issue**
  32¢ **brown** tagged (133,613,000)   .50   .20 ☐☐☐☐☐
CM1847_____ **1996. Iowa Sesquicentennial Issue**
  32¢ **multicolored** tagged (103,400,000)   .50   .20 ☐☐☐☐☐
CM1848_____ **1996. Iowa Sesquicentennial Self-Adhesive Issue**
  32¢ **multicolored** tagged (60,000,000)   .75   .30 ☐☐☐☐☐
CM1849_____ **1996. Rural Free Delivery Centennial Issue**
  32¢ **multicolored** tagged (134,000,000)   .50   .20 ☐☐☐☐☐
CM1850_____ **1996. Riverboats Issue**
  32¢ *Robt. E. Lee,* tagged (32,000,000)   .75   .50 ☐☐☐☐☐
CM1851_____
  32¢ *Sylvan Dell,* tagged   .75   .50 ☐☐☐☐☐
CM1852_____
  32¢ *Far West,* tagged   .75   .50 ☐☐☐☐☐
CM1853_____
  32¢ *Rebecca Everingham,* tagged   .75   .50 ☐☐☐☐☐
CM1854_____
  32¢ *Bailey Gatzert,* tagged   .75   .50 ☐☐☐☐☐
CM1855_____ **1996. Big Band Leaders Issue**
  32¢ **Count Basie,** tagged (23,025,000)   .50   .20 ☐☐☐☐☐
CM1856_____
  32¢ **Tommy & Jimmy Dorsey,** tagged   .50   .20 ☐☐☐☐☐
CM1857_____
  32¢ **Glenn Miller,** tagged   .50   .20 ☐☐☐☐☐
CM1858_____
  32¢ **Benny Goodman,** tagged   .50   .20 ☐☐☐☐☐
CM1859_____ **1996. Songwriters Issue**
  32¢ **Harold Arlen,** tagged (23,025,000)   .50   .20 ☐☐☐☐☐

CM1828

CM1829-1830

CM1836-1839

CM1831-1835

CM1840

CM1841

CM1842-1845

CM1846

CM1850-1854

CM1847, CM1848

CM1849

	MNHVF	UseVF	

CM1860_____
   32¢ **Johnny Mercer,** tagged — .50 — .20 ☐☐☐☐☐
CM1861_____
   32¢ **Dorothy Fields,** tagged — .50 — .20 ☐☐☐☐☐
CM1862_____
   32¢ **Hoagy Carmichael,** tagged — .50 — .20 ☐☐☐☐☐
CM1863_____   **1996. F. Scott Fitzgerald Issue**
   23¢ **multicolored** tagged (300,000,000) — .50 — .20 ☐☐☐☐☐
CM1864_____   **1996. Endangered Species Issue**
   32¢ **Black-footed ferret** — .50 — .20 ☐☐☐☐☐
CM1865_____
   32¢ **Thick-billed parrot** — .50 — .20 ☐☐☐☐☐
CM1866_____
   32¢ **Hawaiian Monk seal** — .50 — .20 ☐☐☐☐☐
CM1867_____
   32¢ **American crocodile** — .50 — .20 ☐☐☐☐☐

CM1855-1858 ←

CM1859-1862 →

CM1863

CM1879

CM1880

CM1864-1878

	MNHVF	UseVF

CM1868_____
   32¢ **Ocelot** | .50 | .20 ☐☐☐☐☐
CM1869_____
   32¢ **Schaus swallowtail butterfly** | .50 | .20 ☐☐☐☐☐
CM1870_____
   32¢ **Wyoming toad** | .50 | .20 ☐☐☐☐☐
CM1871_____
   32¢ **Brown pelican** | .50 | .20 ☐☐☐☐☐
CM1872_____
   32¢ **California condor** | .50 | .20 ☐☐☐☐☐
CM1873_____
   32¢ **Gila trout** | .50 | .20 ☐☐☐☐☐
CM1874_____
   32¢ **San Francisco garter snake** | .50 | .20 ☐☐☐☐☐
CM1875_____
   32¢ **Woodland caribou** | .50 | .20 ☐☐☐☐☐
CM1876_____
   32¢ **Florida panther** | .50 | .20 ☐☐☐☐☐
CM1877_____
   32¢ **Piping plover** | .50 | .20 ☐☐☐☐☐
CM1878_____
   32¢ **Florida manatee** | .50 | .20 ☐☐☐☐☐

CM1879_____ **1996. Computer Technology Issue**
   32¢ **multicolored** tagged (93,612,000) | .50 | .20 ☐☐☐☐☐

CM1880_____ **1996. Hanukkah Issue**
   32¢ **multicolored** tagged (103,520,000) | .75 | .20 ☐☐☐☐☐

CM1881_____ **1996. Cycling Souvenir Sheet**
   50¢ **multicolored** tagged (20,000,000) | 2.50 | 1.00 ☐☐☐☐☐

CM1882_____ **1997. New Years Issue**
   32¢ **multicolored** tagged (160,000,000) | .50 | .20 ☐☐☐☐☐

CM1883_____ **1997. Benjamin O. Davis Issue**
   32¢ **gray, green & black** phosphored paper (112,000,000) | .50 | .20 ☐☐☐☐☐

CM1884_____ **1997. Love Issue**
   32¢ **multicolored** tagged | .50 | .20 ☐☐☐☐☐
CM1885_____
   55¢ **multicolored** tagged | 1.00 | .30 ☐☐☐☐☐

CM1886_____ **1997. Helping Children Learn Issue**
   32¢ **multicolored** tagged | .50 | .20 ☐☐☐☐☐

CM1887_____ **1997. Pacific 97 Issue**
   32¢ **red** phosphored paper (65,000,000) | .50 | .20 ☐☐☐☐☐
CM1888_____
   32¢ **blue** phosphored paper | .50 | .20 ☐☐☐☐☐

NOTE: Because this issue also was made available in full 96-subject printing sheets of six 16-stamp panes, gutter pairs and blocks and cross-gutter multiples also exist.

CM1889_____ **1997. Thornton Wilder Issue**
   32¢ **multicolored** tagged (97,500,000) | .50 | .20 ☐☐☐☐☐

CM1890_____ **1997. Raoul Wallenberg Issue**
   32¢ **multicolored** tagged (96,000,000) | .50 | .20 ☐☐☐☐☐

CM1891_____ **1997. The World of Dinosaurs Issue**
   $4.80 **Sheet of 15,** tagged (14,600,000) | 15.00 | 9.50 ☐☐☐☐☐

CM1892_____ **1997. Bugs Bunny Issue**
   $3.20 **Pane of 10,** tagged | 7.50 | ☐☐☐☐☐

NOTE: Serpentine die cut 11 through stamps and backing.

CM1883

CM1881

CM1882

CM1884

CM1885

CM1886

CM1887   CM1888

CM1892

CM1889

CM1890

	MNHVF	UseVF

CM1893_____
$3.20 **Pane of 10,** tagged   200.00   □□□□□

NOTE: This issue also was made available in top and bottom half printing sheets of six 10-stamp panes each. A single plate number, trimmed away on individual panes, appears adjacent to the bottom-left pane in the bottom half of the printing sheet only. Value of plate number half is $225.

A gummed, non-denominated, untagged item similar to CM1893n on the same backing paper as the normal stamps lacks Bugs' "autograph" and single stamp, the latter of which is replaced by "32 USA" as on the issued stamp. Though printed for the USPS, this item was an advertising piece and was not postally valid.

CM1894_____   **1997. Pacific 97 U.S. Stamp Sesquicentennial Issue**
$6   **Pane of 12,** tagged   11.50   9.00 □□□□□
CM1895_____   **1997. Pacific 97 U.S. Stamp Sesquicentennial Issue**
$7.20 **Pane of 12,** tagged   12.50   10.00 □□□□□

NOTE: Because this issue also was made available to collectors in full six-pane printing sheets, gutter pairs and blocks and cross-gutter multiples also exist.

CM1896_____   **1997. Marshall Plan 50th Anniversary Issue**
32¢ **multicolored** tagged (45,250,000)   .50   .20 □□□□□
CM1897_____   **1997. Classic American Aircraft Issue**
32¢ **North American P-51 Mustang fighter**   .75   .50 □□□□□
CM1898_____
32¢ **Wright Model B Flyer**   .75   .50 □□□□□
CM1899_____
32¢ **Piper J-3 Cub**   .75   .50 □□□□□
CM1900_____
32¢ **Lockheed Vega**   .75   .50 □□□□□

THE WORLD OF DINOSAURS

A scene in Colorado, 150 million years ago

A scene in Montana, 75 million years ago

CM1891

	MNHVF	UseVF	
CM1901_____			
32¢ **Northrop Alpha**	.75	.50	☐☐☐☐☐
CM1902_____			
32¢ **Martin B-10 bomber**	.75	.50	☐☐☐☐☐
CM1903_____			
32¢ **Chance Vought Corsair F4U fighter**	.75	.50	☐☐☐☐☐
CM1904_____			
32¢ **Boeing B-47 Stratojet bomber**	.75	.50	☐☐☐☐☐
CM1905_____			
32¢ **Gee Bee Super-Sportster**	.75	.50	☐☐☐☐☐
CM1906_____			
32¢ **Beech Model C17L Staggerwing**	.75	.50	☐☐☐☐☐
CM1907_____			
32¢ **Boeing B-17 Flying Fortress bomber**	.75	.50	☐☐☐☐☐
CM1908_____			
32¢ **Stearman PT-13 training aircraft**	.75	.50	☐☐☐☐☐
CM1909_____			
32¢ **Lockheed Constellation**	.75	.50	☐☐☐☐☐
CM1910_____			
32¢ **Lockheed P-38 Lightning fighter**	.75	.50	☐☐☐☐☐
CM1911_____			
32¢ **Boeing P-26 Peashooter fighter**	.75	.50	☐☐☐☐☐

CM1894

CM1896

CM1895

		MNHVF	UseVF

CM1912_____

    32¢ **Ford Tri-Motor**   .75   .50 ☐☐☐☐☐

CM1913_____

    32¢ **Douglas DC-3 passenger plane**   .75   .50 ☐☐☐☐☐

CM1914_____

    32¢ **Boeing 314 Clipper flying boat**   .75   .50 ☐☐☐☐☐

CM1915_____

    32¢ **Curtiss JN-4 Jenny training aircraft**   .75   .50 ☐☐☐☐☐

CM1916_____

    32¢ **Grumman F4F Wildcat fighter**   .75   .50 ☐☐☐☐☐

NOTE: Because this issue also was made available to collectors in full six-pane printing sheets, gutter pairs and blocks and cross-gutter multiples also exist.

CM1917_____   **1997. Legendary Football Coaches Issue**

    32¢ **Paul "Bear" Bryant,** tagged (22,500,000)   .50   .20 ☐☐☐☐☐

CM1918_____

    32¢ **Glen "Pop" Warner,** tagged   .50   .20 ☐☐☐☐☐

CM1919_____

    32¢ **Vince Lombardi,** tagged   .50   .20 ☐☐☐☐☐

CM1920_____

    32¢ **George Halas,** tagged   .50   .20 ☐☐☐☐☐

CM1921_____   **1997. Classic American Dolls Issue**

    32¢ **"Alabama Baby" and Martha Chase Doll**   .75   .50 ☐☐☐☐☐

CM1897-1916

	MNHVF	UseVF

CM1922_____
  32¢ **Rutta Sisters "The Columbian Doll"** — .75 — .50 ☐☐☐☐☐
CM1923_____
  32¢ **Johnny Gruelle's "Raggedy Ann"** — .75 — .50 ☐☐☐☐☐
CM1924_____
  32¢ **Martha Chase Cloth Doll** — .75 — .50 ☐☐☐☐☐
CM1925_____
  32¢ **Effanbee Doll Co. "American Child"** — .75 — .50 ☐☐☐☐☐

CM1917-1920

CLASSIC
American Dolls

"Alabama Baby" and Martha Chase   "The Columbian Doll"   Johnny Gruelle's "Raggedy Ann"   Martha Chase   "American Child"
"Baby Coos"   Plains Indian   Izannah Walker   "Babyland Rag"   "Scootles"
Ludwig Greiner   "Betsy McCall"   Percy Crosby's "Skippy"   "Maggie Mix-up"   Albert Schoenhut

The above names include doll makers, designers, trade names and common names.

CM1921-1935

	MNHVF	UseVF

CM1926_____

32¢ **Ideal Novelty & Toy Co. "Baby Coos"** .75 .50 ☐☐☐☐☐

CM1927_____

32¢ **Plains Indian Doll 1920s** .75 .50 ☐☐☐☐☐

CM1928_____

32¢ **Izannah Walker Oil-Painted Cloth Doll** .75 .50 ☐☐☐☐☐

CM1929_____

32¢ **All-Cloth "Babyland Rag" Doll** .75 .50 ☐☐☐☐☐

CM1930_____

32¢ **Rose O'Neill "Scootles" Doll** .75 .50 ☐☐☐☐☐

CM1931_____

32¢ **Ludwig Greiner First U.S. Patent Doll** .75 .50 ☐☐☐☐☐

CM1932_____

32¢ **"Betsy McCall" American Character Doll** .75 .50 ☐☐☐☐☐

CM1933_____

32¢ **Percy Crosby's "Skippy"** .75 .50 ☐☐☐☐☐

CM1934_____

32¢ **Alexander Doll Co. "Maggie Mix-up"** .75 .50 ☐☐☐☐☐

CM1935_____

32¢ **Schoenhut "All Word Perfection Art Dolls"** .75 .50 ☐☐☐☐☐

CM1936_____ **1997. Humphrey Bogart Issue**

32¢ **multicolored** tagged (195,000,000) .50 .20 ☐☐☐☐☐

NOTE: Because this issue also was made available to collectors in full six-pane printing sheets, gutter pairs and blocks and cross-gutter multiples also exist.

CM1937_____ **1997. Vince Lombardi Issue**

32¢ **multicolored** tagged (20,000,000) .50 .20 ☐☐☐☐☐

CM1938_____ **1997. Paul "Bear" Bryant Issue**

32¢ **multicolored** tagged (20,000,000) .50 .20 ☐☐☐☐☐

CM1939_____ **1997. Glen "Pop" Warner Issue**

32¢ **multicolored** tagged (10,000,000) .50 .20 ☐☐☐☐☐

CM1940_____ **1997. George Halas Issue**

32¢ **multicolored** tagged (10,000,000) .50 .20 ☐☐☐☐☐

CM1941_____ **1997. "The Stars And Stripes Forever" Issue**

32¢ **multicolored** tagged (323,000,000) .50 .20 ☐☐☐☐☐

CM1942_____ **1997. Opera Singers Issue**

32¢ **Lily Pons,** tagged (21,500,000) .50 .20 ☐☐☐☐☐

CM1943_____

32¢ **Richard Tucker,** tagged .50 .20 ☐☐☐☐☐

CM1944_____

32¢ **Lawrence Tibbett,** tagged .50 .20 ☐☐☐☐☐

CM1945_____

32¢ **Rosa Ponselle,** tagged .50 .20 ☐☐☐☐☐

CM1946_____ **1997. Classical Composers and Conductors Issue**

32¢ **Leopold Stokowski,** tagged (4,300,000) 20-stamp panes .50 .20 ☐☐☐☐☐

CM1947_____

32¢ **Arthur Fiedler,** tagged .50 .20 ☐☐☐☐☐

CM1948_____

32¢ **George Szell,** tagged .50 .20 ☐☐☐☐☐

CM1949_____

32¢ **Eugene Ormandy,** tagged .50 .20 ☐☐☐☐☐

CM1950_____

32¢ **Samuel Barber,** tagged .50 .20 ☐☐☐☐☐

CM1951_____

32¢ **Ferde Grofe,** tagged .50 .20 ☐☐☐☐☐

CM1936

CM1937

CM1938

CM1939

CM1940

CM1942-1945

CM1941

CM1954

CM1946-1953

CM1955

CM1956-1960

CM1961

	MNHVF	UseVF

CM1952_____
32¢ **Charles Ives,** tagged .50 .20 ☐☐☐☐☐
CM1953_____
32¢ **Louis Moreau Gottschalk, Gottschalk,** tagged .50 .20 ☐☐☐☐☐
CM1954_____ **1997. Padre Felix Varela Issue**
32¢ **purple** tagged (25,250,000) .50 .20 ☐☐☐☐☐
CM1955_____ **1997. U.S. Department of the Air Force Issue**
32¢ **multicolored** tagged (45,250,000) .50 .20 ☐☐☐☐☐
CM1956_____ **1997. Classic Movie Monsters Issue**
32¢ **Lon Chaney, as Phantom of the Opera,** (29,000,000) .50 .20 ☐☐☐☐☐
CM1957_____
32¢ **Bela Lugosi, as Dracula,** tagged .50 .20 ☐☐☐☐☐
CM1958_____
32¢ **Boris Karloff, in Frankenstein,** tagged .50 .20 ☐☐☐☐☐
CM1959_____
32¢ **Boris Karloff, as The Mummy,** tagged .50 .20 ☐☐☐☐☐
CM1960_____
32¢ **Lon Chaney Jr., as The Wolf Man,** tagged .50 .20 ☐☐☐☐☐
NOTE: Because this issue also was made available to collectors in full nine-pane printing sheets, gutter pairs and blocks and cross-gutter multiples also exist.
CM1961_____ **1997. First Supersonic Flight Issue**
32¢ **multicolored** tagged (173,000,000) .50 .20 ☐☐☐☐☐
CM1962_____ **1997. Women in Military Service Issue**
32¢ **multicolored** tagged (37,000,000) .50 .20 ☐☐☐☐☐
CM1963_____ **1997. Kwanzaa Issue**
32¢ **multicolored** tagged (133,000,000) .50 .20 ☐☐☐☐☐
NOTE: Because this issue also was made available to collectors in full six-pane printing sheets, gutter pairs and blocks and cross-gutter multiples also exist.
CM1964_____ **1998. Year of The Tiger New Year Issue**
32¢ **multicolored** tagged .50 .20 ☐☐☐☐☐
CM1965_____ **1998. Winter Sports Issue**
32¢ **multicolored** tagged .50 .20 ☐☐☐☐☐
CM1966_____ **1998. Madam C.J. Walker Issue**
32¢ **multicolored** tagged .50 .20 ☐☐☐☐☐
CM1967_____ **1998. Celebrate the Century 1900s Issue**
$4.80 **Pane of 15,** tagged 12.50 9.50 ☐☐☐☐☐
CM1968_____ **1998. Celebrate the Century 1910s Issue**
$4.80 **Pane of 15,** tagged 12.50 9.50 ☐☐☐☐☐
CM1969_____ **1998. Spanish American War Issue**
32¢ **red & black** tagged .50 .20 ☐☐☐☐☐
CM1970_____ **1998. Flowering Trees Issue**
32¢ **Southern Magnolia,** tagged .50 .20 ☐☐☐☐☐
CM1971_____
32¢ **Blue Paloverde,** tagged .50 .20 ☐☐☐☐☐
CM1972_____
32¢ **Yellow Poplar,** tagged .50 .20 ☐☐☐☐☐
CM1973_____
32¢ **Prairie Crab Apple,** tagged .50 .20 ☐☐☐☐☐
CM1974_____
32¢ **Pacific Dogwood,** tagged .50 .20 ☐☐☐☐☐
CM1975_____ **1998. Alexander Calder Issue**
32¢ **Black Cascade, 13 verticals,** tagged .50 .20 ☐☐☐☐☐
CM1976_____
32¢ **Untitled,** tagged .50 .20 ☐☐☐☐☐

CM1962

CM963

CM1964

CM1965

CM1966

CM1967 →

CM1968 →

	MNHVF	UseVF

CM1977 _____
   32¢ **Rearing Stallion,** tagged   .50   .20 ☐☐☐☐☐
CM1978 _____
   32¢ **Portrait of a young man,** tagged   .50   .20 ☐☐☐☐☐
CM1979 _____
   32¢ **Un Effet du Japonais,** tagged   .50   .20 ☐☐☐☐☐
CM1980 _____ **1998. Cinco de Mayo Issue**
   32¢ **multicolored**   .50   .20 ☐☐☐☐☐
CM1981 _____ **1998. Sylvester and Tweety Issue**
   $3.20 **Pane of 10,** tagged   5.00   ☐☐☐☐☐
CM1981a _____
          ☐☐☐☐☐
CM1982 _____ **1998. Sylvester and Tweety Issue**
   $3.20 **Pane of 10,** tagged   5.00   ☐☐☐☐☐

NOTE: This issue also was made available in top and bottom half printing sheets of six 10-stamp panes each. Vertical rouletting between the two panes is missing on these half sheets. A plate number, trimmed away or individual panes, appears adjacent to the bottom-left pane in the bottom half of the printing sheet only.

CM1983 _____ **1998. Celebrate the Century, 1920s Issue**
   $4.80 **Sheetlet of 15,** tagged   15.00   9.50 ☐☐☐☐☐
CMSP1 _____ **1998. Breast Cancer Research Semipostal Issue**
   40¢ **multicolored**   .80   .30 ☐☐☐☐☐

CM1969

CM1970-1974

CM1975 -1979

CM1980

CM1981-1982

CMSP1

		MNHVF	UseVF

CM1984_____ **1998. Wisconsin Statehood Sesquicentennial Issue**
32¢ **multicolored** — .50 — .20

CM1985_____ **1998. Trans-Mississippi Color Issue**
$3.80 **Pane of 9** — 7.50 — 3.50

CM1986_____ **1998. Trans-Mississippi Color Issue**
$9   **Pane,** 9 examples of CM1985h — 15.00

CM1987_____ **1998. Berlin Airlift Issue**
32¢ **multicolored** — .50 — .20

CM1988_____ **1998. Folk Musicians Issue**
32¢ **Woody Guthrie,** tagged — .50 — .20

CM1989_____
32¢ **Sonny Terry,** tagged — .50 — .20

CM1990_____
32¢ **Huddie "Leadbelly" Ledbetter** — .50 — .20

CM1991_____
32¢ **Josh White** — .50 — .20

CM1992_____ **1998. Spanish Settlement of the Southwest Issue**
32¢ **multicolored** — .50 — .20

CM1993_____ **1998. Gospel Singers Issue**
32¢ **Mahalia Jackson** — .50 — 2.00

CM1994_____
32¢ **Roberta Martin** — .50 — .20

CM1995_____
32¢ **Clara Ward** — .50 — .20

CM1984

CM1983

	MNHVF	UseVF

CM1996_____
32¢ **Sister Rosetta Tharpe** — .50 / .20 ☐☐☐☐☐

CM1997_____ **1998. Stephen Vincent Benét Issue**
32¢ **multicolored** — .50 / .20 ☐☐☐☐☐

CM1998_____ **1998. Tropical Birds Issue**
32¢ **Antillean Euphonia** — .50 / .20 ☐☐☐☐☐

CM1999_____
32¢ **Green-throated Carib** — .50 / .20 ☐☐☐☐☐

CM2000_____
32¢ **Crested Honeycreeper** — .50 / .20 ☐☐☐☐☐

CM2001_____
32¢ **Cardinal Honeyeater** — .50 / .20 ☐☐☐☐☐

CM2002_____ **1998. Alfred Hitchcock Issue**
32¢ **black & gray** — .75 / .20 ☐☐☐☐☐

CM2003_____ **1998. Organ & Tissue Donation Issue**
32¢ **multicolored** — .50 / .20 ☐☐☐☐☐

CM2004_____ **1998. Bright Eyes Pet Issue**
32¢ **Dog,** tagged — .50 / .20 ☐☐☐☐☐

CM2005_____
32¢ **Goldfish,** tagged — .50 / .20 ☐☐☐☐☐

CM2006_____
32¢ **Cat,** tagged — .50 / .20 ☐☐☐☐☐

CM2007_____
32¢ **Parakeet,** tagged — .50 / .20 ☐☐☐☐☐

CM2008_____
32¢ **Hamster,** tagged — .50 / .20 ☐☐☐☐☐

CM2009_____ **1998. Klondike Gold Rush Issue**
32¢ **multicolored** tagged — .50 / .20 ☐☐☐☐☐

CM2010_____ **1998. American Art Issue**
32¢ **John Foster** — .50 / .20 ☐☐☐☐☐

CM2011_____
32¢ **The Freake Limner** — .50 / .20 ☐☐☐☐☐

CM2012_____
32¢ **Ammi Phillips** — .50 / .20 ☐☐☐☐☐

CM2013_____
32¢ **Rembrandt Peale** — .50 / .20 ☐☐☐☐☐

CM2014_____
32¢ **John J. Audubon** — .50 / .20 ☐☐☐☐☐

CM2015_____
32¢ **George Caleb Bingham** — .50 / .20 ☐☐☐☐☐

CM2016_____
32¢ **Asher B. Durand** — .50 / .20 ☐☐☐☐☐

CM2017_____
32¢ **Joshua Johnson** — .50 / .20 ☐☐☐☐☐

CM2018_____
32¢ **William M. Harnett** — .50 / .20 ☐☐☐☐☐

CM2019_____
32¢ **Winslow Homer** — .50 / .20 ☐☐☐☐☐

CM2020_____
32¢ **George Catlin** — .50 / .20 ☐☐☐☐☐

CM2021_____
32¢ **Thomas Moran** — .50 / .20 ☐☐☐☐☐

CM2022_____
32¢ **Albert Bierstadt** — .50 / .20 ☐☐☐☐☐

1998 Bi-Color Re-Issue of the 1898 Trans-Mississippi Stamp Designs

CM1985 (CM1986 is a pane
of 9 examples of
the $1 stamp)

CM1987

CM1992

CM1988-1991

CM1997

CM1993-1996

CM1998-2001

CM2002

CM2003

CM2009

CM2004-2008

	MNHVF	UseVF
CM2023_____		
32¢ **Frederic Edwin Church**	.50	.20
CM2024_____		
32¢ **Mary Cassatt**	.50	.20
CM2025_____		
32¢ **Edward Hopper**	.50	.20
CM2026_____		
32¢ **Grant Wood**	.50	.20
CM2027_____		
32¢ **Charles Sheeler**	.50	.20
CM2028_____		
32¢ **Franny Kline**	.50	.20
CM2029_____		
32¢ **Mark Rothko**	.50	.20
CM2030_____ **1998. Celebrate the Century, 1930s Issue**		
$4.80 **Sheetlet of 15,** tagged	10.00	7.50
CM2031_____ **1998. Ballet Issue**		
32¢ **multicolored**	.50	.20
CM2032_____ **1998. Space Discovery Issue**		
32¢ **Land craft**	.50	.20
CM2033_____		
32¢ **Space ship**	.50	.20
CM2034_____		
32¢ **Figure**	.50	.20

CM2010-2029

	MNHVF	UseVF	

CM2035_____
  32¢ **Jagged hills** — .50 — .20 ☐☐☐☐☐
CM2036_____
  32¢ **Moon** — .50 — .20 ☐☐☐☐☐
CM2037_____ **1998. Giving & Sharing Issue**
  32¢ **multicolored** — .50 — .20 ☐☐☐☐☐
CM2038_____ **1999. Year of the Hare Issue**
  33¢ **multicolored** tagged — .50 — .20 ☐☐☐☐☐
CM2039_____ **1999. Malcolm X Issue**
  33¢ **multicolored** — .50 — .20 ☐☐☐☐☐
CM2040_____ **1999. Victorian Hearts Issue**
  33¢ **multicolored** — .50 — .20 ☐☐☐☐☐
CM2041_____ **1999. Victorian Hearts Issue**
  55¢ **multicolored** — .85 — .25 ☐☐☐☐☐
CM2042_____ **1999. Hospice Care Issue**
  33¢ **multicolored** phosphored paper — .50 — .20 ☐☐☐☐☐
CM2043_____ **1999. Celebrate the Century 1940s Issue**
  $4.95 **Commemorative pane of 15, multicolored** tagged — 10.00 — 7.50 ☐☐☐☐☐
CM2044_____ **1999. Irish Immigration Issue**
  33¢ **multicolored** — .50 — .20 ☐☐☐☐☐
CM2045_____ **1999. Alfred Lunt and Lynn Fontanne Issue**
  33¢ **multicolored** — .50 — .20 ☐☐☐☐☐
CM2046_____ **1999. Arctic Animals Issue**
  33¢ **Arctic Hare, multicolored** — .60 — .20 ☐☐☐☐☐

CM2030
←

	MNHVF	UseVF

CM2047_____
   33¢ **Arctic Fox, multicolored** | .60 | .20 ☐☐☐☐☐
CM2048_____
   33¢ **Snowy Owl, multicolored** | .60 | .20 ☐☐☐☐☐
CM2049_____
   33¢ **Polar Bear, multicolored** | .60 | .20 ☐☐☐☐☐
CM2050_____
   33¢ **Gray Wolf, multicolored** | .60 | .20 ☐☐☐☐☐
CM2051_____ **1999. Sonoran Desert Issue**
   $3.30 **multicolored Sheetlet of 10,** blocked tagged | 7.50 | 3.00 ☐☐☐☐☐
CM2052_____ **1999. Daffy Duck Issue**
   $3.30 **Pane of 10,** tagged | 7.50 | ☐☐☐☐☐

NOTE: This issue also was made available in top- and bottom-half printing sheets of six 10-stamp panes each. Vertical rouletting between the two panes is missing on these half sheets. A single plate number, trimmed away on individual panes, appears adjacent to the bottom-left pane in the bottom half of the printing sheet only.

CM2053_____ **1999. Daffy Duck Issue**
   $3.30 **Pane of 10,** tagged | 7.50 | ☐☐☐☐☐
CM2054_____ **1999. Ayn Rand Issue**
   33¢ **multicolored** | .50 | .20 ☐☐☐☐☐
CM2055_____ **1999. Cinco de Mayo Issue**
   33¢ **multicolored** | .50 | .20 ☐☐☐☐☐
CM2056_____ **1999. Tropical Flowers Issue**
   33¢ **Bird of paradise, multicolored** | .50 | .20 ☐☐☐☐☐
CM2057_____
   33¢ **Royal poinciana, multicolored** | .50 | .20 ☐☐☐☐☐
CM2058_____
   33¢ **Gloriosa lily, multicolored** | .50 | .20 ☐☐☐☐☐

CM2031

CM2032-2036

CM2037

CM2038

CM2039

CM2040

CM2041

CM2042

CM2043

CM2044

CM2045

CM2046-2050

CM2051

	MNHVF	UseVF

CM2059_____
  33¢ **Chinese hibiscus, multicolored** — .50 | .20 ☐☐☐☐☐

CM2060_____ **1999. John & William Bartram Issue**
  33¢ **multicolored** — .60 | .20 ☐☐☐☐☐

CM2061_____ **1999. Celebrate the Century 1950s Issue**
  $4.95 **Commemorative page of 15, multicolored** tagged — 10.00 | 7.50 ☐☐☐☐☐

CM2062_____ **1999. Prostate Cancer Awareness Issue**
  33¢ **multicolored** — .50 | .20 ☐☐☐☐☐

CM2063_____ **1999. California Gold Rush Issue**
  33¢ **multicolored** — .50 | .20 ☐☐☐☐☐

CM2064_____ **1999. Aquarium Fish Issue**
  33¢ **Black-and-white fish** — .50 | .20 ☐☐☐☐☐

CM2065_____
  33¢ **Thermometer** — .50 | .20 ☐☐☐☐☐

CM2066_____
  33¢ **Blue-and-yellow fish** — .50 | .20 ☐☐☐☐☐

CM2052

CM2053

	MNHVF	UseVF

CM2067_____

33¢ **red-and-white fish**   .50   .20 ☐☐☐☐☐

NOTE: This issue was also made available in press sheets.

CM2068_____   **1999. Xtreme Sports Issue**

33¢ **Skateboarding**   .50   .20 ☐☐☐☐☐

CM2069_____

33¢ **BMX biking**   .50   .20 ☐☐☐☐☐

CM2070_____

33¢ **Snowboarding**   .50   .20 ☐☐☐☐☐

CM2071_____

33¢ **In-line skating**   .50   .20 ☐☐☐☐☐

CM2054

CM2055

CM2056-2059

CM2061

CM2060

CM2062

		MNHVF	UseVF	

CM2072_____ **1999. American Glass Issue**

33¢ **Freeblown glass** .50 .20 ☐☐☐☐☐

CM2073_____

33¢ **Mold-blown glass** .50 .20 ☐☐☐☐☐

CM2074_____

33¢ **Pressed glass** .50 .20 ☐☐☐☐☐

CM2075_____

33¢ **Art glass** .50 .20 ☐☐☐☐☐

CM2076_____ **1999. James Cagney Issue**

33¢ **multicolored** .50 .20 ☐☐☐☐☐

CM2077_____ **1999. Honoring Those Who Served Issue**

33¢ **multicolored** .50 .20 ☐☐☐☐☐

CM2078_____ **1999. Universal Postal Union Issue**

45¢ **multicolored** .90 .40 ☐☐☐☐☐

CM2079_____ **1999. All Aboard! Issue**

33¢ **multicolored** .50 .20 ☐☐☐☐☐

CM2080_____

33¢ **multicolored** .50 .20 ☐☐☐☐☐

CM2081_____

33¢ **multicolored** .50 .20 ☐☐☐☐☐

CM2082_____

33¢ **multicolored** .50 .20 ☐☐☐☐☐

CM2063

CM2064-2067

CM2068-2071

CM2072-2075

	MNHVF	UseVF	
CM2083_____			
33¢ **multicolored**	.50	.20	☐☐☐☐☐
CM2084_____　**1999. Frederic Law Olmsted Issue**			
33¢ **multicolored**	.50	.20	☐☐☐☐☐
CM2085_____　**1999. Hollywood Composers Issue**			
33¢ **multicolored**	.50	.20	☐☐☐☐☐
CM2086_____			
33¢ **multicolored**	.50	.20	☐☐☐☐☐
CM2087_____			
33¢ **multicolored**	.50	.20	☐☐☐☐☐
CM2088_____			
33¢ **multicolored**	.50	.20	☐☐☐☐☐

CM2076

CM2077

CM2078　　CM2084

CM2085-2090

CM2079-2083

		MNHVF	UseVF	
CM2089_____				
33¢ **multicolored**		.50	.20 ▢▢▢▢▢	
CM2090_____				
33¢ **multicolored**			▢▢▢▢▢	
CM2091_____	**1999. Celebrate the Century 1960s Issue**			
$4.95 **Commemorative pane of 15, multicolored**, tagged		10.00	7.50 ▢▢▢▢▢	
CM2092_____	**1999. Broadway Songwriters Issue**			
33¢ **multicolored**		.50	.20 ▢▢▢▢▢	
CM2093_____				
33¢ **multicolored**		.50	.20 ▢▢▢▢▢	
CM2094_____				
33¢ **multicolored**		.50	.20 ▢▢▢▢▢	
CM2095_____				
33¢ **multicolored**		.50	.20 ▢▢▢▢▢	
CM2096_____				
33¢ **multicolored**		.50	.20 ▢▢▢▢▢	
CM2097_____				
33¢ **multicolored**		.50	.20 ▢▢▢▢▢	
CM2098_____	**1999. Insects and Spiders Issue**			
33¢ **multicolored**		10.00	7.50 ▢▢▢▢▢	

CM2091

		MNHVF	UseVF	
CM2099_____	**1999. Hanukkah Issue**			
33¢ **multicolored**		.50	.20	☐☐☐☐☐
CM2100_____	**1999. North Atlantic Treaty Organization Issue**			
33¢ **multicolored**		.50	.20	☐☐☐☐☐
CM2101_____	**1999. Kwanzaa Issue**			
33¢ **multicolored**		.50	.20	☐☐☐☐☐
CM2102_____	**1999. Celebrate the Century 1970s Issue**			
$4.95 **Sheetlet of 15,** tagged		10.00	7.00	☐☐☐☐☐
CM2103_____	**1999. Year 2000 Issue**			
33¢ **multicolored**		.50	.20	☐☐☐☐☐
CM2104_____	**2000. Year of the Dragon Issue**			
33¢ **multicolored**		.50	.20	☐☐☐☐☐
CM2105_____	**2000. Celebrate the Century 1980s Issue**			
33¢ **Commemorative pane of 15, multicolored,** tagged		10.00	7.00	☐☐☐☐☐
CM2106_____	**2000. Patricia Roberts Harris Issue**			
33¢ **multicolored**		.50	.20	☐☐☐☐☐
CM2107_____	**2000. U.S. Navy Submarines Issue**			
60¢ **USS Holland**		1.20	1.00	☐☐☐☐☐
CM2108_____				
22¢ **S Class submarine**		.40	.30	☐☐☐☐☐
CM2109_____				
$3.20 **Gato-class submarine**		6.00	2.50	☐☐☐☐☐

CM2099

CM2100

CM2101

CM2092-2097

CM2103

	MNHVF	UseVF

CM2110_____
    33¢ *Los Angeles*-class attack submarine   .60   .30 ☐☐☐☐☐
CM2111_____
    55¢ *Trident-class ICBM submarine*   1.00   1.00 ☐☐☐☐☐
CM2112_____ **2000. Los Angeles Class Submarine Issue**
    33¢ **multicolored**   .50   .20 ☐☐☐☐☐
CM2113_____ **2000. Pacific Coast Rain Forest Issue**
    33¢ **multicolored**   .50   .20 ☐☐☐☐☐
CM2114_____ **2000. Louise Nevelson Issue**
    33¢ **multicolored**   .50   .20 ☐☐☐☐☐
CM2115_____
    33¢ **multicolored**   .50   .20 ☐☐☐☐☐
CM2116_____
    33¢ **multicolored**   .50   .20 ☐☐☐☐☐
CM2117_____
    33¢ **multicolored**   .50   .20 ☐☐☐☐☐
CM2118_____
    33¢ **multicolored**   .50   .20 ☐☐☐☐☐

CM2098

CM2102

CM2106

CM2104

CM2112

CM2107-2111

		MNHVF	UseVF	

CM2119_____   **2000. Edwin Powell Hubble Issue**

33¢ **Eagle Nebula**   .50   .20 ☐☐☐☐☐

CM2120_____

33¢ **Ring Nebula**   .50   .20 ☐☐☐☐☐

CM2121_____

33¢ **Lagoon Nebula**   .50   .20 ☐☐☐☐☐

CM2122_____

33¢ **Egg Nebula**   .50   .20 ☐☐☐☐☐

CM2123_____

33¢ **Galaxy NGC 1316**   .50   .20 ☐☐☐☐☐

CM2105 ←

CM2114-2118

		MNHVF	UseVF

CM2124_____ **2000. American Samoa Issue**

   33¢ **multicolored**   .50   .20

CM2125_____ **2000. Library of Congress Issue**

   33¢ **multicolored**   .50   .20

CM2126_____ **2000. Celebrate the Century 1990's Issue**

   33¢ **Commemorative pane of 15, multicolored,** tagged   10.00   7.00

CM2113

CM2119-2123

CM2124

CM2125

CM2126

		MNHVF	UseVF	
CM2127_____	**2000. Wile E. Coyote & Road Runner Issue**			
33¢ multicolored		7.50		❑❑❑❑❑
CM2128_____				
33¢ multicolored		7.50		❑❑❑❑❑
CM2129_____	**2000. Distinguished Soldiers Issue**			
33¢ multicolored		.50	.20	❑❑❑❑❑
CM2130_____				
33¢ multicolored		.50	.20	❑❑❑❑❑
CM2131_____				
33¢ multicolored		.50	.20	❑❑❑❑❑
CM2132_____				
33¢ multicolored		.50	.20	❑❑❑❑❑
CM2133_____	**2000. Summer Sports Issue**			
33¢ multicolored		.50	.20	❑❑❑❑❑
CM2134_____	**2000. Adoption Issue**			
33¢ multicolored		.50	.20	❑❑❑❑❑
CM2135_____	**2000. Youth Team Sports Issue**			
33¢ multicolored		.50	.20	❑❑❑❑❑
CM2136_____				
33¢ multicolored		.50	.20	❑❑❑❑❑
CM2137_____				
33¢ multicolored		.50	.20	❑❑❑❑❑
CM2138_____				
33¢ multicolored		.50	.20	❑❑❑❑❑
CM2139_____	**2000. Stars and Stripes Issue**			
33¢ multicolored		.50	.20	❑❑❑❑❑
CM2140_____				
33¢ multicolored		.50	.20	❑❑❑❑❑
CM2141_____				
33¢ multicolored		.50	.20	❑❑❑❑❑
CM2142_____				
33¢ multicolored		.50	.20	❑❑❑❑❑
CM2143_____				
33¢ multicolored		.50	.20	❑❑❑❑❑
CM2144_____				
33¢ multicolored		.50	.20	❑❑❑❑❑
CM2145_____				
33¢ multicolored		.50	.20	❑❑❑❑❑
CM2146_____				
33¢ multicolored		.50	.20	❑❑❑❑❑
CM2147_____				
33¢ multicolored		.50	.20	❑❑❑❑❑
CM2148_____				
33¢ multicolored		.50	.20	❑❑❑❑❑
CM2149_____				
33¢ multicolored		.50	.20	❑❑❑❑❑
CM2150_____				
33¢ multicolored		.50	.20	❑❑❑❑❑
CM2151_____				
33¢ multicolored		.50	.20	❑❑❑❑❑
CM2152_____				
33¢ multicolored		.50	.20	❑❑❑❑❑
CM2153_____				
33¢ multicolored		.50	.20	❑❑❑❑❑

CM2133

CM2127

CM2134

CM2135-2139

CM2129-CM2132

CM2139-2158

CM2179

		MNHVF	UseVF	
CM2154_____				
33¢ **multicolored**		.50	.20	☐☐☐☐☐
CM2155_____				
33¢ **multicolored**		.50	.20	☐☐☐☐☐
CM2156_____				
33¢ **multicolored**		.50	.20	☐☐☐☐☐
CM2157_____				
33¢ **multicolored**		.50	.20	☐☐☐☐☐
CM2158_____				
33¢ **multicolored**		.50	.20	☐☐☐☐☐
CM2159_____	**2000. Legends of Baseball Issue**			
33¢ **multicolored**		.50	.20	☐☐☐☐☐
CM2160_____				
33¢ **multicolored**		.50	.20	☐☐☐☐☐
CM2161_____				
33¢ **multicolored**		.50	.20	☐☐☐☐☐
CM2162_____				
33¢ **multicolored**		.50	.20	☐☐☐☐☐
CM2163_____				
33¢ **multicolored**		.50	.20	☐☐☐☐☐
CM2164_____				
33¢ **multicolored**		.50	.20	☐☐☐☐☐
CM2165_____				
33¢ **multicolored**		.50	.20	☐☐☐☐☐
CM2166_____				
33¢ **multicolored**		.50	.20	☐☐☐☐☐
CM2167_____				
33¢ **multicolored**		.50	.20	☐☐☐☐☐
CM2168_____				
33¢ **multicolored**		.50	.20	☐☐☐☐☐
CM2169_____				
33¢ **multicolored**		.50	.20	☐☐☐☐☐
CM2170_____				
33¢ **multicolored**		.50	.20	☐☐☐☐☐
CM2171_____				
33¢ **multicolored**		.50	.20	☐☐☐☐☐
CM2172_____				
33¢ **multicolored**		.50	.20	☐☐☐☐☐
CM2173_____				
33¢ **multicolored**		.50	.20	☐☐☐☐☐
CM2174_____				
33¢ **multicolored**		.50	.20	☐☐☐☐☐
CM2175_____				
33¢ **multicolored**		.50	.20	☐☐☐☐☐
CM2176_____				
33¢ **multicolored**		.50	.20	☐☐☐☐☐
CM2177_____				
33¢ **multicolored**		.50	.20	☐☐☐☐☐
CM2178_____				
33¢ **multicolored**		.50	.20	☐☐☐☐☐
CM2179_____	**2000. Space Achievement and Exploration Issue**			
$11.75 **multicolored**		22.00	10.00	☐☐☐☐☐

NOTE: The foil hologram is affixed with water-soluble adhesive and may release from the stamp while soaking.

CM2180_____	**2000. Landing on the Moon Issue**			
$11.75 **multicolored**		22.00	10.00	☐☐☐☐☐

NOTE: The foil hologram is affixed with water-soluble adhesive and may release from the stamp while soaking.

CM2159-2178

CM2180

	MNHVF	UseVF	

CM2181_____   **2000. Escaping the Gravity of Earth Issue**
$3.20 **multicolored**   6.50   3.00 ☐☐☐☐☐

NOTE: The foil holograms are affixed with water-soluble adhesive and may release from the stamps while soaking.
CM2182_____
$3.20 **multicolored**   6.50   3.00 ☐☐☐☐☐
CM2183_____   **2000. Probing the Vastness of Space Issue**
60¢ **multicolored**   1.10   .60 ☐☐☐☐☐
CM2184_____
60¢ **multicolored**   1.10   .60 ☐☐☐☐☐
CM2185_____
60¢ **multicolored**   1.10   .60 ☐☐☐☐☐
CM2186_____
60¢ **multicolored**   1.10   .60 ☐☐☐☐☐
CM2187_____
60¢ **multicolored**   1.10   .60 ☐☐☐☐☐
CM2188_____
60¢ **multicolored**   1.10   .60 ☐☐☐☐☐
CM2189_____   **2000. Exploring the Solar System Issue**
33¢ **multicolored**   2.00   1.00 ☐☐☐☐☐
CM2190_____
33¢ **multicolored**   2.00   1.00 ☐☐☐☐☐
CM2191_____
33¢ **multicolored**   2.00   1.00 ☐☐☐☐☐
CM2192_____
33¢ **multicolored**   2.00   1.00 ☐☐☐☐☐
CM2193_____
33¢ **multicolored**   2.00   1.00 ☐☐☐☐☐
CM2194_____   **2000. Stampin' the Future Issue**
33¢ **multicolored**   .50   .20 ☐☐☐☐☐
CM2195_____
33¢ **multicolored**   .50   .20 ☐☐☐☐☐
CM2196_____
33¢ **multicolored**   .50   .20 ☐☐☐☐☐
CM2197_____
33¢ **multicolored**   .50   .20 ☐☐☐☐☐
CM2198_____   **2000. California Statehood Issue**
33¢ **multicolored**   .50   .20 ☐☐☐☐☐
CM2199_____   **2000. Deep-Sea Creatures Issue**
33¢ **Fanfin anglerfish**   .50   .20 ☐☐☐☐☐
CM2200_____
33¢ **Sea cucumber**   .50   .20 ☐☐☐☐☐
CM2201_____
33¢ **Fangtooth**   .50   .20 ☐☐☐☐☐
CM2202_____
33¢ **Amphipod**   .50   .20 ☐☐☐☐☐
CM2203_____
33¢ **Medusa**   .50   .20 ☐☐☐☐☐
CM2204_____   **2000. Thomas Wolfe Issue**
33¢ **multicolored**   .50   .20 ☐☐☐☐☐
CM2205_____   **2000. The White House Issue**
33¢ **multicolored**   .50   .20 ☐☐☐☐☐
CM2206_____   **2000. Edward G. Robinson Issue**
33¢ **multicolored**   .50   .20 ☐☐☐☐☐

CM2181-82

CM2198

CM2206

CM2204

CM2205

CM2183-2188

CM2189-2193

CM2199-2203

CM2194-2197

	UnFVF	UseFVF

AIRMAIL

/////

A1 _____ **1918. Curtiss Biplane Issue**
6¢ **red orange** (3,395,854) 75.00 30.00 ⬜⬜⬜⬜⬜
A2 _____
16¢ **green** (3,793,887) 90.00 40.00 ⬜⬜⬜⬜⬜
A3 _____
24¢ **carmine red & blue** (2,134,888) 90.00 45.00 ⬜⬜⬜⬜⬜

NOTE: One sheet of 100 stamps with the blue vignette of the airplane upside down was purchased in a post office at Washington, D.C., by William T. Robey, who sold it to Eugene Klein of Philadelphia, who in turn sold it to Col. Edward H.R. Green. Green retained some of the errors, including the position pieces, and through Klein disposed of the rest. Minkus No. A3v is one of the most famous post office finds in U.S. stamp history.

A4 _____ **1923. The Second Airmail Series Issue**
8¢ **green** (6,414,576) 25.00 15.00 ⬜⬜⬜⬜⬜
A5 _____
16¢ **indigo** (5,309,275) 85.00 30.00 ⬜⬜⬜⬜⬜
A6 _____
24¢ **carmine** (5,285,775) 95.00 30.00 ⬜⬜⬜⬜⬜
A7 _____ **1926-27. Map Issue**
10¢ **blue** (42,092,800) 3.00 .45 ⬜⬜⬜⬜⬜
A8 _____
15¢ **olive brown** (15,597,307) 3.75 2.50 ⬜⬜⬜⬜⬜
A9 _____
20¢ **yellow green** (17,616,350) 9.00 2.00 ⬜⬜⬜⬜⬜
A10 _____ **1927. Lindbergh Airmail Issue**
10¢ **indigo** (20,379,179) 8.00 2.00 ⬜⬜⬜⬜⬜

NOTE: First-day covers for No. A10 are from Washington, D.C., Little Falls, Minn. (where Lindbergh grew up), St. Louis, Mo., and Detroit, Mich. (his birthplace). FDCs for No. A10n are from Washington, D.C., and Cleveland, Ohio.

A11 _____ **1928. Air Mail Beacon Issue**
5¢ **carmine red & blue** (106,887,675) 4.50 .75 ⬜⬜⬜⬜⬜
A12 _____ **1930. Winged Globe Issue**
5¢ **purple** (97,641,200) 10.00 .50 ⬜⬜⬜⬜⬜
A13 _____ **1930. Graf Zeppelin Issue**
65¢ **green** (93,536) 325.00 240.00 ⬜⬜⬜⬜⬜
A14 _____
$1.30 **yellow brown** (72,428) 650.00 450.00 ⬜⬜⬜⬜⬜
A15 _____
$2.60 **blue** (61,296) 975.00 700.00 ⬜⬜⬜⬜⬜
A16 _____ **1931-34. Winged Globe Issue**
5¢ **reddish violet** (57,340,000) 5.50 .60 ⬜⬜⬜⬜⬜
A17 _____
6¢ **orange** (302,205,100) 2.50 .35 ⬜⬜⬜⬜⬜
A18 _____
8¢ **yellow olive** (76,648,803) 2.50 .35 ⬜⬜⬜⬜⬜
A19 _____ **1933. Century of Progress Zeppelin Issue**
50¢ **green** (324,070) 90.00 75.00 ⬜⬜⬜⬜⬜
A20 _____ **1935-37. China Clipper Over Pacific Issue**
20¢ **green** (12,794,600) 10.00 1.50 ⬜⬜⬜⬜⬜
A21 _____
25¢ **blue** (10,205,400) 1.50 1.00 ⬜⬜⬜⬜⬜
A22 _____
50¢ **carmine** (9,285,300) 10.00 4.50 ⬜⬜⬜⬜⬜
A23 _____ **1938. Eagle and Shield Issue**
6¢ **indigo & carmine** (349,946,500) .50 .20 ⬜⬜⬜⬜⬜

A1

A2

A3

A3v

A4

A5

A6

A7-A9

A10

A11

A-12

A13

A14

A15

A16-A18

A19

A33-A34

A20

A23

A24

A25

A32

A35

	UnFVF	UseFVF	

A24 _____ **1939. Transatlantic Issue**
30¢ **slate blue** (19,768,150) — 9.00 — 1.50 ☐☐☐☐☐

	MNHVF	UseVF

A25 _____ **1941-44. Twin Motored Transport Plane Issue**
6¢ **rose red** (4,746,527,700) — .25 — .20 ☐☐☐☐☐
A26 _____
8¢ **light olive green** (1,744,878,650) — .30 — .20 ☐☐☐☐☐
A27 _____
10¢ **violet** (67,117,400) — 1.40 — .20 ☐☐☐☐☐
A28 _____
15¢ **brown carmine** (78,434,800) — 2.75 — .40 ☐☐☐☐☐
A29 _____
20¢ **emerald** (42,359,850) — 2.75 — .40 ☐☐☐☐☐
A30 _____
30¢ **light blue** (59,880,850) — 2.75 — .50 ☐☐☐☐☐
A31 _____
50¢ **orange** (11,160,600) — 14.00 — 4.00 ☐☐☐☐☐
A32 _____ **1946. Skymaster Issue**
5¢ **carmine** (864,753,100) — .25 — .20 ☐☐☐☐☐
A33 _____ **1947. Small 5¢ Skymaster Issue**
5¢ **carmine** (971,903,700) — .25 — .20 ☐☐☐☐☐
A34 _____ **1947. Small 5¢ Skymaster Coil Issue**
5¢ **carmine** (33,244,500) — 1.00 — 1.00 ☐☐☐☐☐
A35 _____ **1947. Pictorial Airmail Issue**
10¢ **black** (207,976,550) — .40 — .20 ☐☐☐☐☐
A36 _____
15¢ **blue green** (756,186,350) — .50 — .20 ☐☐☐☐☐
A37 _____
25¢ **blue** (132,956,100) — 1.25 — .20 ☐☐☐☐☐
A38 _____ **1948. New York City Issue**
5¢ **carmine red** (38,449,100) — .25 — .20 ☐☐☐☐☐
A39 _____ **1949. Small 6¢ Skymaster Issue**
6¢ **carmine** (5,070,095,200) — .25 — .20 ☐☐☐☐☐
A40 _____ **1949. Small 6¢ Skymaster Coil Issue**
6¢ **carmine** — 3.50 — .20 ☐☐☐☐☐
A41 _____ **1949. Alexandria Bicentennial Issue**
6¢ **carmine** (75,085,000) — .20 — .20 ☐☐☐☐☐
A42 _____ **1949. Universal Postal Union Issue**
10¢ **violet** (21,061,300) — .40 — .30 ☐☐☐☐☐
A43 _____
15¢ **cobalt** (36,613,100) — .50 — .40 ☐☐☐☐☐
A44 _____
25¢ **carmine** (16,217,100) — .85 — .60 ☐☐☐☐☐
A45 _____ **1949. Wright Brothers Issue**
6¢ **carmine purple** (80,405,000) — .30 — .20 ☐☐☐☐☐
A46 _____ **1952. Hawaii Airmail Issue**
80¢ **bright purple** (18,876,800) — 6.00 — 1.50 ☐☐☐☐☐
A47 _____ **1953. Powered Flight Issue**
6¢ **carmine** (78,415,000) — .25 — .20 ☐☐☐☐☐
A48 _____ **1954. Eagle Issue**
4¢ **blue** (40,483,600) — .25 — .20 ☐☐☐☐☐
A49 _____ **1957. Air Force Issue**
6¢ **bright Prussian blue** (63,185,000) — .25 — .20 ☐☐☐☐☐

A36

A37

A38

A39-A40

A41

A42

A43

A44

A45

A46

A47

A48, 50

A49

A51-A52, A60-61

A53

A54

A55

A56

A57

A58

A59

A62

A63

	MNHVF	UseVF	

A50 _____   **1958. Eagle Issue**
5¢   **carmine red** (72,480,000)   .25   .20 ☐☐☐☐☐
A51 _____   **1958. Jet Silhouette Issue**
7¢   **blue** (1,326,960,000)   .25   .20 ☐☐☐☐☐
A52 _____   **1958. Jet Silhouette Coil Issue**
7¢   **blue** (157,035,000)   2.00   .20 ☐☐☐☐☐
A53 _____   **1959. Alaska Statehood Issue**
7¢   **deep blue** (90,055,200)   .30   .20 ☐☐☐☐☐
A54 _____   **1959. Balloon Jupiter Issue**
7¢   **deep blue & scarlet** (79,290,000)   .30   .20 ☐☐☐☐☐
A55 _____   **1959. Pan American Games Issue**
10¢   **deep blue & scarlet** (38,770,000)   .35   .30 ☐☐☐☐☐
A56 _____   **1959. Hawaii Statehood Issue**
7¢   **dull scarlet** (84,815,000)   .30   .20 ☐☐☐☐☐
A57 _____   **1960. Liberty Bell Issue**
10¢   **black & green** (39,960,000)   1.75   .80 ☐☐☐☐☐
A58 _____   **1959. Statue of Liberty Issue**
15¢   **black & orange** (98,160,000)   .50   .20 ☐☐☐☐☐
A59 _____   **1966. Abraham Lincoln Issue**
25¢   **black & brown purple**   .75   .20 ☐☐☐☐☐
A60 _____   **1960. Jet Silhouette Issue**
7¢   **bright red** (1,289,460,000)   .25   .20 ☐☐☐☐☐
A61 _____   **1960. Jet Silhouette Coil Issue**
7¢   **bright red** (87,140,000)   4.50   .40 ☐☐☐☐☐
A62 _____   **1961. Statue of Liberty Issue**
15¢   **black & orange**   .50   .20 ☐☐☐☐☐
A63 _____   **1961. Liberty Bell Issue**
13¢   **black & scarlet**   .50   .20 ☐☐☐☐☐
A64 _____   **1962. Airliner Over Capitol Issue**
8¢   **carmine**   .30   .20 ☐☐☐☐☐

NOTE: Type I tagging: mat tagging, using four separate mats that did not cover entire sheet of 400 stamps (untagged areas identify the variety). Stamps from the four corners of a pane have two untagged margins.

Type II tagging: roll tagging, where continuous rolls replaced the tagging mats. Only the plate number selvage margin is partially tagged.

A65 _____   **1962. Airliner Over Capitol Coil Issue**
8¢   **carmine**   .60   .20 ☐☐☐☐☐
A66 _____   **1963. Montgomery Blair Issue**
15¢   **red, maroon & blue** (42,245,000)   .75   .60 ☐☐☐☐☐
A67 _____   **1963. Bald Eagle Issue**
6¢   **carmine**   .25   .20 ☐☐☐☐☐
A68 _____   **1963. Amelia Earhart Issue**
8¢   **carmine red & brown purple** (63,890,000)   .35   .20 ☐☐☐☐☐
A69 _____   **1964. Robert H. Goddard Issue**
8¢   **multicolored** (65,170,000)   .45   .20 ☐☐☐☐☐
A70 _____   **1967. Alaska Purchase Issue**
8¢   **brown & light brown** (64,710,000)   .40   .20 ☐☐☐☐☐
A71 _____   **1967. Columbia Jays Issue**
20¢   **blue, brown & yellow,** tagged (165,430,000)   1.25   .20 ☐☐☐☐☐
A72 _____   **1968. Star Runway Issue**
10¢   **red** tagged   .40   .20 ☐☐☐☐☐
A73 _____   **1968. Star Runway Coil Issue**
10¢   **red**   .40   .20 ☐☐☐☐☐
A74 _____   **1968. Airmail Service Issue**
10¢   **black, red & blue** (74,180,000)   .40   .20 ☐☐☐☐☐

A64-65

A66

A67

A68

A69

A70

A71

A72-73

A74

A75 (A81 has "21¢")

FIRST MAN ON THE MOON

A76

A77

A78-A79

A82

A83

A80

A84

A85, A86

A87

A88

A89

A90

	MNHVF	UseVF	

A75 _____ **1968. USA and Jet Issue**
20¢ **multicolored** .75 .20 ☐☐☐☐☐
A76 _____ **1969. Moon Landing Issue**
10¢ **multicolored** (152,364,800) .40 .20 ☐☐☐☐☐

NOTE: A76v. must have missing red from the entire design, including the dots on top of the yellow area as well as the astronaut's shoulder patch. Stamps with any red present are worth far less than the true red-omitted error.

A77 _____ **1971. Delta Wing Silhouette Issue**
9¢ **red** (25,830,000) .30 .20 ☐☐☐☐☐
A78 _____ **1971. Jet Silhouette Issue**
11¢ **red** tagged (317,810,000) .40 .20 ☐☐☐☐☐
A79 _____ **1971. Jet Silhouette Coil Issue**
11¢ **red** .40 .20 ☐☐☐☐☐
A80 _____ **1971. Head of Liberty Issue**
17¢ **multicolored** tagged .60 .20 ☐☐☐☐☐
A81 _____ **1971. Jet and "USA" Issue**
21¢ **multicolored** tagged (49,815,000) .75 .20 ☐☐☐☐☐
A82 _____ **1972. National Park Issue**
11¢ **multicolored** (78,210,000) .35 .20 ☐☐☐☐☐
A83 _____ **1972. Olympic Issue**
11¢ **multicolored** (92,710,000) .40 .20 ☐☐☐☐☐
A84 _____ **1973. Progress in Electronics Issue**
11¢ **multicolored** tagged (56,000,000) .30 .20 ☐☐☐☐☐
A85 _____ **1973. Winged Envelope Issue**
13¢ **red** tagged .40 .20 ☐☐☐☐☐
A86 _____ **1973. Winged Envelope Coil Issue**
13¢ **red** .50 .20 ☐☐☐☐☐
A87 _____ **1974. Statue of Liberty Issue**
18¢ **multicolored** tagged .60 .50 ☐☐☐☐☐
A88 _____ **1974. Mount Rushmore Issue**
26¢ **multicolored** tagged .75 .20 ☐☐☐☐☐
A89 _____ **1976. Plane and Globes Issue**
25¢ **multicolored** tagged .75 .20 ☐☐☐☐☐
A90 _____
31¢ **multicolored** tagged .90 .20 ☐☐☐☐☐
A91 _____ **1978. Orville and Wilbur Wright Issue**
31¢ **multicolored large portraits & biplane** 1.75 1.50 ☐☐☐☐☐
A92 _____
31¢ **multicolored, small portraits, biplane and hangar** 1.75 1.50 ☐☐☐☐☐
A93 _____ **1978. Octave Chanute Issue**
21¢ **multicolored, large portrait** 1.75 1.50 ☐☐☐☐☐
A94 _____
21¢ **multicolored, small portrait** 1.75 1.50 ☐☐☐☐☐
A95 _____ **1979. High Jumper Issue**
31¢ **multicolored** tagged 1.00 .35 ☐☐☐☐☐
A96 _____ **1979. Wiley Post Issue**
25¢ **multicolored, large portrait,** tagged 3.00 2.00 ☐☐☐☐☐
A97 _____
25¢ **multicolored, small portrait,** tagged 3.00 2.00 ☐☐☐☐☐
A98 _____ **1982. Philip Mazzei Issue**
40¢ **multicolored** tagged 1.25 .25 ☐☐☐☐☐
A99 _____ **1980. Blanche Stuart Scott Issue**
28¢ **multicolored** tagged .90 .25 ☐☐☐☐☐
A100 _____ **1980. Glenn Curtiss Issue**
35¢ **multicolored** tagged 1.00 .25 ☐☐☐☐☐

A91, A92   A93, A94

A95

A100

A96, A97

A98

A99

A101, A102,
A103, A104

A105, A106, A107, A108

A109, A110,
A111, A112

A113

A114

A115

A116

A117

A118

	MNHVF	UseVF	

A101 _____ **1983. Olympic Issues**
40¢ **Men's shot put,** tagged | 1.25 | .25 ☐☐☐☐☐
A102 _____
40¢ **Men's gymnastics,** tagged | 1.25 | .25 ☐☐☐☐☐
A103 _____
40¢ **Women's swimming,** tagged | 1.25 | .25 ☐☐☐☐☐
A104 _____
40¢ **Men's weight lifting,** tagged | 1.25 | .25 ☐☐☐☐☐
A105 _____ **1983. Olympics Second Issue**
28¢ **Women's gymnastics,** tagged | 1.25 | .25 ☐☐☐☐☐
A106 _____
28¢ **Men's hurdles,** tagged | 1.25 | .25 ☐☐☐☐☐
A107 _____
28¢ **Women's basketball,** tagged | 1.25 | .25 ☐☐☐☐☐
A108 _____
28¢ **Soccer,** tagged | 1.25 | .25 ☐☐☐☐☐
A109 _____ **1983. Olympics Third Issue**
35¢ **Fencing,** tagged | 1.25 | .25 ☐☐☐☐☐
A110 _____
35¢ **Cycling,** tagged | 1.25 | .25 ☐☐☐☐☐
A111 _____
35¢ **Women's volleyball,** tagged | 1.25 | .25 ☐☐☐☐☐
A112 _____
35¢ **Pole vaulting,** tagged | 1.25 | .25 ☐☐☐☐☐
A113 _____ **1985. Alfred V. Verville Issue**
33¢ **multicolored** tagged | 1.00 | .30 ☐☐☐☐☐
A114 _____ **1985. Lawrence and Elmer Sperry Issue**
39¢ **multicolored** tagged | 1.25 | .40 ☐☐☐☐☐
A115 _____ **1986. Transpacific Airmail Issue**
44¢ **multicolored** tagged | 1.25 | .40 ☐☐☐☐☐
A116 _____ **1985. Junipero Serra Issue**
44¢ **multicolored** tagged | 1.75 | .60 ☐☐☐☐☐
A117 _____ **1988. Settlement of New Sweden Issue**
44¢ **multicolored** tagged (22,975,000) | 1.40 | .50 ☐☐☐☐☐
A118 _____ **1988. Samuel P. Langley Issue**
45¢ **multicolored** tagged | 1.40 | .30 ☐☐☐☐☐
A119 _____ **1988. Igor Sikorsky Issue**
36¢ **multicolored** tagged | 1.25 | .40 ☐☐☐☐☐

NOTE: Traces of red have been detected in all copies of a so-called "red-omitted" error of this stamp. Such stamps, on which even minute traces of red are present, are worth far less than a genuine color-omitted error would be.

A120 _____ **1989. French Revolution Bicentennial Issue**
45¢ **multicolored** tagged (38,532,000) | 1.40 | .40 ☐☐☐☐☐
A121 _____ **1989. America Issue**
45¢ **multicolored** tagged (39,325,000) | 1.50 | .30 ☐☐☐☐☐
A122 _____ **1989. Future Mail Transportation Souvenir Sheet**
$1.80 **multicolored,** souvenir sheet, tagged (1,944,000) | 7.00 | 5.00 ☐☐☐☐☐
A123 _____ **1989. Future Mail Transportation Issue**
45¢ **Hypersonic airliner,** tagged | 1.25 | .25 ☐☐☐☐☐
A124 _____
45¢ **Hovercraft,** tagged | 1.25 | .25 ☐☐☐☐☐
A125 _____
45¢ **Service rover,** tagged | 1.25 | .25 ☐☐☐☐☐
A126 _____
45¢ **Space Shuttle,** tagged | 1.25 | .25 ☐☐☐☐☐
A127 _____ **1990. America Issue**
45¢ **multicolored** tagged | 1.50 | .50 ☐☐☐☐☐

	MNHVF	UseVF

A128 _____ **1991. Harriet Quimby Issue**

50¢ **multicolored** tagged — 1.50 — .50 ⬜⬜⬜⬜⬜

A129 _____ **1991. William T. Piper Issue**

40¢ **multicolored** tagged — 1.40 — .50 ⬜⬜⬜⬜⬜

A130 _____ **1991. Antarctic Treaty Issue**

50¢ **multicolored** tagged — 1.50 — .60 ⬜⬜⬜⬜⬜

A131 _____ **1991. America Issue**

50¢ **multicolored** tagged — 1.50 — .50 ⬜⬜⬜⬜⬜

A132 _____ **1993. William T. Piper Issue**

40¢ **multicolored,** _(July 1993)_ tagged — 1.50 — .50 ⬜⬜⬜⬜⬜

A119

A120

A121

A122

A123, A124,
A125, A126

A127

A128

A129

A130

A131

A132

		UnFVF	UseFVF

SPECIAL DELIVERY STAMPS

		UnFVF	UseFVF	
SD1 _____	**1885. Messenger, First Issue**			
10¢ **Prussian blue**		115.00	22.50	☐☐☐☐☐
SD2 _____	**1888. Messenger, Second Issue**			
10¢ **Prussian blue**		120.00	7.00	☐☐☐☐☐
SD3 _____	**1893. Messenger, Third Issue**			
10¢ **orange yellow**		75.00	10.00	☐☐☐☐☐
SD4 _____	**1894. Messenger Issue**			
10¢ **deep blue**		300.00	20.00	☐☐☐☐☐
SD5 _____	**1895. Messenger Issue**			
10¢ **blue**		65.00	1.75	☐☐☐☐☐
SD6 _____	**1902. Messenger on Bicycle Issue**			
10¢ **ultramarine**		75.00	3.00	☐☐☐☐☐
SD7 _____	**1908. Helmet of Mercury Issue**			
10¢ **green**		50.00	30.00	☐☐☐☐☐
SD8 _____	**1911. Messenger on Bicycle Issue**			
10¢ **ultramarine**		75.00	4.50	☐☐☐☐☐
SD9 _____	**1914. Messenger on Bicycle Issue**			
10¢ **ultramarine**		140.00	5.00	☐☐☐☐☐
SD10 _____	**1916. Messenger on Bicycle Issue**			
10¢ **pale ultramarine**		225.00	22.50	☐☐☐☐☐
SD11 _____	**1917. Messenger on Bicycle Issue**			
10¢ **ultramarine**		14.50	.50	☐☐☐☐☐
SD12 _____	**1922. Messenger and Motorcycle Issue**			
10¢ **gray blue**		22.50	.25	☐☐☐☐☐
SD13 _____				
15¢ **red orange**		19.00	1.00	☐☐☐☐☐
SD14 _____	**1925. Post Office Delivery Truck Issue**			
20¢ **black**		2.25	1.50	☐☐☐☐☐
SD15 _____	**1927. Messenger and Motorcycle Issue**			
10¢ **dark lilac**		1.00	.20	☐☐☐☐☐

		MNHVF	UseVF	
SD16 _____	**1944. Messenger and Motorcycle Issue**			
13¢ **blue**		1.00	.20	☐☐☐☐☐
SD17 _____	**1931. Messenger and Motorcycle Issue**			
15¢ **yellow orange**		.75	.20	☐☐☐☐☐
SD18 _____	**1944. Messenger and Motorcycle Issue**			
17¢ **yellow**		3.50	3.00	☐☐☐☐☐
SD19 _____	**1951. Post Office Delivery Truck Issue**			
20¢ **black**		17.50	.20	☐☐☐☐☐
SD20 _____	**1954. Letter and Hands Issue**			
20¢ **gray blue**		.75	.20	☐☐☐☐☐
SD21 _____	**1957. Letter and Hands Issue**			
30¢ **maroon**		.75	.20	☐☐☐☐☐
SD22 _____	**1969. Dual Arrows Issue**			
45¢ **carmine & violet blue**		1.50	.50	☐☐☐☐☐
SD23 _____	**1971. Dual Arrows Issue**			
60¢ **violet blue & carmine**		1.50	.25	☐☐☐☐☐

SD1

SD2, SD3

SD4, SD5

SD6

SD7

SD8-SD11

SD12, SD13, SD15-SD18

SD14, SD19

SD20, SD21

SD22, SD23

	UnFVF	UseFVF

AIRMAIL/SPECIAL DELIVERY

ASD1_____   **1934. Blue Airmail Special Delivery Stamp Issue**

16¢ **Prussian blue** (9,215,750)   .90   .75 ☐☐☐☐☐

NOTE: An imperforate, ungummed version of the blue airmail special delivery issue, CM161, is listed with other so-called Farley Series stamps among the commemorative listings.

ASD2_____   **1936. Red and Blue Airmail Special Delivery Stamp Issue**

16¢ **carmine & blue**   .60   .30 ☐☐☐☐☐

ASD1

ASD2

	UnFVF	UseFVF

PARCEL POST STAMPS

PP1 _____ **1912. Parcel Post Stamps**

1¢ **carmine** (209,691,094)	3.00	1.25 ☐☐☐☐☐
PP2 _____		
2¢ **carmine** (206,417,253)	3.50	1.00 ☐☐☐☐☐
PP3 _____		
3¢ **carmine** (29,027,433)	6.50	4.50 ☐☐☐☐☐
PP4 _____		
4¢ **carmine** (76,743,813)	17.50	2.50 ☐☐☐☐☐
PP5 _____		
5¢ **carmine** (108,153,993)	17.50	1.75 ☐☐☐☐☐
PP6 _____		
10¢ **carmine** (56,896,653)	30.00	2.50 ☐☐☐☐☐
PP7 _____		
15¢ **carmine** (21,147,033)	45.00	8.00 ☐☐☐☐☐
PP8 _____		
20¢ **carmine** (17,142,393)	85.00	16.00 ☐☐☐☐☐
PP9 _____		
25¢ **carmine** (21,940,653)	42.50	5.00 ☐☐☐☐☐
PP10 _____		
50¢ **carmine** (2,117,793)	190.00	32.50 ☐☐☐☐☐
PP11 _____		
75¢ **carmine** (2,772,615)	55.00	25.00 ☐☐☐☐☐
PP12 _____		
$1 **carmine** (1,053,273)	250.00	20.00 ☐☐☐☐☐

PARCEL POST/POSTAGE DUE STAMPS

PPD1 _____ **1912. Parcel Post Postage Due Stamps**

1¢ **green** (7,322,400)	6.00	3.50 ☐☐☐☐☐
PPD2 _____		
2¢ **green** (3,132,000)	55.00	15.00 ☐☐☐☐☐
PPD3 _____		
5¢ **green** (5,840,100)	9.00	3.50 ☐☐☐☐☐
PPD4 _____		
10¢ **green** (2,124,540)	125.00	40.00 ☐☐☐☐☐
PPD5 _____		
25¢ **green** (2,117,700)	65.00	3.75 ☐☐☐☐☐

SPECIAL HANDLING STAMPS

SH1 _____ **1925-29. Issue**

25¢ **green**	22.50	5.50 ☐☐☐☐☐
SH2 _____		
10¢ **yellow green**	2.25	1.00 ☐☐☐☐☐
SH3 _____		
15¢ **yellow green**	2.25	1.00 ☐☐☐☐☐
SH4 _____		
20¢ **yellow green**	3.00	1.75 ☐☐☐☐☐
SH5 _____		
25¢ **yellow green** (1929)	17.50	7.50 ☐☐☐☐☐

	UnFVF	UseFVF

REGISTRATION STAMP
REG1_____   **1911. Registration Stamp**

   10¢ **bright blue**   65.00   5.00 □□□□□

	MNHVF	UseVF

CERTIFIED MAIL STAMP
CER1_____   **1955. Certified Mail Stamp**

   15¢ **red**   .50   .35 □□□□□

PP1

PP2

PP3

PP4

PP5

PP6

PP7

PP8

PP9

PP10

PP11

PP12

PPD1-PPD5

SH1-SH5

REG1

CER1
→

	UnFVF	UseFVF

POSTAGE DUE

First Printing

PD1 _____   **1879. Postage Due Stamps Issue**

   1¢   **yellow brown**   40.00   8.00 ☐☐☐☐☐

PD2 _____

   2¢   **yellow brown**   250.00   6.50 ☐☐☐☐☐

PD3 _____

   3¢   **yellow brown**   35.00   5.00 ☐☐☐☐☐

PD4 _____

   5¢   **yellow brown**   400.00   38.00 ☐☐☐☐☐

PD5 _____

   10¢   **yellow brown**   450.00   30.00 ☐☐☐☐☐

PD6 _____

   30¢   **yellow brown**   200.00   47.50 ☐☐☐☐☐

PD7 _____

   50¢   **yellow brown**   350.00   55.00 ☐☐☐☐☐

Later Printings   ☐☐☐☐☐

PD8 _____

   1¢   **brown**   40.00   8.00 ☐☐☐☐☐

PD9 _____

   2¢   **brown**   250.00   5.00 ☐☐☐☐☐

PD10 _____

   3¢   **brown**   35.00   5.00 ☐☐☐☐☐

PD11 _____

   5¢   **brown**   400.00   18.00 ☐☐☐☐☐

PD12 _____

   10¢   **brown**   450.00   30.00 ☐☐☐☐☐

PD13 _____

   30¢   **brown**   200.00   50.00 ☐☐☐☐☐

PD14 _____

   50¢   **brown**   350.00   55.00 ☐☐☐☐☐

1887. *Previous designs in changed colors.*

PD15 _____

   1¢   **brown red**   40.00   5.00 ☐☐☐☐☐

PD16 _____

   2¢   **brown red**   50.00   5.00 ☐☐☐☐☐

PD17 _____

   3¢   **brown red**   700.00   150.00 ☐☐☐☐☐

PD18 _____

   5¢   **brown red**   350.00   20.00 ☐☐☐☐☐

PD19 _____

   10¢   **brown red**   350.00   15.00 ☐☐☐☐☐

PD20 _____

   20¢   **brown red**   175.00   50.00 ☐☐☐☐☐

PD1-28 →

		UnFVF	UseFVF	

PD21 _____

| | 50¢ **brown red** | 1,225.00 | 175.00 | ⬜⬜⬜⬜⬜ |

1891. Previous designs in changed colors. Imperforate varieties of PD22-28 exist, but they were not regularly issued.

⬜⬜⬜⬜⬜

PD22 _____

| | 1¢ **claret** | 20.00 | 1.00 | ⬜⬜⬜⬜⬜ |

PD23 _____

| | 2¢ **claret** | 25.00 | 1.00 | ⬜⬜⬜⬜⬜ |

PD24 _____

| | 3¢ **claret** | 50.00 | 8.00 | ⬜⬜⬜⬜⬜ |

PD25 _____

| | 5¢ **claret** | 60.00 | 8.00 | ⬜⬜⬜⬜⬜ |

PD26 _____

| | 10¢ **claret** | 100.00 | 17.50 | ⬜⬜⬜⬜⬜ |

PD27 _____

| | 30¢ **claret** | 350.00 | 150.00 | ⬜⬜⬜⬜⬜ |

PD28 _____

| | 50¢ **claret** | 375.00 | 150.00 | ⬜⬜⬜⬜⬜ |

PD29 _____   **1894. New Designs Issue**

| | 1¢ **vermilion** *(1894)* | 1,300.00 | 300.00 | ⬜⬜⬜⬜⬜ |

PD30 _____   **1879. Special Printings**

| | 1¢ **brown carmine** *(Aug. 14, 1894)* | 32.50 | 5.50 | ⬜⬜⬜⬜⬜ |

PD31 _____

| | 2¢ **vermilion** *(1894)* | 550.00 | 130.00 | ⬜⬜⬜⬜⬜ |

PD32 _____

| | 2¢ **brown carmine** *(July 20, 1894)* | 35.00 | 4.00 | ⬜⬜⬜⬜⬜ |

PD33 _____

| | 3¢ **brown carmine** *(April 27, 1895)* | 130.00 | 26.00 | ⬜⬜⬜⬜⬜ |

PD34 _____

| | 5¢ **brown carmine** *(April 27, 1895)* | 200.00 | 27.50 | ⬜⬜⬜⬜⬜ |

PD35 _____

| | 10¢ **brown carmine** *(Sept. 24, 1894)* | 200.00 | 25.00 | ⬜⬜⬜⬜⬜ |

PD36 _____

| | 30¢ **brown carmine** *(April 27, 1895)* | 350.00 | 90.00 | ⬜⬜⬜⬜⬜ |

PD37 _____

| | 50¢ **brown carmine** *(April 27, 1895)* | 900.00 | 250.00 | ⬜⬜⬜⬜⬜ |

1895. Same as previous designs. Double-line USPS watermark.

PD38 _____

| | 1¢ **brown carmine** *(Aug. 29, 1895)* | 7.50 | .75 | ⬜⬜⬜⬜⬜ |

PD39 _____

| | 2¢ **brown carmine** *(Sept. 14, 1895)* | 7.50 | .70 | ⬜⬜⬜⬜⬜ |

PD40 _____

| | 3¢ **brown carmine** *(Oct. 30, 1895)* | 47.50 | 1.50 | ⬜⬜⬜⬜⬜ |

PD41 _____

| | 5¢ **brown carmine** *(Oct. 15, 1895)* | 50.00 | 1.50 | ⬜⬜⬜⬜⬜ |

PD28

PD29-68

	UnFVF	UseFVF

PD42 _____
   10¢ **brown carmine** *(Sept. 14, 1895)* — 47.50 — 3.50 ☐☐☐☐☐

PD43 _____
   30¢ **brown carmine** *(Aug. 21, 1897)* — 450.00 — 50.00 ☐☐☐☐☐

PD44 _____
   50¢ **brown carmine** *(March 17, 1896)* — 275.00 — 35.00 ☐☐☐☐☐

1910. Same as previous designs. Single-line USPS watermark.

PD45 _____
   1¢ **brown carmine** *(Aug. 30, 1910)* — 27.50 — 2.75 ☐☐☐☐☐

PD46 _____
   2¢ **brown carmine** *(Nov. 25, 1910)* — 27.50 — 1.25 ☐☐☐☐☐

PD47 _____
   3¢ **brown carmine** *(Aug. 31, 1910)* — 450.00 — 30.00 ☐☐☐☐☐

PD48 _____
   5¢ **brown carmine** *(Aug. 31, 1910)* — 75.00 — 6.25 ☐☐☐☐☐

PD49 _____
   10¢ **brown carmine** *(Aug. 31, 1910)* — 95.00 — 12.50 ☐☐☐☐☐

PD50 _____
   50¢ **brown carmine** *(Sept. 23, 1912)* — 750.00 — 120.00 ☐☐☐☐☐

1914. Same as previous designs. Perforated 10.

PD51 _____
   1¢ **rose red** — 50.00 — 11.00 ☐☐☐☐☐

PD52 _____
   2¢ **vermilion** — 45.00 — .30 ☐☐☐☐☐

PD53 _____
   2¢ **rose red** — 45.00 — .30 ☐☐☐☐☐

PD54 _____
   3¢ **rose red** — 750.00 — 38.00 ☐☐☐☐☐

PD55 _____
   5¢ **rose red** — 32.00 — 2.50 ☐☐☐☐☐

PD56 _____
   10¢ **rose red** — 50.00 — 2.00 ☐☐☐☐☐

PD57 _____
   30¢ **rose red** — 200.00 — 16.00 ☐☐☐☐☐

PD58 _____
   50¢ **rose red** — 8,200.00 — 650.00 ☐☐☐☐☐

1916. Same as previous designs. Unwatermarked.

PD59 _____
   1¢ **rose red** — 2,000.00 — 300.00 ☐☐☐☐☐

PD60 _____
   2¢ **rose red** — 125.00 — 20.00 ☐☐☐☐☐

1917-25. Same as previous designs. Perforated 11.

PD61 _____
   1/2¢ **carmine** *(April 13, 1925)* — 1.00 — .25 ☐☐☐☐☐

PD62 _____
   1¢ **carmine** — 2.25 — .25 ☐☐☐☐☐

PD63 _____
   2¢ **carmine** — 2.25 — .25 ☐☐☐☐☐

PD64 _____
   3¢ **carmine** — 10.00 — .25 ☐☐☐☐☐

PD65 _____
   5¢ **carmine** — 10.00 — .25 ☐☐☐☐☐

PD66 _____
   10¢ **carmine** — 15.00 — .30 ☐☐☐☐☐

PD67 _____
   30¢ **carmine** — 80.00 — .75 ☐☐☐☐☐

	UnFVF	UseFVF	

PD68 _____
50¢ **carmine** — 10.00 — .30 ☐☐☐☐☐

1930. New Designs Issue

PD69 _____
1/2¢ **carmine** — 4.00 — 1.25 ☐☐☐☐☐

PD70 _____
1¢ **carmine** — 2.50 — .25 ☐☐☐☐☐

PD71 _____
2¢ **carmine** — 3.50 — .25 ☐☐☐☐☐

PD72 _____
3¢ **carmine** — 20.00 — 1.50 ☐☐☐☐☐

PD73 _____
5¢ **carmine** — 20.00 — 2.50 ☐☐☐☐☐

PD74 _____
10¢ **carmine** — 40.00 — 1.00 ☐☐☐☐☐

PD75 _____
30¢ **carmine** — 110.00 — 2.00 ☐☐☐☐☐

PD76 _____
50¢ **carmine** — 140.00 — .75 ☐☐☐☐☐

PD77 _____
$1 **carmine** — 25.00 — .25 ☐☐☐☐☐

PD78 _____
$5 **carmine** — 40.00 — .25 ☐☐☐☐☐

1931. Same as previous design. Rotary press printing, perforated 11 x 10 1/2.

PD79 _____
1/2¢ **vermilion** — 1.00 — .15 ☐☐☐☐☐

PD80 _____
1¢ **vermilion** — .20 — .15 ☐☐☐☐☐

PD81 _____
2¢ **vermilion** — .20 — .15 ☐☐☐☐☐

PD82 _____
3¢ **vermilion** — .20 — .15 ☐☐☐☐☐

PD83 _____
5¢ **vermilion** — .40 — .15 ☐☐☐☐☐

PD84 _____
10¢ **vermilion** — 1.00 — .15 ☐☐☐☐☐

PD85 _____
30¢ **vermilion** — 8.00 — .25 ☐☐☐☐☐

PD86 _____
30¢ **vermilion** — 10.00 — .25 ☐☐☐☐☐

1956. Perforated 10 1/2 x 11.

PD87 _____
$1 **vermilion** — 35.00 — .25 ☐☐☐☐☐

PD88 _____ **1959-85. New Designs Issue**
1/2¢ **red & black** — 1.25 — .85 ☐☐☐☐☐

PD68

PD69-76, 79-86

PD76

PD77, 87

PD78

		UnFVF	UseFVF	

PD89 _____
   1¢ **red & black**   .15   .15 ☐☐☐☐☐

PD90 _____
   2¢ **red & black**   .15   .15 ☐☐☐☐☐

PD91 _____
   3¢ **red & black**   .15   .15 ☐☐☐☐☐

PD92 _____
   4¢ **red & black**   .15   .15 ☐☐☐☐☐

PD93 _____
   5¢ **red & black**   .15   .15 ☐☐☐☐☐

PD94 _____
   6¢ **red & black**   .15   .15 ☐☐☐☐☐

PD95 _____
   7¢ **red & black**   .15   .15 ☐☐☐☐☐

PD96 _____
   8¢ **red & black**   .20   .15 ☐☐☐☐☐

PD97 _____
   10¢ **red & black**   .20   .15 ☐☐☐☐☐

PD98 _____
   30¢ **red & black**   .50   .15 ☐☐☐☐☐

PD99 _____
   50¢ **red & black**   1.00   .15 ☐☐☐☐☐

PD100 _____
   $1 **red & black**   1.75   .15 ☐☐☐☐☐

PD101 _____
   $5 **red & black**   9.00   .20 ☐☐☐☐☐

PD102 _____
   11¢ **red & black** *(Jan. 2, 1978)*   .25   .15 ☐☐☐☐☐

PD103 _____
   13¢ **red & black** *(Jan. 2, 1978)*   .25   .15 ☐☐☐☐☐

PD104 _____
   17¢ **red & black** *(June 10, 1985)*   .40   .15 ☐☐☐☐☐

PD88-100

PD101

	UnFVF	UseFVF

MIGRATORY BIRD HUNTING PERMIT

		UnFVF	UseFVF	
RH1 _____	**1934. Mallard Issue**			
$1 blue		575.00	115.00	☐☐☐☐☐
RH2 _____	**1935. Canvasback Duck Issue**			
$1 crimson		525.00	135.00	☐☐☐☐☐
RH3 _____	**1936. Canada Geese Issue**			
$1 brown black		300.00	65.00	☐☐☐☐☐
RH4 _____	**1937. Scaup Ducks Issue**			
$1 dull green		250.00	45.00	☐☐☐☐☐
RH5 _____	**1938. Pintail Duck Issue**			
$1 violet		250.00	45.00	☐☐☐☐☐
RH6 _____	**1939. Green-Winged Teal Issue**			
$1 sepia		140.00	40.00	☐☐☐☐☐

		MNHVF	UseVF	
RH7 _____	**1940. Black Mallard Issue**			
$1 black brown		140.00	40.00	☐☐☐☐☐
RH8 _____	**1941. Ruddy Ducks Issue**			
$1 red brown		140.00	35.00	☐☐☐☐☐
RH9 _____	**1942. Baldpates Issue**			
$1 sepia		140.00	35.00	☐☐☐☐☐
RH10 _____	**1943. Wood Duck Issue**			
$1 carmine red		60.00	35.00	☐☐☐☐☐
RH11 _____	**1944. White-Fronted Geese Issue**			
$1 red orange		60.00	25.00	☐☐☐☐☐
RH12 _____	**1945. Shoveller Ducks Issue**			
$1 black		45.00	18.00	☐☐☐☐☐
RH13 _____	**1946. Redhead Ducks Issue**			
$1 chestnut brown		35.00	13.50	☐☐☐☐☐
RH14 _____	**1947. Snow Geese Issue**			
$1 black		35.00	13.50	☐☐☐☐☐
RH15 _____	**1948. Bufflehead Ducks Issue**			
$1 light blue		45.00	13.50	☐☐☐☐☐
RH16 _____	**1949. Goldeneye Ducks Issue**			
$2 emerald		50.00	13.50	☐☐☐☐☐
RH17 _____	**1950. Trumpeter Swans Issue**			
$2 violet		60.00	10.00	☐☐☐☐☐
RH18 _____	**1951. Gadwall Ducks Issue**			
$2 gray black		60.00	10.00	☐☐☐☐☐
RH19 _____	**1952. Harlequin Ducks Issue**			
$2 deep ultramarine		60.00	10.00	☐☐☐☐☐
RH20 _____	**1953. Blue-Winged Teal Issue**			
$2 lavender brown		60.00	12.00	☐☐☐☐☐
RH21 _____	**1954. Ring-Necked Ducks Issue**			
$2 black		60.00	8.00	☐☐☐☐☐
RH22 _____	**1955. Blue Geese Issue**			
$2 deep blue		60.00	8.00	☐☐☐☐☐
RH23 _____	**1956. American Merganser Issue**			
$2 black		60.00	8.00	☐☐☐☐☐
RH24 _____	**1957. American Eider Issue**			
$2 yellow emerald		60.00	8.00	☐☐☐☐☐
RH25 _____	**1958. Canada Geese Issue**			
$2 black		60.00	8.00	☐☐☐☐☐
RH26 _____	**1959. Retriever Carrying Mallard Issue**			
$3 blue, orange brown & black		85.00	8.00	☐☐☐☐☐
RH27 _____	**1960. Redhead Ducks Issue**			
$3 multicolored		65.00	8.00	☐☐☐☐☐

RH1

RH2

RH3

RH4

RH5

RH6

RH7

RH8

RH9

RH10

RH11

RH12

RH13

RH14

RH15

RH16

RH17

RH18

		MNHVF	UseVF	

RH28 _____ **1961. Mallards Issue**
$3   blue, brown & yellow brown .... 70.00 ..... 8.00 ☐☐☐☐☐

RH29 _____ **1962. Pintails Issue**
$3   multicolored .... 70.00 ..... 8.00 ☐☐☐☐☐

RH30 _____ **1963. Pacific Brant Issue**
$3   multicolored .... 70.00 ..... 8.00 ☐☐☐☐☐

RH31 _____ **1964. Nene Geese Issue**
$3   multicolored .... 70.00 ..... 8.00 ☐☐☐☐☐

RH32 _____ **1965. Canvasbacks Issue**
$3   multicolored .... 70.00 ..... 8.00 ☐☐☐☐☐

RH33 _____ **1966. Whistling Swans Issue**
$3   deep green, black & blue .... 70.00 ..... 8.00 ☐☐☐☐☐

RH34 _____ **1967. Old Squaw Ducks Issue**
$3   multicolored .... 70.00 ..... 8.00 ☐☐☐☐☐

RH35 _____ **1968. Hooded Mergansers Issue**
$3   multicolored .... 55.00 ..... 8.00 ☐☐☐☐☐

RH36 _____ **1969. White-Winged Scoters Issue**
$3   multicolored .... 40.00 ..... 7.00 ☐☐☐☐☐

RH37 _____ **1970. Ross' Geese Issue**
$3   multicolored .... 40.00 ..... 7.00 ☐☐☐☐☐

RH38 _____ **1971. Cinnamon Teal Issue**
$3   multicolored .... 35.00 ..... 7.00 ☐☐☐☐☐

RH39 _____ **1972. Emperor Geese Issue**
$5   multicolored .... 22.50 ..... 7.00 ☐☐☐☐☐

RH40 _____ **1973. Steller's Eider Issue**
$5   multicolored .... 20.00 ..... 7.00 ☐☐☐☐☐

RH41 _____ **1974. Wood Ducks Issue**
$5   multicolored .... 18.00 ..... 7.00 ☐☐☐☐☐

RH42 _____ **1975. Canvasbacks Issue**
$5   multicolored .... 14.00 ..... 7.00 ☐☐☐☐☐

RH43 _____ **1976. Canada Geese Issue**
$5   green & black .... 14.00 ..... 7.00 ☐☐☐☐☐

RH44 _____ **1977. Ross' Geese Issue**
$5   multicolored .... 14.00 ..... 7.00 ☐☐☐☐☐

RH45 _____ **1978. Hooded Merganser Issue**
$5   multicolored .... 14.00 ..... 7.00 ☐☐☐☐☐

RH46 _____ **1979. Green-Winged Teal Issue**
$7.50 **multicolored** .... 17.50 ..... 7.00 ☐☐☐☐☐

RH47 _____ **1980. Mallards Issue**
$7.50 **multicolored** .... 17.50 ..... 7.00 ☐☐☐☐☐

RH48 _____ **1981. Ruddy Ducks Issue**
$7.50 **multicolored** .... 17.50 ..... 7.00 ☐☐☐☐☐

RH49 _____ **1982. Canvasbacks Issue**
$7.50 **multicolored** .... 17.50 ..... 7.00 ☐☐☐☐☐

RH50 _____ **1983. Pintails Issue**
$7.50 **multicolored** .... 17.50 ..... 7.00 ☐☐☐☐☐

RH51 _____ **1984. Widgeons Issue**
$7.50 **multicolored** .... 17.50 ..... 7.00 ☐☐☐☐☐

NOTE: After No. RH51's period of use had expired, 15 uncut sheets of 120 (four panes of 30 stamps per sheet, separated by gutters) were overprinted "1934-84" and "50th Anniversary" along the margins. These sheets were auctioned off by the U.S. Fish and Wildlife Service, beginning Sept. 1, 1985, with a minimum acceptable bid for each sheet of $2,000. Face value of the sheets, when valid for use, was $900. Fourteen sheets were sold, and one was donated to the Smithsonian Institution. Individual stamps of the sheet cannot be differentiated from normal copies of No. RH51. Various configurations were formed from the sheets and sold to collectors: horizontal and vertical pairs with a gutter between, cross-gutter blocks of four, and margin blocks. Sheets were submitted to The Philatelic Foundation for certification prior to being broken up, and each stamp from each of the sheets has a mark of the expertizer on the reverse. With such marks in place, individual stamps not attached to a margin were sold along with configurations noted above.

RH51a _____ **1984. Special Commemorative Issue**
$7.50 **Special Commemorative Issue** (All examples must have P.F. certificates) .... ☐☐☐☐☐

RH19

RH20

RH21

RH22

RH23

RH24

RH25

RH26

RH27

RH28

RH29

RH30

RH31

RH32

RH33

RH34

RH35

RH36

		MNHVF	UseVF	

RH52 _____ **1985. Cinnamon Teal Issue**
  $7.50 **multicolored**   17.50   7.00 ☐☐☐☐☐
RH53 _____ **1986. Fulvous Whistling Duck Issue**
  $7.50 **multicolored**   17.50   7.00 ☐☐☐☐☐
RH54 _____ **1987. Redhead Issue**
  $10 **multicolored**   20.00   10.00 ☐☐☐☐☐
RH55 _____ **1988. Snow Goose Issue**
  $10 **multicolored**   20.00   7.00 ☐☐☐☐☐
RH56 _____ **1989. Lesser Scaup Issue**
  $12.50 **multicolored**   22.50   7.00 ☐☐☐☐☐
RH57 _____ **1990. Black-Bellied Whistling Duck Issue**
  $12.50 **multicolored**   22.50   7.00 ☐☐☐☐☐

NOTE: printing on back of stamp normally is on top of gum. No. RH57v can only exist unused. Beware of copies with gum removed.

RH58 _____ **1991. King Eiders Issue**
  $15 **multicolored**   27.50   12.50 ☐☐☐☐☐
RH59 _____ **1992. Spectacled Eider Issue**
  $15 **multicolored**   27.50   12.50 ☐☐☐☐☐
RH60 _____ **1993. Canvasback issue**
  $15 **multicolored**   27.50   12.50 ☐☐☐☐☐
RH61 _____ **1994. Red-Breasted Mergansers Issue**
  $15 **multicolored**   25.00   10.00 ☐☐☐☐☐
RH62 _____ **1995. Mallard Issue**
  $15 **multicolored**   25.00   10.00 ☐☐☐☐☐
RH63 _____ **1996. Surf Scoter Issue**
  $15 **multicolored**   25.00   10.00 ☐☐☐☐☐
RH64 _____ **1997. Canada Goose Issue**
  $15 **multicolored**   25.00   10.00 ☐☐☐☐☐
RH65 _____ **1998. Barrow's Goldeneye Issue**
  $15 **multicolored**   25.00   10.00 ☐☐☐☐☐
RH66 _____ **1998. Barrow's Goldeneye Self-Adhesive Issue**
  $15 **multicolored**   30.00   15.00 ☐☐☐☐☐
RH67 _____ **1999. Greater Scaup Issue**
  $15 **multicolored**   30.00   15.00 ☐☐☐☐☐
RH68 _____ **1999. Greater Scaup Self-adhesive Issue**
  $15 **multicolored**   30.00   15.00 ☐☐☐☐☐
RH69 _____ **2000. Mottled Duck Issue**
  $15 **multicolored**   25.00   15.00 ☐☐☐☐☐
RH70 _____ **2000. Mottled Duck Issue**
  $15 **multicolored**   25.00   15.00 ☐☐☐☐☐

RH37

RH38

RH39

RH40

RH41

RH42

RH43

RH44

RH45

RH46

RH47

RH48

RH49

RH50

RH51

RH52

RH53

RH54

RH55

RH56

RH57

RH58

RH59

RH60

RH61

RH62

RH63

RH64

RH66

RH65

RH68

RH67

RH70

RH69

FREE

Minkus-Scott cross-reference

As a purchaser of this new Krause-Minkus Stamps and Prices Mini-Catalog of United States Stamps, you are entitled to receive free a cross-reference booklet. This booklet contains both Minkus-to-Scott and Scott-to-Minkus United States catalog number cross-references in an easy-to-use format.

To receive a copy, send the coupon below to Philatelic Division, Krause Publications, 700 E. State St., Iola WI 54990-0001.

Yes, please send my **free**
Minkus-Scott Mini-Catalog of United States Stamps
cross-reference.

Name: _____

Address: _____

City: _____

State: _____ ZIP: _____